PUBLIC PROPERTY, LAW AND SOCIETY

This book examines the almost entirely neglected realm of public property, identifying and describing a number of key organizing principles around which a nascent jurisprudence of public property may be developed.

In property law terms, the public realm is lost to plain view. Despite the vast acreage of public lands, or the extensive tracts of private lands over which public rights subsist, there is little commensurate scholarly discussion of the ideas, theories, practices, and laws of public property. This is no accident. Public property has been marginalized and pushed to the periphery for centuries, a consequence of the dominant discourse of private property, and its enclosing, encroaching tendencies. This book explores the rich diversity of the public estate, of what the public realm means for us, the general public, canvassing what we may 'own', where we may 'belong', or not, and how we may 'connect' through a shared use and enjoyment of public place and space. To better understand public property is to better value its critical public-wealth. Whether overlooked, over-used, or under threat of imminent loss, this book maintains that our loved (and not so loved) public spaces are essential components of our diverse, functioning, and optimistically livable human geographies. As such, they demand legal protection.

This important and original book will be of considerable interest to scholars and others with interests in property and land law, socio-legal studies, legal geography and urban studies.

John Page is a Professor of Law at the School of Law and Justice at Southern Cross University, Australia.

PUBLIC PROPERTY, LAW AND SOCIETY

Owning, Belonging, Connecting in the Public Realm

John Page

Routledge
Taylor & Francis Group
LONDON AND NEW YORK

First published 2021
by Routledge
2 Park Square, Milton Park, Abingdon, Oxon OX14 4RN

and by Routledge
52 Vanderbilt Avenue, New York, NY 10017

Routledge is an imprint of the Taylor & Francis Group, an informa business

British Library Cataloguing-in-Publication Data
A catalogue record for this book is available from the British Library

Library of Congress Cataloging-in-Publication Data
A catalog record has been requested for this book

ISBN: 978-0-367-69100-4 (hbk)
ISBN: 978-0-367-37598-0 (pbk)
ISBN: 978-0-367-80837-2 (ebk)

Typeset in Bembo
by Newgen Publishing UK

CONTENTS

TABLES

ACKNOWLEDGMENTS

This book has been a long time in gestation. I have been thinking about public property for many years, fortunate in having grown up and lived for so long amongst the 'wide open synergies' of the (publicly owned) public spaces of the Northern Rivers of New South Wales, Australia, the lands of the Widjabul peoples of the Bundjalung Nation.

Nascent thoughts started taking recognizable structure three years ago, when I floated early ideas around 'connection' at the Association of Law, Property, and Society's (ALPS) annual meeting at the University of Michigan, Ann Arbor. Since then, there have been other conferences, and conversations with colleagues. Especially helpful have been the numerous links to news stories and journal articles that colleagues have sent, thinking I might find them useful. Some of the best ideas have come from these generous gestures.

Luckily, my family are also enthusiastic fans and advocates of public property. We have a rich storehouse of memorable holidays spent on the public terrain of Australia, New Zealand and the United States. They too, are keen spotters of the indicia (and quirks) of public property, and similarly, their observations have proved inspiring.

So I would like to thank my colleagues, especially Dr. Cristy Clark and Professor William MacNeil, for some of the 'gems' they have given me over the years. I would also like to give special thanks to the members of ALPS, which is truly a generous and good-hearted scholarly group. I am likewise very grateful to the support of Dr. Colin Perrin and the editorial team at Routledge, who embraced this project readily, and have brought these disparate thoughts to fruition. To my dear family, Myeka, Nicholas, Henry and Coco, thank you for your love, time, enthusiasm, and support. And to my nephew, Alex in London, who has also given me some great leads and insights. Finally, thanks to the green, subtropical landscape of the Australian Northern Rivers, which has shown me how to see and appreciate *things public*, both here and everywhere.

Any errors and omissions are entirely my own.

1

INTRODUCTION

Our relationships with public real property are as diverse and varied as the vast public estate itself. Whether grid-locked on Los Angeles' Interstate 405, trudging through London's sunless, unremarkable Passing Alley, or tramping the wild emptiness of New Zealand's high country, we engage with public property in ways that stretch the limits of description – and imagination. Our very public sharing of this public space never ceases in an infinite, ever-changing constancy of time and place, the social, inherently propertied interactions that shape who we are, where we belong, and how we connect. Yet, despite its centrality, the public estate remains sorely under-theorized and under-documented in the common law – a legal poverty out of all proportion to the vast acreage of public lands, the diversity of intangible public rights, and the cognate literature of public *space* that fires the scholarly imagination in disciplines such as geography or urban design. This book is a response to this incongruity, its objectives to first capture the scattered literature of public property jurisprudence, and second to develop a theoretical framework that explains, or at least contextualizes, the public realm in the common law tradition.

To engage with public real property is to resist a dominant narrative, to challenge the universalizing notion that all property is private, and to refute its corollary – that the public estate is 'bereft of property, a *terra nullius*' (Blomley 2008, p. 321). Non-private property has been marginalized for centuries, pushed to the periphery and diminished from plain view. Indeed, since (near) time immemorial, the forces of enclosure and privatization have conspired to transform legal landscapes from rich heterogeneous patchworks to 'improved' private monotones.[1] The normalization of 'private property' as 'property' impugns both the *fact* and the *idea* of property's *other*, a physical and metaphysical encroachment that renders the concept of non-private property awkward to propertied ears. What prevails is a counter-factual paradigm entrenched by centuries of precedent. Thus, the once widely accepted common right to glean was reduced by an English court in 1768 to a 'mere practice' characterized by its 'vulgarity' and 'promiscuity.'[2] Just over two hundred years later, the Australian High Court re-affirmed property in singularly private terms, where 'a [property] right … does not mean a public right; it means an individual right of a proprietary nature', and 'interest' mean 'interests held by persons in their individual capacity.'[3] Collective rights have long been suspect, mired in their feudal origins (Rose 1998, p. 179) and dismissed as the mere practices of custom, not rights of property.

Another implication is the widespread confusion that marks the blurred delineations between different types of non-private property. Public property is state property, federal lands, the commons, collective property, Crown land, and so on. As Chapter 2 details, the task of categorizing public property is fraught, its amorphous boundaries open to conjecture, and wide institutional uncertainty. Indeed, in its opening words, this book fares little better – its several references to 'non-private' property a concession to the rhetorical (and intrinsically diminishing) power of defining something by what it is not.

With these challenges in mind, the book asks a core question – how should we define the essence of public real property? Its approach is to identify and interrogate a number of key organizing principles, divergent themes around which ideas of public real property coalesce. It pinpoints five, beginning with *ownership* and ending with *democracy and protest*. In between these two bookends, the strengths and flaws of *sociability*, *belonging*, and *connection* are in individual turn explored. The book's trajectory can be measured in several ways. Doctrinally, it begins with the law, yet ends ostensibly beyond it. It commences with the black letter, the formality of legal title but shifts to the study of the extra-legal or performative effects of connection. Theoretically, it follows a similar path, radicalizing as it shifts from the orthodoxies of ownership to the fallout of protest, and moving away from an abstract, rights-based understanding of property to a relational, material one. However, its scrutiny remains lawful, its objective to capture a jurisprudential snapshot of the common law public estate.

In each chapter, specific enquiries are canvassed pertinent to the theme or organizing principle under scrutiny. For *public order*, the question is asked, should we be content to define public real property descriptively, accepting half-hearted attempts at legal hierarchy as good enough? Or is *ownership* the golden thread, and if so, who owns public real property, and in what capacity? Is the 'owner' the government, a state agency, or is it 'us'? And if the latter, what does 'us' mean? Leaving behind doctrine, and its orthodox imperatives to own, the book crosses over to property's *otherness*. It starts in the safer territory of progressive property, Aristotelian theories the likes of property as propriety, the rationales of sociability, even the promotion of happiness. The book scrutinizes the implications of these proprietarian accounts, and critiques their relevance as both optimal and all-encompassing explanations of the public estate. It then strays into the more radical terrain of *property as belonging*, an arguably fuller explanation of property that opens up a 'black box' of unofficial, sometimes utopian claims, practices and norms – performances of property beyond the private model. Belonging segues to *connection*, an organizing principle viewed through the eyes of the pedestrian trope. It observes how connection and movement enjoy nuanced yet robust links with the common law at justiciable, theoretical and normative levels, links that enact and contextualize our propertied relations with the public estate. Last, it ends in the convergence of public and democratic terrain, remarking upon the telltale, unassuming centrality of public real property to democratic discourse and civil protest.

In terms of structure, Chapter 2 begins by outlining how certain jurisdictions have instilled their own semblance of *public order* into the public estate. While not an organizing principle in itself, this chapter canvasses the ways in which four jurisdictions: Scotland, England, the United States and New Zealand, have sought to acknowledge, classify and structure the public realm. These jurisdictions exemplify very different approaches to the task, from a conscious design based on a rich albeit little-known history, to a resigned sense that there is little, if anything left to catalogue – the meagre remnants of an exhausted public estate.

The chapter observes that the public taxonomic project has been an underwhelming one. Attempts at legal order have been largely *ad hoc*, reactions to context or the imperatives of exigency. While they yield a diversity of form – corporeal, incorporeal and *sui generis* – unsurprisingly, they tend to end messily, taxonomies replete with loose ends. Such inconclusiveness institutionalizes performances of failure. It also exhausts theoretical curiosity, a preference to put the threadbare public house in order rather than rationalize *why*. That being said, taxonomy has its upsides. As Wesley Hohfield argues, it sharpens intellectual rigor (1913). It helps to prune, to discard unhelpful categories. Ancient Scots law identified *regalia minora,* the likes of royal swans, wild salmon and the sovereign's castle as a unique type of public property. Today, such *regalia minora* are analogous to Crawford Macpherson's 'state' or 'corporate public property', essentially private lands where the exclusion stick is held by individual state agencies, not the public at large (1978). Rigor suggests these ostensibly public interests could be parked elsewhere, safely sidelined in their own public sub-ledger.

The chapter also offers an opening definition of the 'public estate', or its interchangeable equivalents, 'public real property' or the 'public realm'. These are terms used liberally throughout this book, along with 'public realty' and 'public property in land.' Such descriptors rarely appear in land law texts, nor are they commonly taught in property law curricula. Where they do manifest, they are exceptional, at odds with the common law's erstwhile focus on the private right. Outlier examples include the study of federal public lands in the western United States, or public real rights within the *numerus clausus* of Scots law. Otherwise, the study of the vast public estate is lost to plain sight – and scrutiny.

Chapter 3 introduces the reader to the first of the organizing principles of the public realm, the prism of *ownership*. The chapter seeks to find value in the idea of public owning, scrutinizing title from divergent theoretical, metaphoric, spectral and spatial perspectives. There is an inherent risk that the question *who* 'owns' public real property, is an inapt enquiry, a construct designed in the private paradigm, and thus ill-suited to the public. If this premise is correct, logically the answers it yields may be compromised, or at best, problematic.

Despite such misgivings, Chapter 3 begins by exploring familiar property terrain, the metaphor of the bundle of sticks, a private paradigm where divisible 'stick' rights are detached and re-assembled at will. Here, almost immediately things go awry. The public estate's dilemma lies in identifying which 'stick' best highlights its core 'public-ness'. Indeed, private property has long struggled with its own analogous conundrum. For example, if exclusion is the private right's *sina qua non*, then logic might suggest that inclusion is the public estate's inverse gatekeeper. Yet in practice, inclusion is, at best, patchy and inconclusive. Contrarily, Carol Rose argues that possession is the first right, the origin of property, but possession finds little literal or theoretic traction in public lands. Indeed, use and enjoyment better describes the exercise of public rights, where sharing seems the key. Curiously, though, this particular stick right remains as vague as the jurisprudence of public real property itself. By and large, private metaphors tend to lock public real property into closed loops – endless circularities that are both stale and wearying.

Employing the image of the *spectrum* is another way to posit the various meanings of public real property ownership. As canvassed elsewhere,[4] seeing public ownership as gradations along an axis helps to explain many of its key iterations. The unitary state as owner, the state as trustee, even the unorganized public, fit defensibly on a continuum where position on the axis turns on owner-identity. The chapter then shifts to a *spatial* analysis of ownership, and the unique porousness of public borders. It ends in disruption, contesting colonial assumptions about public ownership in the settler colonial state, and challenging the emphasis on owner-identity, when owner-purpose may be a less vexing explanation of public owning.

Chapter 4 is, as foreshadowed, Aristotelian. It explores literature devoted to sociability, human flourishing, and the emergent 'science' of happiness. In this chapter, property is not the majoritarian 'land as commodity' private model. Rather, property serves virtuous ends, the citizen's well-lived life. Through this perspective, public realty promises an enhanced, perhaps leading role. Carol Rose's 1986 article, 'The Comedy of the Commons: Custom, Commerce, and Inherently Public Property' is a seminal work that concludes that *sociability* is the overarching modern rationale for public property. Gregory Alexander's 'other-half' explanation of property, 'property as propriety', likewise offers a plausible justification for the public estate (1997). Equally, the happiness of public spaces, and the ever-growing roll call of 'livable cities' boasting rich public infrastructure compounds the utopia that public spaces are an Elysian amalgam of happiness, sociability and propriety rolled into one.

Yet the comedy of the public commons is not universally comedic. Other literature speaks of the grinding loneliness of dispersed commuter neighborhoods, scattered from the metropolis to the suburb, to the exurb, and forever outwards. In these ubiquitous 'geographies of nowhere' (Kunstler 1993), the common denominator is the freeway, the long thin lifeline of public concrete that links the commuter to employment and a remote social life. These far-flung places may be 'dysfunctional suburb[s] of people shuttling from private interior to private interior' (Solnit 2001, p. 255) but they are enabled and connected by the public road, the thoroughfare that began as a pastoral footway and metamorphosed into the ten-lane interstate. This dystopian alt-account suggests that public real property is more than sociable national parks and loved public squares. The sunniness of sociability, let alone happiness, is not always the inexorable outcome of every manifestation of the public realm.

Chapter 5 analyzes the implications of 'property as belonging' to the public estate. Belonging is a school of property theory that re-imagines property relationships on the bases of proximity, attachment or connection. Belonging underscores that property is intrinsically a social institution, with constitutive human connections to 'proper or rightful place'. Belonging is thus intimately contextual, and spatial. As Sarah Keenan explains, 'focusing on belonging rather than exclusion brings into view spatial factors that tend to be otherwise overlooked in exclusion-focused theorizations of property' (2015, p. 72). Belonging also makes sense of property's 'otherness', its 'unofficial black box' of informal norms, claims and behaviors (Cooper 2013).

Belonging helps to explain public real property because the public estate is mostly beyond the orthodox terrain of justiciable rules, subject-object relationships, and 'exclusion focused theorizations of property'. Importantly, belonging cuts both ways, describing places that are well loved and those that are not. In this way, belonging accounts for the inconvenient gaps that sociability ignores. If there is a flaw of belonging, it is its equal plausibility for private property or common property. After all, *all* property is belonging.

Connection in Chapter 6 builds on belonging in Chapter 5, observing that connecting includes within its meanings, a joining together through a sense of affinity. But of course, this interpretation is not all-encompassing – connection has another practical and material meaning of bringing together, of physically linking A to B. Thus, in both senses of the word, public property connects; a symmetry of purpose that is simultaneously intuitive and material, intangible and tangible. Moreover, connection depends on movement; legal and non-legal acts that evidence our passing from one space to another. In this chapter, movement is traced through the eyes of the bipedal pedestrian, a convenient trope through which the connections of public real property are seen.

Chapter 6 employs the rich literature of walking – its joys, philosophies, and anthropologies – to prise open a gateway that shows the way ahead for this pedestrianized journey. Authors such as Rebecca Solnit and her *Wanderlust, A History of Walking* (2001) reveal the powerful yet deeply understated links between movement, connection, and the norms, laws and theories of public real property. For example, movement is the basis of prescription, an acquisitive doctrine given force in both the private and public realms, and often critical for the vexed issue of wet sand access in the United States. Movement is also critical to rights to roam and rights of passage in England and Scotland, where the public footpath and public highway emplace its flow, and statute endows it with black-letter specificity. And in the antipodean south, connection finds form in New Zealand walkways, or the *sui generis* Australian travelling stock reserve. At the theoretical level, movement and connection attract juristic attention. Hence, Olivia Barr describes a jurisprudence of *movement*, a convergence of the common law, walking and unsettling place. Kevin Gray writes of the pedestrian democrat, while conversely, Nicholas Blomley explains pedestrianism in remorselessly practical terms, its goal to preserve unimpeded flow and circulation on finite public resources.

Connection sits awkwardly in modern property law, with its emphasis on individual rights and private owners. As noted earlier, connection is not a legal doctrine but a crude observation of the *effects* of public real property, an interloper in a propertied landscape. Yet away from the private monotone and its orthodox rules and assumptions, connection and movement are recurring themes in public real property, the 'stuff' of its laws, customs, practices, and nascent theory. Chapter 6 purports to leave the law behind, but connection cannot escape it. Nor can the law of public realty escape its connecting urges.

Democracy and protest comprise the final organizing principle – scrutinized in Chapter 7. The rules of private property are adept at curtailing protest, but on the public domain, there are fewer constraints. Indeed, constitutional doctrines and ancient custom facilitate free speech, political communication, and the performance of dissent. In short, look for democratic self-expression and one finds public real property. Protest, or what Lucy Finchett-Maddock calls the 'proprietorial right of resistance' (2016, p. 121), play out on the fault-line where private-wealth confronts public-wealth, the public terrain that (imperfectly) aspires, both in spirit and in deed, to be likewise, democratic terrain.

Chapter 8 concludes by drawing together the core lessons of previous chapters and exploring a series of dualities that this analysis provokes. The chapter is discerning, highlighting how key aspects of each of the organizing principles best explains the public estate. For instance, law's order sharpens intellectual rigor, and discards unhelpful understandings that muddy the public waters. Ownership gives us pause, a chance to consider *why* we own – rather than *who* publicly owns. Sociability is the genius of Rose's comedy of the commons, and the irrepressible appeal of her 'unorganized public at large.' Belonging is relational, a way of thinking about property that clears a discrete theoretical space for the public realm. Conversely, connection is instrumentalist, yet accurate in describing what public real property does – and does not do. And democratic dissent bells the cat on what is ours, and the lengths we go to protect and defend the public square.

In beginning this public journey, it is useful to lighten the load, to jettison unhelpful legal baggage: the sticks in the bundle, or doctrine's insatiable need for ownership. Such comforting assumptions, the well tested but inappropriate tenets of private property will likely stand in the way, conceptual distractions that ignore that public real property is a distinctive institution with its own legal practices and knowledges. As Blomley observes of pedestrianism, *sui generis* approaches and methodologies may be more illuminating. We should treat public real property 'on its own terms', and explore it from the perspective of its 'own particular effects'. At its heart, Blomley opines, 'perhaps, it is better to think of pedestrianism as a particular legal knowledge, with its own networks, logic and internal truth' (2011, p. 4). The same leap of logic may be needed for public real property, an embrace of blue-sky thinking, and the limitless fresh ideas this imaginative departure offers.

Likewise, it is useful to discard a mentality where '[public] streets are the spaces left over between [private] buildings' (Solnit 2001, p. 175), or 'the void between workplaces, shops and dwellings' (p. 176). Perhaps the dominant image should be the reverse. Amidst the global, bustling city that is 21st-century London, an observant walker may stumble across glimpses of an ancient past – the plethora of narrow, human-scale passageways, the 'spaces left over' that crisscross city blocks, the likes of Passing Alley in Clerkenwell or Vicarage Way in Crouch End. To busy Londoners, these quirky paths no doubt merge into the milieu, as one of many.[5] But to a curious outsider, these footways are remarkable for what they represent, an epiphany of sorts that symbolizes the public estate's intimacy with place, and the connections it engenders.

Public real property is a contested, little understood notion in the common law of property. It is under-theorized, under-studied and under-documented. Where it does populate legal space, it exists in a miscellany, a rag-tag of marginal doctrine, unanchored statute, and hollow rationales. In observing the 'revelation' that is Solnit's 'magic of the street ... the mingling of the errand and the epiphany' (p. 178), this Introduction draws a parallel between ordinary footways, such as Passing Lane, and their high profile public equivalents – iconic national parks like John Muir's Yosemite, or much-loved urban spaces such as New York's elevated High Line.[6] Similarly high profile is the public indicia of livable cities – the cycle paths, cultural precincts, and community food gardens – that fill the tomes of sustainable literature. This book sets out to discover what the public mundane and the public sublime all share in common – the Yosemites, High Lines, Passing Lanes and clogged interstates – a jurisprudence of the vast public estate.

As Davina Cooper observes, understanding property through alternative perspectives, such as the prism of public lands, is *utopian*. To Cooper, 'utopian perspectives emphasize the importance of society imagined otherwise, rather than merely society imagined' (2013, p. 33). The public estate merits a place at the real property table, to be a phrase less awkward to propertied ears. To get there requires a transformative vision of public real property imagined otherwise, a simultaneously imaginative, at times utopian, yet doctrinally grounded journey, one that reaches back to the past and forward to the future. In better understanding our shared public spaces, both glorious and not, we gain better insight into what we own as a public citizenry, how we belong to place and community, and why we traverse the public ways of connection.

Notes

1 Legal memory or 'time immemorial' in the common law is deemed to begin in 1189. Chapter 7 explores the public customary implications of the Forest Charter of 1217, a remarkable statute that was given legal force only some 28 years after legal memory 'began'.

2 *Steel v Houghton* (1788) 126 ER 32.
3 *Stow v Mineral Holdings (Australia) Pty Ltd* (1977) 51 ALJR 672, 679.
4 Page and Brower (2017).
5 Of course, such passageways are far from unique to London. In vieux Lyon, secret 'traboules' transport locals through a maze of unmarked passages, and in Lisbon, steep public stairways exhaust pedestrians with their never-ending ascents, yet captivate with their entrée into sociable plazas or stunning vistas. Even in the so-called 'New World', in the inner suburbs of Sydney, Melbourne or Christchurch, pedestrian laneways re-materialize before one's eyes as forgotten yet critical components of the urban landscape.
6 Described as 'a former elevated railway that has been converted to a linear park, perhaps the most delightful piece of civic art to have been created since midcentury … a real boon to the livability of neighborhoods and well used in all but the worst weather' (Speck 2012, pp. 97–98). However, as Chapter 4 details, this view is far from unanimous.

References

Alexander, G 1997, *Commodity & Propriety: Competing Visions of Property in American Thought 1776–1970*, University of Chicago Press, Chicago.

Blomley, N 2008, 'Enclosure, Common Right and the Property of the Poor', *Social & Legal Studies*, vol. 17, 311–331.

Blomley, N 2011, *Rights of Passage: Sidewalks and the Regulation of Public Flow*, Routledge, Abingdon.

Cooper, D 2013, *Everyday Utopias: The Conceptual Life of Promising Spaces*, Duke University Press, Durham, NC.

Finchett-Maddock, L 2016, *Protest, Property and the Commons: Performances of Law and Resistance*, Routledge, Abingdon.

Hohfield, W 1913, 'Some Fundamental Legal Conceptions as Applied in Legal Reasoning', *Yale Law Journal*, vol. 23, 16–59.

Keenan, S. 2015, *Subversive Property: Law and the Production of Spaces of Belonging*, Routledge, Abingdon.

Kuntsler, J H 1993, *The Geography of Nowhere: The Rise and Decline of America's Man-Made Landscape*, Simon & Schuster, New York.

Macpherson, C B 1978, 'The Meaning of Property' in C B Macpherson (ed.) *Property: Mainstream and Critical Positions*, University of Toronto Press, Toronto.

Page, J and Brower, A 2017, 'The Four Dimensions of Public Property', in R Hickey and H Conway (eds), *Modern Studies in Property Law*, Hart Publishing, Oxford.

Rose, C M 1986, 'The Comedy of the Commons: Custom, Commerce, and Inherently Public Property', *University of Chicago Law Review*, vol. 53, no. 3, 711–781.

Rose, C M 1998, 'The Several Futures of Property: Of Cyberspace and Folk Tales, Emission Trades and Ecosystems', *Minnesota Law Review* vol. 83, 129–182.

Solnit, R 2001, *Wanderlust: A History of Walking*, Penguin Books, New York.

Speck, J 2012, *Walkable City: How Downtown Can Save America One Step at a Time*, North Point Press, New York.

2

OF PUBLIC ORDER

This chapter sets out to identify and describe various schema or categories into which types of public realty may fall. Its quest for order is paradoxical, since the public estate itself cannot be found in most mainstream real property taxonomies. As observed in the Introduction, 'public real property' or the 'public estate' are terms rarely seen in property curricula or land law texts. As an institution hidden to plain view, the public estate defies easy description – and categorization.

2.1 Introduction

Chapter 2's task is made doubly difficult given that property is likewise an institution where an imprecision of order, combined with a looseness of legal terminology, provides a 'striking example' of 'ambiguity'. As Wesley Hohfield explains,

> Both with lawyers and with laymen [property] has no definite or stable connotation. Sometimes it is employed to indicate the physical object to which various legal rights, privileges, etc., relate; then again-with far greater discrimination and accuracy the word is used to denote the legal interest (or aggregate of legal relations) appertaining to such physical object. Frequently there is a rapid and fallacious shift from the one meaning to the other. At times, also, the term is used in such a "blended" sense as to convey no definite meaning whatever.
>
> *(1913, p. 18)*

Such a perfect storm of *property* and the *public* has profound implications, combining as it does the ambiguously indefinite with the little known. In Hohfieldian terms, this is conducive to a lack of rigor. The converse is where 'good order' and a clarity of terminology encourages us to 'think straight' (ibid.) about the law and legal relations. 'Straight thinking', for instance, may help to de-clutter unhelpful categories of public realty, and re-imagine a pared back, coherently clearer public estate. This is one upside of the taxonomic task. A downside is the risk to engage in hollow churn. If the purpose of classification becomes self-serving, order for order's sake, there is an opportunity cost to be paid. What is foregone is the oxygen needlessly consumed, the absence of 'clear air' for public theory to take root and flourish. Moreover, a tendency to end the taxonomic exercise with a litany of loose ends is underwhelming. Performance theorists would cite this as reiterated performances of failure, acts that repeat and compound the public institution's flaws and omissions (Blomley 2013).

Being mindful of these risks – and opportunities – this chapter identifies a number of organizing filters in its brief survey of the public estate. These include the legacies of Roman law, the identity of state agency managers, and the dominant purpose(s) to which public realty is put. It identifies these filters through four case studies; its discussion ranging over the public (and private) lands of the western United States, England, Scotland, and New Zealand. These case studies explore not only space, but also time – from 17th-century Scots law to modern statutory hierarchies of public realty. Finally, they demonstrate a spectrum of sorts, from discernible yet inchoate systems of classification, graduating through to a jurisdiction where no apparent taxonomy corresponds to a hollowed out public realm.

This chapter also begins with a definition of 'public real property', and its meta-analogues, the 'public estate' or the 'public realm'. This definition is a work in progress – provided here to set early parameters around this book's core content, and to act as a point of departure for the journey ahead. As a definition of the 'little known', it places more qualifications on public realty than, say Brett Christophers's straightforward explanation that 'public land is simply land owned by public bodies' (2018, p. 6). It sidesteps the very real question (for the moment at least) that the public-private divide with 'its particularly strong connections to property' (Blomley 2005, pp. 283–284)[1] is not a simple binary; but porous, complex, and at times indistinct. Nor does it engage with the dilemma as to whether *public property* and *public space* are co-constitutive.[2] Its wording is likewise not without internal inconsistencies, proposing in its headlong rush to order a contested duality of corporeal versus incorporeal, flawed (at least in Hohfield's eyes) since 'all legal interests [in property] are incorporeal, consisting as they do of more or less limited aggregates of *abstract* legal relations' (1913, p. 24). Moreover, it follows the near-universal style of property statutes that construe property – not as a statement of its elusive essence – but as open-ended shopping lists; of interests real and personal, vested and contingent, legal and equitable, and so on.[3]

With these (many) limitations acknowledged, 'public real property' is thus defined as those corporeal and incorporeal interests in land; common law or statutory; traditional or *sui generis*, that are used or enjoyed by the public at large, or serve public purposes. The corporeal include lands owned, managed or controlled by the state, the likes of national parks, public cultural spaces, or national monuments, as well as less esteemed public spaces: roads, sidewalks, or nondescript municipal reserves. For present purposes, it also includes state-owned corporeal property such as public hospitals, housing or schools. The incorporeal comprise non-possessory interests or rights appurtenant to (public or private) land that are again used or enjoyed by the public at large, or serve public purposes. They include public recreational easements, rights of passage, or rights to roam. 'Traditional' is used to describe interests recognizable as orthodox things of property, such as rights of way or covenants. *Sui generis* interests are typically creatures of statute, sometimes modelled on traditional rights and sometimes not, modified by geography, time or context into unique, stand-alone rights, exemplified by the Australian travelling stock reserve.

As an opening gambit, this definition is premised around three anchor points: the alternate notions of 'use or enjoyment' or 'public purpose', the amorphous scope of the 'public at large', and the meaning of the 'state'. *Use and enjoyment* is used non-technically in this chapter. Here, it does not invite any rights-based analysis – that is postponed to Chapter 3. To *use or enjoy* in this context is simply an observation of the public's factual enjoyment of public realty, corporeal and incorporeal. In *Otto v Inn at Watervale Inc.*,[4] the Michigan Supreme Court described children 'building sand castles, throwing stones in the water, and splashing around' as public uses of lakefront beaches. In *Hay*, customary public rights over Oregonian dry sands are similarly described as picnickers 'gathering wood, building warming fires, … or rang[ing] over the foreshore.'[5] Nor need the *use* be leisurely; it may encompass acts as mundane as passing and re-passing, with or without vehicles. Articulated in such language, public use and enjoyment is not a term of legal art, simply a statement of observable fact. If there is another property law analogy, it is the distinction between *occupation* and *possession*, occupation being a crude factual claim, possession a determination of the legal quality of that occupation (Wonnacott 2006).[6] Analogously, *public purpose* is left matter-of-fact at this stage, an analysis of its purposive uniqueness postponed to later in this chapter, and in Chapter 3.

The *public at large* tends to be the citizenry of the state. In a globalized world this constraint may seem anachronistic, but this sub-definition is faithful to the Roman law concept of *res publicae*, things ostensibly restricted to the use of a state's citizens, and at the state's invitation, to the lawful use and enjoyment of others. US national parks may be famously 'your national parks', but the possessive pronoun employed is a citizen-premised one. Like performative use and enjoyment, the *who* in the public at large is largely self-evident to the casual observer's gaze.

State is an expansive term that includes all levels of government – central, federal, state, provincial and local. Patrick Dunleavy (1995) defines the 'state' as a recognizably cohesive set of institutions that operate within a discrete space, whose existence serves to 'define and enforce collectively binding decisions' on society and its members (Jessop 1990, p. 341). The state claims to advance the public will of its citizens, regulating the affairs of its citizens by law, and deriving legitimacy from (in these case studies at least) the democratic compact between the governed and the governing. Importantly, the state's collective decision-making is said to delineate between private and public spheres.[7]

This book also resists the noetic call of the *commons* in its first-blush demarcation of public real property. The extent of the modern commons is a reminder of Hohfield's cautionary advices about imprecise terminology at law. Is the 'commons' a reference to open-access natural resources, the likes of Roman law's *res communes*? Or should the commons be construed narrowly? And to what extent should concepts such as 'commoning' enter the public field?[8] History suggests that the commons is both a bounded and boundless concept, bounded in its agrarian roots as land capable of only being used and enjoyed by members of a local group, yet (alternatively) boundless as an idea of the earth's resources, universally open to all. This book prefers the former interpretation. While the distinction may seem arcane to some, the difficulty in freely interchanging 'public property' with the 'commons' lies in the further erosion this causes to the public estate's integrity. There are technical and very real distinctions between common and public property. As flagged, the former is the exclusive right of a member of a community, enjoyed in common with others similarly qualified, but denied to the public at large. The latter by contrast is available to all, irrespective of one's communitarian status.[9] Common property rights tend to be micro, public property interests macro. To the extent of any overlap, it stems from a conflation of the two, a lack of Hohfieldian discipline where 'the term is used in such a "blended" sense as to convey no definite meaning whatever' (1913, p. 24). Michael Brill reduces the distinction to sociable terms, common property provides for community life, a sociability 'with people you somewhat know', while public property provides for public life and a shared sociability 'with a diversity of strangers.' (2002, p. 50). Like performative use and enjoyment, and the self-evident public at large, this deceptively simple explanation captures a key point of difference.

As this initial discussion shows, to engage with taxonomy is a fraught exercise. Indeed, as seen in the above paragraph, the discussion can get bogged down at the *genus* stage, well before the finer distinctions of public *species* are reached. The record suggests that there is a dearth of 'straight thinking' around public property – and the ways it has been marshalled. Yet, fraught-ness or difficulty aside, and with the pluck of Chapter 6's pedestrian, this chapter nonetheless aspires to persist, to ignore false signposts, and reach some satisfactory endpoint. Along its way, it will identify filters used to sort the public realm, whether deliberately designed or the product of happenstance, and whether patent or latent. Its key enquiry is to discern taxonomy's implications for the public estate; to identify various themes around which certain hierarchies are constructed, and to ask what insights, if any, these hierarchies provide.

2.2 Scotland – a rich history of public real rights

Of the four public hierarchies canvassed in this chapter, the first case study is the most extensively explored, and perhaps, the least known. Scots law boasts a sophisticated history of public real rights, and an equally sophisticated modern public jurisprudence. Discussion of the latter is confined to Chapter 6, where the human pedestrian roams its vast, open, and often wild outdoors. This part's focus lies in the *history* of its public estate taxonomy, a hierarchy *par excellence,* a valiant attempt at structure developed over centuries but ultimately discarded, one that reflected complex, at times confusing interplays between things communal, things public, and the notion of *regalia*. Despite its final failings, it is a structure that nonetheless leaves a beneficial legacy.

As Jill Robbie argues, such juristic concern with order is (in part) a legacy of Scots law's institutional writers,[10] and their articulation of the little regarded Division of Things (2015). Described by Robbie as 'the classification of certain objects with regard to their inherent nature and characteristics, the law by which such objects are governed, or the uses to which they can be put' (p. 10), the Division of Things was a formal taxonomy of Scots law that flourished in the Institutional period,[11] principally, though not exclusively, through the writings of Sir Thomas Craig and Viscount Stair. The Division of Things canvassed all forms of property in varying degrees of detail and description, including the categories of *communal things* and *public things*. Citing Kevin Gray, Jill Robbie acknowledges (as does this book) that a general lack of scholarly discussion about public property and its organization makes 'this topic a challenging one to analyse' (p. 10).[12]

The challenge with analyzing the Division of Things (here from the perspective of public real property) is that its processes of classification meant different things to different writers. Its background was Roman law, and the notionally public categories of *res communes* and *res publicae*. *Res communes* were essentially natural resources, the air, seas, and running water. Such resources were incapable of appropriation, a consequence of their natural state – although water could be owned once captured and minus its 'running' quality. *Res communes* were open to universal use, by citizen and non-citizen alike. By contrast, *res publicae* were a category based on paramount public rights to use, not questions of ownership. Indeed, the *situs* of *res publicae* could be owned privately. *Res publicae* were rights of trade and travel; public rights of navigation and fishing in ports, harbors and highways. *Res publicae,* unlike res communes, were rights of citizens only. Overlap between the two was considerable and contested, and often manifested in grey zones such as the foreshore. As Daniel Coquillette observes of the middle ground between the two:

> Scholars have long debated the nature of the ownership rights in *res communes* and *res publicae*. … [T]he Romans clearly conceived of a 'middle ground' between absolute individual ownership and ownership by the state that was not limited to property owned by no one. It was … public property 'not the object of commerce' and did 'not absolutely belong to the people' but was used 'for public purposes'.
>
> *(1979, p. 803)*

The millennial-long hiatus between Justinian's Digests and 'the writing of the first Scottish institutional work at the turn of the 17th century, [saw] categories of *res communes* and *res publicae* … subject to substantial interpretation and alteration in the western legal tradition' (Robbie 2015, p. 13). In particular, this took form as the 'intermingling' of *regalia* with *res publicae. Regalia* were the sovereign's property, the patrimony of the Crown. Such intermingling infused Crown jurisdiction and control into what Carol Rose would later call 'inherently public property'.

The rise of *regalia* as an iteration of public property, and its conflation with *res publicae,* was evident in Craig's Division of Things, written at the beginnings of the 17th century.[13] Craig ignored the Roman *res communes*, and thereby transformed many common things into *public things*, thus shifting their characterization from natural resources to rights of public use. For instance, Craig categorized the foreshore as a public thing, a place subject to public rights of use, but it was not allocated as *regalia*, and therefore not specifically owned. Despite this emphasis, Robbie observes that public things were not explored or enumerated by Craig in any detail. By contrast, Craig dug into the granular of *regalia*, the core idea of Crown ownership or control. Craig described two sub-categories of *regalia*; *regalia majora* and *regalia minora*. The former comprised things closely connected to government, held by the Crown in the public interest, where the resulting trust meant they were conceptually inalienable and subject to overriding public rights of use.[14] *Regalia minora* by contrast were things subject to exclusive Crown use and control. *Minora* were *not* things held by the Crown for the public, and therefore could be sold or otherwise disposed of, like rights to fish wild salmon.

In Craig's taxonomy, certain things were also both *regalia majora* and public things. Highways and navigable rivers fell into this complicated hybrid, one where the rules of *regalia majora* took precedence. Hence, public things could be blended and subject to Crown ownership, or else were essentially owner-less things distinguished by an overriding public right to use, such as the foreshore. As Table 2.1 indicates, Craig devised four categories of public property, which ranged on a spectrum from public things focused on public use not ownership, to exclusive and alienable Crown-owned things.

The later writings of Viscount Stair (first published in 1681) are described by Robbie as the 'first general and systematic account of the laws of Scotland.' In an edited collection of Stair's Institutes published 300 years later, the editor's verdict is similar – with due deference to Stair's institutional predecessor, Sir Thomas Craig:

> The literature of Scots law existing in 1681 immediately prior to the publication of Stair's Institutions was amazingly scanty. … Of earlier writings, three deserve mention, including Craig's Jus Feudale and Hope's Major and Minor Practicks. Jus Feudale is a detailed narrative account of land law based on principles and the earliest reasoned examination of a major area of Scots law.
> *(Walker 1981, p. 13)*

Stair's 'account' of land law, particularly its public real rights, departs in a number of significant respects from Craig's. Stair revived and re-configured natural resources as 'real rights of commonty', resources that could be appropriated according to community need, yet available to all, being rights 'which all men [*sic*] have of all things.'[15] Robbie notes the paradox at the heart of Stair's commonty, that while such resources inherently 'cannot be appropriated', they were capable of being taken subject to Lockean-like qualifiers of 'enough and as good'. Commonty included 'the air ... running water, the vast oceans, [and] all the wild and free creatures subject to the common right of appropriation.'[16] The *real* rights of commonty represented the practical ability to appropriate such resources for community need. The right of commonty is described by Stair as a 'promiscuous and conjunct power.'[17]

Commonty was the first real right in Stair's taxonomy, followed by possession, private property,[18] and servitudes. Public things and regalia were also listed and discussed. Servitudes included *rights of passage* that were either public or private, a distinction recognized in Roman law and maintained 'with us' in Scots law.[19] Public ways or highways were 'constitute for public use ... which go from one public place to another, as from one burgh to another, or from a burgh to a public port ...'.[20] As rights open and available to all,[21] public rights of passage were not (citizen-only) *public things*.[22] Robbie notes that the foreshore was an ancillary incident of the public right of passage in Stair's Division.

Stair's *public things*, like Craig's, were public rights of use unrelated to questions of the land's ownership. Their use was similarly restricted to nationals only. While distinct, Stair's account of public things is said to be 'brief and unclear which makes analysis difficult' (Robbie 2015, p. 22). *Regalia* were a separate category again, with a heavy textual emphasis by Stair on *regalia minora*. Indeed, Stair suggests two further variants of *regalia*: jura *publica*, 'which the law appropriates to princes and states ... exempted from private use, unless the same be expressly granted and disponed by the king'; and *barony* or *inter regalia*. *Jura publica* included Crown property in royal minerals, treasure, and swans. *Inter regalia* comprised Crown privileges over forests, the hunting of deer, 'salmond fishings', and 'ports with their petty customs'.[23] In both cases, the Crown property was exclusive to the monarch and not held for the public.

Table 2.1 lists the four broad categories of *public* real rights found in each of Craig's and Stair's Divisions of Things. These taxonomies were complex and often porous, with individual emphases that had the consequence of robbing other under-regarded public rights of any substantive detail. In the case of Craig it was his focus on *regalia* and public rights to use, in the case of Stair it was an 'original interpretation' of commonty (Robbie 2015, p. 24). Elsewhere, there was unanimity between the two – the consistent characterization of *regalia,* and the shared understanding

TABLE 2.1 Categories of *public* real rights in the institutional writings of Craig and Stair

Craig's Division of Things	*Stair's Division of Things*
Public things (subject to public rights but not *regalia*)	Real rights of commonty
Blended public things/*regalia*	Public rights of passage
Regalia majora	Public things
Regalia minora	*Regalia* (mainly *minora*)

TABLE 2.2 Three public real rights respectively categorized under Craig's and Stair's Divisions of Things

	The shore	*Public ways*	*The port*
Craig	Public thing	Hybrid public thing and *regalia majora*	Public thing
Stair	Ancillary right of public right of passage	Public right of passage	*Regalia minora* (at least the concession to grant)

that *public things* are concerned with 'public rights of use', not issues of ownership or infeudation (p. 15).

Table 2.2 conversely, takes a resource or use-centric approach to Craig's and Stair's Divisions of Things. It takes three well-used public things and indicates where each fell as categories within the hierarchies. Table 2.2 highlights the unpredictable and uncertain nomenclatural outcomes that divergent (and incomplete) taxonomies produce.

The Division of Things fell into decline in the period of the Later Institutional Writers – roughly the period from the 18th to the mid-19th centuries. Robbie observes three trends unfolding over this time: a 'withering of common things'; the further 'rise of regalia'; and the disappearance of the nomenclature of the Division of Things itself. By the time of modern Scots law literature, '[t]here was to be no return to the Division of Things' in any formal sense (p. 30).

Nonetheless, Robbie claims optimistic grounds to 'build a modern Division of Things' around this 'historical framework' (p. 43). Irrespective of the merits or otherwise of re-creating a modern construct, the enduring appeal of this very Scots taxonomy has (at least) two lasting legacies for the jurisprudence of the public estate; first, the clarity given to *regalia*, and second, the symbolism of public rights of passage as an entrenched 'main real right' of Scots property law.

While the category of *public things* was subsumed within the class of *regalia*, the conceptual certainty surrounding *regalia* marks out two very distinct categories of public realty, the first held by the Crown in trust for the public, and thus inalienable (*regalia majora*), and the second, an exclusive Crown property not held for the public and hence disposable (*regalia minora*). This clarity had been evident for some time. For example, the later institutional writer John Erskine described *regalia majora* in the following terms in 1773:

> But as the regalia of this sort are little capable of property, and chiefly adapted to public use, the King's right in them is truly no more than a trust for the behoof of his people, for he cannot hurt the navigation of rivers, or shut up highways, or demolish bridges …[24]

In 1892, scholar John Rankine re-affirms the key distinction between the two forms of *regalia*, being 'those which cannot and those which can be alienated by the

Crown to a subject, [and] those rights which the Crown holds as trustee for the public, and those which it holds for its own profit' (p. 211). Such consistent 'straight thinking' about the public estate is refreshing.

Similarly, the credence that these taxonomies delivered for the public right of passage ensured its consolidation as a 'main real right' in the modern *numerus clausus* of Scots property law (Anderson 2016, p. 13). This represents a powerful symbolic affirmation, a rare elucidation of a public real right within the property mainstream. Again, this invokes a technical 'straight thinking' around the ambit of the public right. Thus, the public right of way is said to distinguishable from the private servitude in four clear-cut ways, 'title to sue in a public right of way rests with every member of the public; the decree granted for [the public right] is *res judicata* for or against the whole public; the public right of way is for the public's use, a servitude is not; and in the case of the public right, each *termini* must be a public place' (Cusine and Paisley 1998, p. 720).

The counter-legacy of the Division of Things is its decline and eventual disappearance from Scots law. For the public estate, this performance of taxonomic failure sets an unhelpful precedent, amplified given the *gravitas* Scots law otherwise accords its institutional writers. Likewise, eminent jurists of the time could not agree on the status of key public realty, as Table 2.2 shows. Amidst a few examples of clarity, there was also much ambiguity and confusion, a first glimpse of the paradox that is the taxonomic public endeavor.

If there is a modern Division of Things in the Scots public realm, it is a structure where *corporeal* public realty is relegated to a secondary, subsidiary tier. In addition to traditional rights of passage, the rise of the incorporeal public right of 'responsible access' under the *Law Reform (Scotland) Act 2003* is a dramatic and supervening addition to the hierarchy. In a jurisdiction where the majority of lands are owned by a small private few,[25] this right of 'responsible access' ensures that the public realm is seen through an incorporeal, rights-based lens. This perspective contrasts starkly with that of the western United States, next to be canvassed, where the prism is unambiguously one of corporeal public lands. This robust Scots 'universalist' right to 'be on land and to cross land'[26] is testament to many social and political factors, discussed in detail in Chapter 6. One less traversed is the juristic legacy that strived over centuries (albeit imperfectly) to find a rational and principled place for public realty within the taxonomy of property law.

2.3 US federal public lands – one-third of a nation, one-half of the West

Federal public lands comprise around 670 million acres, or nearly 30% of the United States' land area. This grandiloquent figure was the title of the landmark (and last) report of the Public Land Law Review Commission in 1970, 'One Third of the Nation's Land'.[27] In the 11 continental western states, the public estate exceeds 47% of the footprint, and in Nevada, Utah and Oregon, the figure soars proportionately again to 82%, 64% and 52% respectively (Lehmann 1995, pp. 4, 22–23).[28]

Unsurprisingly then, the vast majority of federal lands are in the West. While 'federal land and resources law may be increasingly national [with] principal cases being drawn from all regions of the country' (Coggins et al 2007, p. 12), this discussion reflects the dominance of federal western land holdings, compared to 'east of the Mississippi where the federal government owns only 4 percent of the land' (Bui and Singer-Katz 2016).

Originally 'acquired' to promote the nation's Manifest Destiny, the federal government's storehouse of public lands incentivized development through a closer settlement program based on principles of 'first in time, first in right', rewarding white settlers with 160-acre land grants under the Homestead Act of 1862.[29] This bonanza, fed by a seemingly inexhaustible land bank available for private disposal drew to a close by the late 19th century, when federal land retention policies coupled with principles of utilitarian conservation or 'scientific management' came to the fore.[30] The frontier reputedly closed with the passage of the Taylor Grazing Act in 1934, which regulated grazing on the fragile western ranges and 'reversed homestead entry onto the public domain' (Page 2009, p. 412).[31] Of course, much of the land 'retained' was geographically ill suited to intensive settlement or agriculture, being arid, at high altitude, and inaccessible, and whose chief value lay in grazing or pastoral purposes, not homesteading.[32] Robert Keiter describes this historical narrative, and the value of western federal lands to the United States in the following terms:

> The federal estate … has long been regarded as a literal storehouse for the nation. Awash in valuable natural resources, uncluttered open spaces, and breathtaking vistas, the public lands historically served as a catalyst for westward expansion, then as a development bank for the growing nation, and more recently as a last bastion of wilderness. Western states and communities have long looked to the public lands for their economic sustenance, whether through royalty payments, job opportunities, or as magnets for tourism. Over time, public land law and policy have evolved to accommodate the felt necessities of the day.
>
> *(2005, p. 1128)*

Moreover, the federal estate's superlative acreage and vast natural resources fostered a rich public land law and policy scholarship in western law schools. In 1915, it was seen as a subject 'largely neglected', notwithstanding its importance 'for the practitioner in the states of the West … especially when consideration is given to the vast area of public lands belonging to the federal government' (Arnold 1915, pp. 316–317). The later spread of the discipline amongst western law schools confirmed the sense that 'this subject is one of vital concern to the western states' (ibid., p. 317).[33]

Federal landholdings are mostly categorized and defined by the *identity* of the four responsible federal agencies: the Bureau of Land Management (BLM), National Park Service, US Forest Service, and the US Fish and Wildlife Service.[34] Other taxonomies struggle for recognition or adoption. For instance, a resource-premised structure could be feasible, suggesting a categorization of public lands based on the resource exploited: minerals, oil or gas extraction, timber, forage, wildlife, recreation, or wilderness. The difficulty in adopting a resource-premised taxonomy however is the 'multiple use sustained yield' mandate that dates from the 1960 Act (of the same name), and re-affirmed in the *Federal Land Management and Planning Act 1976* (FLMPA). Hence, BLM lands or national forests can host a multiplicity of simultaneous resource uses, from forestry to grazing, to wildlife refuge and recreation. Even in lands with dominant uses such as national parks, the needs of recreation, conservation and preservation may sit uneasily. Jedidah Britton-Purdy describes this in 2019 terms as a 'structured normative pluralism', an 'integrat[ion of] a range of competing values' (p. 939). Values-compatibility is far from universal; indeed much of modern public land law in the United States is concerned with legal responses to the problems of 'avoiding or resolving resource conflicts' (Coggins et al 2007, p. 15). Ultimately, competing resource uses make a resource-premised taxonomy difficult when public lands fail to fit neatly in their respective pigeonholes.

Other novel thematic taxonomies have been floated, for example, identifying discrete resources, land-based resources, and the commons (Freyfogle 2007). In 1974, Jerome Muys proposed a three-way classification system for federal lands; *resource preservation lands* (national parks, wildlife refuges), *multiple resource use lands* (BLM grazing lands, national forests) and a catchall *lands used for specific non-resource oriented purposes* (defense lands etc.).[35] This smorgasbord of taxonomic choice mirrors 'like so much of public land law' – an approach where 'consistency is not a hallmark and generalization is hazardous' (Coggins et al. 2007, p. 14). Muys' trio of categories did not gain traction, despite the bright-line clarity that its first two classes offered. Taxonomies often suffer the curse of the 'catchall,' into which miscellaneous loose ends find a less-than-logical, or discomfortingly large home.

Hence, in the absence of any compelling alternative, western public lands remain strongly identified with the federal agency charged with the land's management and control. BLM lands are the most extensive, comprising some 247.3 million acres. The agency's jurisdiction covers once unallocated public domain lands, the lands rejected as unsuitable for purchase or homesteading, the colloquial 'lands nobody wanted' (Dombeck et al 2003, p. 2). Its original remit, reflecting its Grazing Service roots, was regulation of the range for grazing and mining activities. But over time, other resource uses, such as conservation came within its ambit. The BLM is long criticized as an example of 'agency capture,' wherein vested (that is, private grazing) interests unduly control agency decision-making processes. Conversely, rancher groups are scathing of BLM practices and forage pricing regimes (Hage 1989; cf Ferguson and Ferguson 1983). The BLM's 'organic statute' is the FLMPA of 1976.

Federal lands under the control of the US Forest Service (USFS) comprise 'the second largest system by acreage' (Coggins et al 2007, p. 21) at 192.9 million acres. The timber resource is managed by the USFS for harvesting and conservation purposes, guided for decades by principles of 'scientific management' championed by its founding progressive-era director, Gifford Pinchot. The national forest system is required under statute 'to improve and protect the forest … for the purpose of securing favorable conditions of water flows, and to furnish a continuous supply of timber' (16 USC sect. 475). The National Forest Management Act of 1976 is the agency's organic statute. Recreation, conservation and grazing are other resource uses widely undertaken on Forest Service lands.

The US Fish and Wildlife Service (FWS) administers a wildlife refuge system of 89.1 million acres, which like the Forest system, dates from the progressive era of the early 20th century, and unilateral proclamations of 'bird refuges' by President Theodore Roosevelt (Britton-Purdy 2019, p. 958). It includes fee simple refuges set aside for wildlife conservation, and less than fee interests such as waterfowl easements. Refuge lands exhibit a 'bewildering taxonomic diversity of units', including migratory bird refuges, waterfowl production areas, game ranges, and wildlife and fish refuges (Coggins et al 2007, p. 847).

Lastly, the National Park Service (NPS) is an iconic American institution. The United States invented the concept of the national park with the opening of Yellowstone four years after the Civil War. Twenty-six new parks followed in the period up to 1916, when the Park Service was formed under first director Stephen Mather.[36] While its primary objective remains the preservation of approximately 60 national parks, the Park Service also administers an increasing and divergent array of other lands and units, such as recreation areas, urban parks, cultural and historic sites, national monuments, national seashores, and national trails, comprising a total area of 79.6 million acres.[37] Indeed, 'the ever increasing number of national park units and their diversity of categories has led to criticism of '"park barrel" politics' that allegedly dilute the integrity of the National Park estate (Coggins et al. 2007, pp. 23–24).[38]

While this agency-based public land taxonomy has not proved 'an exact science' (p. 20), it has proved to be lasting. Unlike the highly technical classifications of Scottish institutional writers, the US methodology is a porous early 20th century construct that evolved as exigency required. As George Coggins and his colleagues observe:

> No classification of public lands is exclusive or immutable (even classifications chosen expressly by Congress) and overlapping functions and common problems are more of a rule than an exception. The distribution of federal lands to agencies with delegated management powers is as much a function of historical contingency as it is rational deliberation.
>
> *(p. 20)*

This agency-based schema has its drawbacks. It is incomplete, failing to capture other public lands managed by other state agencies. Moreover, its myopic preoccupation with public *lands* (emphasis added) also ignores the plethora of less than fee public interests; such as public trust rights famously enforced at Mono Lake, California (see Chapter 3), or customary public access rights along the Oregon Pacific coast (see Chapter 6). Nor does this blunt categorization expand theoretical understandings of the public estate; rather, by emphasizing government centrality, it entrenches simplistic definitions of public lands as 'lands owned by the United States' or 'federally-owned lands for limited purposes' (Coggins et al. 2007, p. 14).

Moreover, this federal agency taxonomy ignores important critiques of public lands in the West. So-called agency capture of the BLM by grazing interests has long been blamed for the parlous ecological state of the rangelands, with attendant causes and effects of overgrazing, native vegetation loss, and soil erosion (Page 2009). In recent years, the increasing incidence of catastrophic wildfires and 'smoke apocalypse' in the Pacific Northwest and California has been laid at the door of not only the 'multifaceted effects of climate change' but also, critically the environmentally suspect 'practice of fire suppression rather than fire management by the U.S. Forest Service' (Kindig 2018). On the left, public lands in the American West have become a 'verb' for colonial dispossession, settler violence, and the institutionalization of a 'settler commons' (Anson 2019). On the right, public lands are symbolic of federal government overreach, 'land grabs' and a loss of local control. Such diverse critiques of the western public estate reveal complexities that no crude agency-premised taxonomy could ever meaningfully address.

Nonetheless, public lands enjoy a high profile in the western United States – for all the right and wrong reasons. They are loved to death in the summer gridlock at Yosemite, yet loathed in equal measure by aggrieved ranchers. Public lands do not fade to an existential grey; the well-known BLM, NPS, USFS and FWS reinforce a public understanding that agency lands are 'your public lands.'[39] The quintessential westerner Wallace Stegner writes of prevailing 'attitudes to the federal presence' and describes how each of the four federal bureaus charged with administering 'all the empty space', contribute to a sense of western pride and self-image (2008, p. 87):

> All I can do is repeat that the land bureaus have a strong, often disregarded, influence on how life is lived in the West. They provide and protect the visible, available, unfenced space that surrounds almost all western cities and towns – surrounds them as water surrounds fish, and is their living element. … Neither state ownership nor private ownership could offer anywhere near the disinterested stewardship that these imperfect and embattled federal bureaus do, while at the same time making western space available to millions.
>
> *(p. 91)*

Stegner elevates federal agency lands to a plane beyond ownership, private or state. Rather, these are lands open to all, 'unfenced' and 'available', analogous to the public places of Scots jurisprudence, where the emphasis lay on public use, not questions of title. Taxonomy in the western United States may be a crude administrative device, an inexact science, but it yields a profile for public lands that is clear, robust, and widely understood within its narrow remit.

2.4 New Zealand's public outdoors – predominant purpose, bi-cultural context

If the delineation of federal lands in the western United States turns on bureau identity, in New Zealand, public lands and public rights in land are organized around a comprehensive legislative architecture – one based on the predominant *purpose* to which the public realty is put. Statutory schemes cover the (public property) field, both in terms of their breadth, and their consistent application across all legislated forms of a vast public estate, corporeal and incorporeal.

While undoubtedly wide-ranging, consistent and detailed, what makes the New Zealand public taxonomy remarkable is the way this structure molds to societal change as ideas of public purpose evolve. In Aotearoa/New Zealand, the public estate finds itself at the vanguard of a profound cultural shift – one where public places – ex-national parks, rivers or mountains – have been, or are proposed to be endowed with a legal personhood that reflects the nation's bi-cultural identity.[40] Maori worldviews about place disrupt western mono-cultural perspectives of public ownership; yet in the process re-shape (and re-organize) the public estate in ways truthful to their spatio-temporal setting. While no doubt a work in progress, this re-ordering of the public and Maori estates is achieved in a systematic, legislated fashion, a quiet triumph of taxonomic order set amidst the swirl of a deep socio-cultural and ontological shift.

The foundational architecture of the New Zealand public estate is premised on four key public property statutes: the *Reserves Act 1977*, the *National Parks Act 1980*, the *Conservation Act 1987*, and the *Land Act* of 1948. The *Reserves Act 1977* gives statutory validity to 'the control, management, development, use, maintenance and preservation of reserves' through a classification scheme that turns on the public land's 'principal or primary purpose' (Sect. 16(1)). Broadly speaking, 'reserves' or 'public reserves' are lands 'set apart for any public purpose' (Sect. 2(1)). The concept of 'public purpose' is defined to mean 'the use, benefit, enjoyment, safety, or defense of the people of New Zealand or the inhabitants of any district or locality therein' (Sect. 2(2)). Section 3(1) likewise expands on what public 'purpose' encompasses, to include *inter alia,* recreational, environmental, landscape, ecological, community, and access values. The Act envisages seven categories of reserve, 'set apart' for recreation, historic, scenic, natural, scientific, government and local purposes (Sects.17–23). Statutory purposes thus cover a diverse field, from 'sporting activities and the physical welfare and enjoyment of the public' to 'protecting and preserving in perpetuity indigenous flora and fauna', and more.

Similarly, the *National Parks Act 1980* regulates and administers public parks for the general *purpose* of '(preserving in perpetuity as national parks, for their intrinsic worth and for the benefit, use and enjoyment of the public areas of New Zealand that contain scenery of such distinctive quality, ecological systems, or natural features so beautiful, unique, or scientifically important that their preservation is in the national interest [*sic*]' (Sect. 4(1)). The later *Conservation Act 1987* permits the declaration of conservation areas 'held for conservation purposes' that do not fit the prescriptive definitions of reserves or national parks. This Act creates further conservation sub-hierarchies, variously designated as stewardship areas, concessions, conservation parks, and wilderness, ecological, sanctuary, watercourse, amenity or wildlife management areas (Sects. 19–23).

Finally, the oft-amended *Land Act 1948* completes (much of) the remaining public corporeal jigsaw,[41] with its sweeping up of 'land vested in Her Majesty … not for the time being set aside for any public *purpose* or held by any person in fee simple' (Sect. 2(1), emphasis added). The purpose of 'Crown land' is in effect, its public non-purpose, namely to catch all lands not otherwise dealt with, and excluding lands disposed of as private freehold. Like its Australian cousins, the *Land Act* has a contextual heritage extending back to the mid-19th century, with colonial-era imperatives of settling the remote hinterlands, or in New Zealand parlance, the backcountry. The 1948 Act created a diverse array of public tenures, from pastoral leases under the now repealed Section 66 (which at its height covered 30% of the nation's acreage), to idiosyncratic flax leases granted for terms of up to 33 years '[f]or the purpose of growing, cutting, or removing flax' (Sect. 166), an Indigenous perennial plant used for sundry textile uses.

In its incorporeal iterations, the New Zealand public estate is likewise motivated by public purpose. For example, under the *Queen Elizabeth the Second National Trust Act 1977*, open space covenants are purposed on preserving landscape-scale open spaces, and public access to them (Sects. 22 and 33). Similar provisions exist in the *Conservation Act 1987*.

Unlike the western United States, this unassuming (and largely uncontroversial) taxonomy turns on statutorily defined purpose, not agency management. In New Zealand, the Department of Conservation (DoC) manages a vast portfolio of public lands, including under the *Conservation Act*, the *National Parks Act*, and some lands under the *Reserves Act*. In the case of lands under the *Reserves Act*, land managers could also include local authorities or domain trusts. The identity of the public manager is administratively important, but it is not determinative of the public carve-up.

Unique to New Zealand, the public estate also sits alongside the Maori estate. The two are mostly separate, with different statutory bases and distinct mechanisms for the adjudication and determination of property rights.[42] The *Te Ture Whenua Maori Act 1993* (or *Maori Land Act 1993*) explains this parallel co-existence through a taxonomy that requires all land in New Zealand to 'have one of the following statuses': Maori customary land, Maori freehold land, General land (i.e. private freehold); General land owned by Maori, Crown land; and Crown land preserved for Maori (Sect. 129(1)). The public estate is found in the last two classes; in particular, stand-alone 'Crown land' is defined for the purposes of the Act to mean 'land (other than Maori customary land) that has not been alienated from the Crown for a subsisting estate in fee simple' (Sect. 129(2)(e)), a classic definition by exclusion where public land is non-private. As this taxonomy implies, there is scope for overlap (for example, Crown land preserved for Maori) (Sect. 129(2)(f)), and as the Act likewise makes clear, there is wide power for the status of individual parcels of land to be altered through court order (Sects. 130–137).

As noted, public lands have been at the vanguard of a distinctly New Zealand paradigm shift in the last decade, a trend that transcends the erstwhile neat division of land between Maori and the Crown. Three recent Acts of the New Zealand parliament exemplify this gathering shift; the *Coastal and Marine Area (Takutai Moana) Act 2011*, the *Te Urewera Act 2014*, and the *Te Awa Tupua (Whanganui River Claims Settlement) Act 2017*.[43] In 2011, the *Coastal and Marine Area (Takutai Moana) Act* legislated that the foreshore and seabed, the liminal zone between land and sea that confounded Scots Institutional Writers (and Roman lawyers a millennium before), was legally 'ownerless'. Section 11 divested Crown ownership and replaced it with the concept of a 'common marine and coastal area', lands ostensibly owned by no one. This Act in turn replaced the *Foreshore and Seabed Act* 2004, which Maori regarded as 'discriminatory and a confiscation of property rights in the foreshore area' (Jones 2016, p. 80). Critics of the 2011 Act may describe it as 'spin-doctoring', but coastal and submerged public lands were the context through which efforts at bi-cultural accommodation were enacted by de-centering notions of ownership.

In 2014, the former Urewera National Park in the North Island, described in its organic Act as 'ancient and enduring, a fortress of nature, alive with history, its scenery abundant with mystery, adventure and remote beauty' (Sect. 3(1) Te Urewera Act 2014) was de-gazetted as a national park after 60 years. The land was re-constituted as Te Urewera, a legal entity in its own right with all the rights, powers, duties and liabilities of a legal person (Sect. 11). In effect, the land has become its own registered 'owner' (Sect. 12(3)). While Te Urewera must be seen in its unique spatio-temporal and cultural context, it nonetheless remains a part of the New Zealand public estate, as Section 4 – in particular Section 4(c) – underscores:

> The *purpose* (emphasis added) of this Act is to establish and preserve in perpetuity a legal identity and protected status for Te Urewera for its intrinsic worth, its distinctive natural and cultural values, the integrity of those values, and for its national importance, and in particular to:
>
> (a) strengthen and maintain the connection between Tūhoe and Te Urewera; and
> (b) preserve as far as possible the natural features and beauty of Te Urewera, the integrity of its indigenous ecological systems and biodiversity, and its historical and cultural heritage; and
> (c) provide for Te Urewera as a place for public use and enjoyment, for recreation, learning, and spiritual reflection, and as an inspiration for all.

Moreover, in Section 12(2), the Act affirms the four-part New Zealand public taxonomy, making it clear that while Te Urewera's 'establishment land' is exceptional, in that it is no longer classified as reserve, national park, conservation area or Crown land, it nonetheless must be seen as an exception to the dominant statutory architecture.

Better known globally is the legal personhood conferred on the North Island's Whanganui River in 2017, or Te Awa Tupua (Clark et al 2019; Sect. 14(1) Te Awa Tupua (Whanganui River Claims Settlement) Act 2017). Again, this development must be seen within its specific national and cultural context, of treaty settlement, apology, historical account, and cultural redress (Jones 2016, pp. 93–4). Its organic Act, the *Te Awa Tupua (Whanganui River Claims Settlement) Act 2017* similarly acknowledges its exceptionality to the public *status quo*; declaring that any river lands previously classified as reserve, national park, conservation area or Crown land, are removed from such status (Sects. 40 and 53(2)).

Te Awa Tupua and Te Urewera reflect the emerging significance of Indigenous legal traditions in the settler colonial state, of a de-centering of dominant state law, and a concomitant 're-centering of Indigenous legal orders' (Jones 2016, p. 47). In de-colonizing property law, for instance, the incorporation of property-holding entities that reflect a Maori worldview is seen by Maori legal scholars as critical. As Jacinta Ruru writes (of the Whanganui River):

> I think that it is incredibly exciting what the legislation has done because it sees a joining of a Western perspective of law – legal personality – but really seeing it from a Maori perspective. Our lands around us have always had that personality. And this is probably the first time our legislation, our laws have really moved beyond the usual as to what we had, to be disrupted in many ways, and be transformed to embrace a Maori understanding of the worldview around us. … Being respectful to both knowledge systems [is] to see what it means to be Aotearoa/New Zealand, to see what it means to be of this place here.
>
> *(2017)*

Carwyn Jones likewise sees these changes as steps toward Indigenous self-determination. However, he is more qualified, saying that while 'these innovative mechanisms have provided creative solutions to difficult issues … and rightly heralded … as "groundbreaking" [they] still fall far short' (p. 98). Indeed while the Western concept of legal personality comes close to a Maori worldview, 'it confirms that Maori legal traditions will not be recognized on their own terms, but only through the closest equivalent … deploying a mechanism from the common law that is deemed by the Crown to be a close enough match' (ibid.).

In New Zealand, this de-colonization debate, and all its nuances, has flourished within its vast and rich public realm. Conversely, on private land, it has less purchase. What this shows is the maturity of public property jurisprudence in the antipodes, an understanding of *public purpose* expressed with understated confidence in its legislative architecture. It also demonstrates that this understanding of public purpose is equally capable of adapting to the contours of social and cultural change.

2.5 England – the invisible, disappearing public realm?

The last case study explores the English public estate. Surprisingly, it has a shorter history than its equivalents in former colonies such as New Zealand or the United States. As a creature of the later 19th century, the English public estate's (relative) lack of provenance has fed into a low public recognition. As Brett Christophers' pithily surmises, public real property flies below the English 'social and scholarly radar' (2018, p. 330):

> It is not only the privatization of land that is poorly visible in Britain, it is also the related fact that the state was a significant landowner in the first place. … Public landownership, and its putative purposes, was only very dimly visible to the general public when the neoliberal era began.
>
> *(pp. 330–331)*

Antonia Layard argues similarly. In 2012, she observed that English courts have left the question of 'what we mean by public property' unanswered. Layard offers to fill the judicial lacuna, suggesting that 'its simplest explanation … is that the land is public because the site is owned [via statute] by a public body' (2012, p. 269). As to statute, Layard argues that the analogous term 'public land' likewise is 'very rarely used in legislation' (ibid.). Only outlier examples exist, such as Section 48(12) of the Anti Social Behaviour Act, which in the context of *graffiti removal* defines public land as 'land to which the public are entitled or permitted to have access with or without payment …' Layard makes it plain that 'there is no *ex ante* distinction between private and public property in [English] land law … and there is no generic group of landowners that can be easily identified as "public"' (2016, p. 16). As a logical corollary, the 'true public realm, as something to which we should "return" to, does not then exist' (p. 20).

Upon reflection, what seems at first glance *surprising* about the English public realm is not. A brief public lands history – contrasted to ancient, well-understood common rights – and recent waves of ongoing land privatizations at rates far in excess of 18th century parliamentary enclosures, have combined to diminish an already weak public estate, and feed its existential angst.

The short history that Christophers cites begins with *The Return of Owners of Land* of 1875.[44] This national audit of land ownership – completed a mere 800 years after its predecessor the Domesday Book of 1086 – was designed to refute the widespread perception that landownership was the province of a privileged few. While its findings confirmed this perception as fact – and thus exposing the landed elite – it also revealed the virtual absence of any public estate:

> What is striking and important about the picture contained in the *Return* is the role in that era – or rather the lack of a role in that era – for public land and public landownership. The simple reality is that the British state was not, and never had been, a significant landowner. There was 'an almost complete absence' of state ownership. … The days of the state being a significant owner of land were, in short, yet to come.
>
> *(pp. 83–85)*

The Return was 'swiftly buried because of its embarrassing findings [that showed] that 95% of the population owned nothing at all' (Shrubsole 2019, p. 26). Eventually, political fallout, however, saw the central government and local authorities start to acquire public lands for public purposes (ibid.), an acquisition that ebbed, but mostly flowed in the century that followed. Thus by 1979, Christophers calculates that 20% of British lands were in public ownership.[45] Major concentrations of public property could be found in postwar cities, where council estates mushroomed, and in rural areas, where the public forest estate accounted for 1.2 million hectares, or 5% of the British landmass.[46]

Christophers' account of the *recent* history of the English public realm is open to contest, but criticisms mostly fall on the chronological or semantic fringes. For example, the advent of council housing may be traced back to a slightly earlier date of 1869, when St. Martin's Cottages in Vauxhall, Liverpool were built under the auspices of the *Labouring Classes Dwellings Act* of 1866, which enabled municipalities to buy land and build working-class homes (Boughton 2019, pp. 13–14).[47] Similarly, the (already canvassed) Hohfieldian risk of imprecise terminology muddies English public waters. So, if one includes *Crown lands* under the public moniker, the history of royal landownership extends the English public estate back a millennium or more, and 'then of course, things look very different' (Christophers 2018, p. 87). But as Christophers argues, the sovereign herself was in most cases an absolute or effective owner, holding land under a type of *regalia minora*. As a result, '[t]he monarch, was … one of the privileged few individuals whose extensive holdings were "outed" in the *Return*' (ibid.).[48] This aside also reveals that Crown land takes a distinctly different hue in England. Unlike the colonial context, in New Zealand, Canada or Australia, Crown land is not the monarch's exclusive property. Rather, the term is a descriptor of public lands (Shore and Williams 2019). In England, the monarch's holdings were renamed the Crown Estate in 1955, ostensibly to avoid confusion, however there are also 'Crown Lands' which are defined by statute to mean 'land in which there is Crown or Duchy interest' (Section 293, Town and Country Planning Act 1990).[49] As Layard comments (more widely), this is but one example of many 'contested dichotomies' in the English public realm.

Similarly, the contested demarcation between the commons and public lands, again the subject of earlier discussion, problematizes a clear(er) understanding of the English public realm. Commons have a rich and ancient history in English land law, where idiosyncratic rights such as pannage or estovers validated localized uses of local resources. But for outsiders beyond that community, and excluded by its customary laws, such lands were not universally accessible. Likewise, in recent times, many 'commons' in English cities (for example, Southampton Common) have migrated in practical terms from common to public land. Whether in the abstract or the grounded, such imprecision stands in the way of Hohfield's ideal of legal 'straight-thinking.' So when the commons, or town and village greens are raised in English property discourse, it is easy to blur an already hazy line between common and public.

The modern English public estate, diminished to around 10% of the national acreage in 2018 (Christophers 2018, pp. 258–263; Shrubsole 2019, pp. 144 and 298), appears to lack any central organizing principle. In some cases, the public realty's *use* is its key. In others, it is the identity of the public body that ostensibly owns or manages the land. Or, its rationale could fall to its public designation. It is perhaps safer to compile a type of public shopping list. So, in rural areas, public lands include the forest estate, nature conservation zones such as green belts, the county farming estate, the ancient public footpath network, countryside and coastal rights to roam, and some ten national parks (Shrubsole 2019, p. 248). The latter are a case in point of qualified public-ness, 'made up of a patchwork of public and private landowners' where designation as national park does not 'make [the] land either public or private. The[ir] status is a regulatory designation introducing national park authorities to exercise management responsibilities rather than changing land ownership' (Layard 2016, p. 17). To make the lines even more blurred, in July 2019, London declared itself the world's first 'national park city'.[50]

In cities, the public estate includes parks (such as the eight well-loved royal parks in London), allotments, and council-owned housing estates (Christophers 2018, p. 100; Shrubsole 2019, p. 62). Beyond the urban/rural duality, other components of the public realm include the National Health Service estate, defense bases, lands owned by public education authorities, lands owned by nationalized entities, public highways, and public remnants of the rail network.

In the absence of an organizing rationale, the public estate's 'public-ness' is often contested or challenged. More prosaically, its acreage has been sharply reduced. School playgrounds and sporting ovals have been subdivided off and sold, the Right to Buy cut a swathe through public housing, the NHS's landowning arm has been corporatized, and so on. The neoliberal ideology of privatization is no doubt chiefly responsible for this loss of public faith (and acreage), but it springs from a low base. And it persists despite the empirical evidence to the contrary, the little-regarded statistics that suggested (not so long ago) that 20% of England was in public hands.

If there is an iconic symbol or metaphor of the public estate in England, it is the council housing estate, the poster-child of the postwar Welfare State. As a metaphor, its rise and fall is potent. Its highpoint was from 1945 to 1951, when the Atlee Government sought to make good its 1945 campaign pledge to 'now win the peace' for its working-class constituency. In building public bricks and mortar, the rapid expansion of the council estate aspired to a 'simple decency' (Boughton 2019, p. 90)[51] progressive ideals that for a time captured hopes that 'what had once seemed radical, even utopian, [was now] mainstream' (p. 67):

> A spirit of companionship was the higher goal. This was an ideal sometimes understood nostalgically as a revival of community feeling lost to industrialization and urbanization. It was a criticism too of the design failings of the interwar cottage suburbs and their alleged lack of community. And it embodied hopes that frequently invoked, perhaps exaggerated, wartime sentiments of social solidarity and shared purpose could be maintained and strengthened in the post-war world. Practically, the expectation of higher

> living standards, more universally enjoyed, and a belief in the fuller quality of life they enabled were strong, even heartfelt.
>
> *(ibid.)*

As a guiding *public purpose*, this sentiment comes close to a public lodestar. Yet, these aspirations were short-lived. By the Thatcher era of the 1980s, public housing stock was sold in large numbers, the Right to Buy made former council tenants private freeholders (sometimes briefly), and public investment declined markedly. Fleeting utopian ideals of 'social solidarity' or 'shared purpose' became secondary to the imperatives of the market. In its place, a philosophy emerged which deemed public housing to be a shelter of last resort, and concomitantly relegated its residents to 'second-rate' status (p. 107). The decline of a once-great foundation of the English public realm was symbolized to many by the Grenfell Tower tragedy in June 2017, when over 70 council tenants died in a shocking fire attributed to flammable external cladding.

Like its metaphor, the decline of the English public realm, in both its idea and its materiality, has fed a particularly English sense of public existentialism. While public rights to roam may have been legislated in 2000 – in a brief win for the pedestrian democrat (see Chapter 6) – the public estate seems to have suffered disproportionate loss. As to why, Christophers cuts to the chase. Over the last 40 years, he argues, 'Britons have not mourned public landownership because ... they have not associated it with public benefit; they did not regard the land as genuinely, meaningfully, theirs' (p. 327).

2.6 Conclusions

This chapter's quest to seek public order has yielded a mixed bag. As the Division of Things showed, high levels of technicality may work in the finer micro, but in the messier macro, they fail to cover the field. At the spectrum's other end, the absence of any overarching public narrative coincides with an English quasi-nihilism, a sense that public lands serve no public benefit. Meanwhile in the American West, simple administrative categorizations produce equally simple understandings of 'your public lands.' It seems that some modicum of hierarchy is useful. But it is not an end in itself, and particularly not if the task becomes a substitute for 'thinking straight' about the public estate.

Piecemeal outcomes reveal that we need to look beyond simply putting the public house in order. If, like the US West, '[i]t is difficult to locate a common legal denominator among the many diverse instances of present federal ownership' (Coggins et al 2007, p. 19) then the superficial commonality that 'explains all' may not be there. So, what insights, if any, does this paradoxical seeking of order provide? In closing, this chapter suggests two. First, is the significance of *public purpose* to public real property. Second, is the desirability to account for what C.B. Macpherson calls 'state property,' one potential upside to the taxonomic exercise that might result in a coherently clearer, or at least, more differentiated and defensible public realm.

Where the public purpose of public real property is well understood, the latter tends to flourish. In Aotearoa/New Zealand, public purpose is quietly and clearly articulated in the legislative hierarchy. Indeed, like property itself, public purpose is optimal when it adapts to, and reflects changing contexts. The shift from a colonial mono-cultural view of public lands to de-colonized understandings of purpose – as is unfolding in New Zealand – illustrates how lofty public purposes may suit the times. Contrast this to the hollowing out of public purpose in England, where faith in postwar, utopian-like 'municipal dreams' has faded after four decades. In drawing on the scholarship of geographer Doreen Massey, Christophers argues that 'Massey's key contribution was to show that public ownership only means something different from private ownership if it is allowed to.' Public purpose loses its point when it becomes a pale(r), indistinguishable version of private purpose. As Christophers reiterates, '[if] public ownership … really does mean anything different, one cannot repeat this truth often enough' (p. 38). This 'truth' is developed further in Chapter 3.

The second insight draws on the experience of Scots Institutional Writers, and their simultaneous grappling of the Roman law's *res communes* and *res publicae* with different understandings of *regalia*. While 'fluid' Roman taxonomies *also* 'did not develop various types of nonexclusive property at any great length' (Rose 2003, p. 91), their influential rigor did yield a semblance of Scots law 'straight thinking' around the public property of the monarch. The differentiation between Crown property owned for the monarch's exclusive purposes, and that held in a form of inalienable public trust may be carried forward to modern state property. This differentiation marks out certain public lands – like Macpherson's corporate office buildings – from those public real interests impressed with wider public purpose(s). Indeed, the Roman law category of *res universitas*, which neither Craig nor Stair brought into the Divisional fold, might help better. These *res* were the corporate property of public bodies, 'of municipal theaters, racecourses and other income-producing public property'. Carol Rose describes them as 'bounded', in contrast to the 'wide-open synergies' of *res publicae* (2003, pp. 108 and 108). 'Bounded' government offices, and their like, may be best parked in a public sub-category of their own, quarantining their corporate qualities from the 'wide-open synergies' of the public estate in the main. That is not to say that Inland Revenue offices or high-security military bases do not serve a public purpose. But they do act as a distraction, relative outliers that mark down the public estate as nothing more than a diluted private variant, where the only difference is that a state agency holds the stick right of exclusion, not a private owner. Or worse still, that they create a mindset where there is no distinction at all.

So here's the thing about Chapter 2, taxonomy only takes you so far. It opens up a (mostly) unhelpful Pandora's box of a million shades of grey. But what it does reveal is the inevitability of distinction in the public estate, and the concomitant need to tolerate and accept this vast public diversity – in all its messiness. It also highlights that when it comes to the *public purposes* of public real property, distinctly public rationales are both desirable, and necessary.

Notes

1 Blomley argues that this 'great dichotomy' is not as exhaustive or mutually exclusive as some proponents would argue, a simple binary 'that exhausts all viable options for property' (2005 pp. 283–284).
2 Layard argues that public space and public property are not one and the same (2016). See Chapter 8.
3 For example, section 7 *Conveyancing Act (1919)* NSW defines property as *including* 'any real and personal property, and any estate or interest in any property real or personal, and any debt, and any thing in action, and any other right or interest'.
4 *Kerrie Hunter Otto v Inn at Watervale, Inc.* SC: 155380, Benzie CC: 14-009969-NO (April 6, 2018).
5 *State ex rel. Thornton v Hay* 462 P.2d 671 (1969), 724.
6 To give multiple meanings to the one word has a rich property provenance. *Tenant* describes both the lessor/lessee relationship, and the remainderman/life tenant relationship.
7 Others would ascribe the modern division between public and private to the rise of industrial capitalism, not the state (Zaretsky 2012, p. 155).
8 Commoning' is used to describe actions that contest the private status of land and give it a collective effect. Its use reveals little thought for the distinction between common and public lands. There is no equivalent verb of 'public-ing'.
9 For instance, Scottish public real rights are said to be exercised in full with no limitation on the number of people entitled to use (Cusine and Paisley 1998, p. 767).
10 'Institutional writers have a special place in Scots law, in that their writings are considered to be a formal source of law in their own right' (Anderson 2016, p. 9).
11 The institutional period in Scots law dates from the early 17th to the first half of the 19th centuries, from jurists Craig and Stair to Hume and Bell.
12 Robbie cites Kevin Gray, 'Property Law in Thin Air' (1991) 50 *CLJ* 252 at 256.
13 Although, it was not published as *Jus Feudale* until 1655.
14 Reserved exclusively for subjects of the Crown.
15 Book II, Title I, Para. 5.
16 Book II, Title I, Para. 5.
17 Book II, Title I, Para. 7.
18 Property is the 'main real right ... standing in the middle betwixt community [or commonty] and possession, which precede it, and servitude and pledge which follow it. But the nature of property is best understood, when it is compared to community; for in this they both agree, that either hath a power to dispose of things, and in this they differ, that community is a promiscuous and a conjunct power, but property is a disjunct and separate power of disposal', Book II, Title I, Para. 28.
19 Other servitudes include pasturage, watering, fueling and thirlage (rights restricted to mills).
20 Book II, I, Para. 9.
21 '[Y]ea and to all strangers having freedom of traffic' (Stair II, vii, 10).
22 Ways were described as 'part of the reservation from property, and the necessary vestige of the ancient community of the earth, and which are understood as the common pertinents of all grounds; for free ish and entry are implied in the very right of property', Book II, I. Para. 10.

23 Book II, I, Para. 61.
24 Erskine, Book II,VI, 17 (cited in Cusine and Paisley 1998, p. 716).
25 Outside the cities, a small number of estate holders own most of the countryside. Lovett cites that in 1995, 1,411 owners held 57.8% of Scotland (2003, p. 771).
26 Section 1(2) *Law Reform (Scotland) Act* 2003.
27 *One Third of the Nation's Land: A Report to the President and to the Congress by the Public Land Law Review Commission* (1970).
28 Even in urbanized California, the percentage of public lands stands at a respectable 44% (Coggins et al 2007, p. 14).
29 Strictly, the federal government never acquired unallocated public lands; they were ceded by new states joining the Union. In the case of Native Americans, their lands were 'acquired' under one-sided treaty arrangements and other dubious land transactions; see for example (Banner 2007).The Homestead Act of 1862 permitted US citizens (and prospective citizens) to settle 160 acres of public land, and through five years of settlement, labor, and improvement, and gain private title to that land. The maximum acreage was later increased to 320 and 640 acres, respectively (e.g. Desert Lands Act 1877), but the areas still remained unviable. The Homestead Act of 1862, ch. 75, 12 Stat. 392 expired in 1976 in all states but Alaska; it expired in Alaska in 1986.
30 Gifford Pinchot, first director of the US Forest Service, famously personifies scientific management principles that dominated federal land management until the 1960s, when principles of MUSY, 'multiple use, sustained yield' sanctioned multiple resource use; extractive uses include forestry and grazing, and non-extractive uses include recreation, conservation and preservation.
31 See also Farrington R. Carpenter, 'Carpenter on Grazing in National Forests', *American Cattle Producer,* February 1940, 11.
32 'The [Taylor Grazing] Act deals with … the leftover land- the culls as it were. Three generations of settlers passed them by. They are the most arid and least productive land in the Union. In and of themselves they are almost valueless. But when considered … in connection to private lands and water that are largely dependent upon them, they are indispensable' Theodore A Walters, First Assistant Secretary of the Interior, January 13, 1937, 'The Use and Abuse of the Public Range', 40th annual convention, American National Livestock Association.
33 Today there are several texts in this field, the subject is taught in numerous law schools from Colorado to Washington, and a specialist law review, the *Public Land and Resources Law Review* published by the School of Law at the University of Montana, is devoted to public land issues.
34 The taxonomy is articulated in diverse sources, in texts such as Coggins et al (2007), or in op-ed pieces such as Bui and Sanger-Katz (2016).
35 Jerome Muys, 'The Federal Lands' in *Federal Environmental Law* (1974) 495 (cited in Coggins et al 2007, pp. 19–20).
36 'Other Progressive conservation measures [largely brought within the national park system] included the protection of scenic and historic lands as "national monuments" under the Reclamation Act 1902 and the Antiquities Act 1906' (Fischer 2012, p. 319).
37 For example, the Stonewall National Monument in New York City was established in 2015 as one of the last executive acts of the Obama administration.
38 In 2017, the Trump administration opened up the Bears Ears and Grand Staircase Escalante National Monuments in Utah to drilling, mining and grazing by sharply reducing their area (Britton-Purdy 2019). Conversely, Sheldon Lyke critiques the gazettal of new national parks in 2018 by the Trump administration to sites with questionable conservation value but located in key electoral swing states.

39 Similarly, the campaign by outdoor-clothing company Patagonia against the shrinking of the Bears Ears National Monument in Utah by nearly 80% in 2017 used the catch line, 'The President Stole Your Land' (Gelles 2018).
40 These include the Te Urewera forest and ranges, the Whanganui River, and Mt. Taranaki, all in New Zealand's North Island.
41 Exceptions to this statement include, for instance, public lands reserved for road or railway purposes, or walkways under the *Walkways Act 2008* (NZ); see Chapter 6. The Queen Elizabeth II National Trust may also acquire corporeal lands for the purposes of preserving open space and public access, *Queen Elizabeth the Second National Trust Act 1977* (NZ).
42 For example, the Act establishes the Maori Land Court under Part 1, and the Maori Appellate Court under Part 2.
43 These three Acts are not intended to be exhaustive of this paradigm shift, for example, section 6X *Conservation Act 1987*, amended in 1990, allows for the appointment of Guardians of Lakes Manapouri, Monowai and Te Anau, by Ngai Tahu, the local Maori iwi.
44 There are four 'modern Domesdays' (Shrubsole 2019, p. 26).
45 Massey arrives at the same figure in 1980. She estimates that around 10% is owned by central government (significantly forestry land) with 7% owned by local authorities (with one-third of that 7% being common land). Nationalized industries and public services own less than 2%. Another (separate) category is land owned by the 'venerable institutions' at around 4%, namely the Crown Estate (lands owned ex officio by the monarch) and the establishment Church of England (1980, pp. 255–256).
46 The postwar expansion of public forests was not without controversy. Niemann (2016) argues an emphasis on the large-scale planting of sylvan monocultures, such as the Scandinavian pine, came at the cost of ancient woodlands, public accessibility, and woodland diversity.
47 These 'cottages' were in fact 'bleak' two four-story blocks of tenements demolished in 1977.
48 Conversely, Horowitz says that the private-public distinction could be traced back to 'the two different roles of the monarch as landowner', the lands the King owned as 'feudal lord [which] he could alienate as private property' and 'a second category of crown lands – in essence public lands – which he could not alienate' (Horowitz 1982, p. 1423). Horowitz cites tidal lands between high and low water marks as within the latter category.
49 An account of the byzantine nature of the Crown Estate can also be found in Shrubsole 2019 pp. 45–64.
50 https://theconversation.com/london-becomes-the-worlds-first-national-park-city-committed-to-giving-people-access-to-nature-120714.
51 A total of 804,921 council houses were built between 1945 and 1951 (Boughton 2019, p. 105).

References

Anderson, C 2016, *Property: A Guide to Scots Law*, Thomson Reuters, Edinburgh.

Anson, A 2019, 'The President Stole Your Lands: Public Lands and the Settler Commons', *Western American Literature* vol. 54, 49–62.

Arnold, E 1915, 'The Study of Public Land Law in the Western Law Schools', *California Law Review* vol. 4, 316–318.

Banner, S 2007, *How the Indians Lost Their Land: Law and Power on the Frontier*, Harvard University Press, Cambridge, MA.

Blomley, N 2005, 'Flowers in the Bathtub: Boundary Crossings at the Public–Private Divide', *Geoforum* vol. 36, 281–296.

Blomley, N 2013, 'Performing Property: Making the World', *Canadian Journal of Law and Jurisprudence* vol. 26, 23–48.

Boughton, J 2019, *Municipal Dreams: The Rise and Fall of Council Housing,* Verso Books, London.

Brill, M 2002, 'Problems with Mistaking Community Life for Public Life', *Places* vol. 14, no. 2, 48–55.

Britton-Purdy, J 2019, 'Whose Lands? Which Public? The Shape of Public-Lands Law and Trump's National Monument Proclamations', *Ecology Law Quarterly*, vol. 45, 921–963.

Bui, Q and Sanger-Katz, M 2016, 'Why the Government Owns So Much Land in the West', *The New York Times,* January 5, 2016 at www.nytimes.com/2016/01/06/upshot/why-the-government-owns-so-much-land-in-the-west.html?_r=0 (accessed 1 July 2019).

Christophers, B 2018, *The New Enclosure: The Appropriation of Public lands in Neoliberal Britain,* Verso Books, London.

Clark, C et al, 2019, 'Can You Hear the Rivers Sing? Legal Personhood, Ontology, and the Nitty-Gritty of Governance', *Ecology Law Quarterly,* vol. 45, 787–844.

Coggins, G et al, 2007 *Federal Public Land and Resources Law* (6th edn.) Foundation Press, New York.

Coquillette, D R 1979, 'Mosses from an Old Manse: Another Look at Some Historic Property Cases About the Environment', *Cornell Law Review* vol. 64, 761–821.

Cusine D J and Paisley, R R M 1998, *Servitudes and Rights of Way*, W Green, Edinburgh.

Dombeck, M P et al., 2003, *From Conquest to Conservation: Our Public Lands Legacy,* Island Press, Washington, DC.

Dunleavy, P 1995, 'The State', in R Goodin and P Pettit (eds.), *A Companion to Contemporary Political Philosophy,* Blackwell Publishers, Oxford.

Ferguson, D and Ferguson F, 1983, *Sacred Cows at the Public Trough,* Maverick Publications, Bend, OR.

Fischer, D H 2012, *Fairness and Freedom: A History of Two Open Societies New Zealand and the United States,* Oxford University Press, Oxford.

Freyfogle, E 2007, *Natural Resources Law: Private Rights and Collective Governance*, Thomson West, Minneapolis, MN.

Gelles, D 2018, 'Patagonia v Trump', *The New York Times*, May 5, 2018, at www.nytimes.com/2018/05/05/business/patagonia-trump-bears-ears.html?searchResultPosition=1 (accessed 1 November 2019).

Hage, W 1989, *Storm over Rangelands: Private Rights in Federal Lands*, Free Enterprise Press, Bellevue, WA.

Hohfield, W 1913, 'Some Fundamental Legal Conceptions as Applied in Legal Reasoning', *Yale Law Journal* vol. 23, 16–59.

Horowitz, M 1982, 'The History of the Public/Private Distinction', *University of Pennsylvania Law Review* vol. 130, 1423–1428.

Jessop, R 1990, *State Theory: Putting Capitalist States in their Place,* Polity Press, Cambridge.

Jones, C 2016, *New Treaty, New Tradition: Reconciling New Zealand and Maori Law,* Victoria University Press, Wellington.

Keiter, R B, 2005, 'Public Lands and Law Reform: Putting Theory, Policy, and Practice in Perspective' *Utah Law Review*, 1127–1226.

Kindig, J 2018, 'Defensible Space' *Boston Review*, Oct. 22, 2018 at http://bostonreview.net/science-nature/jessie-kindig-wildfires-western-myth (accessed 5 June 2019).

Layard, A 2012, 'Property Paradigms and Place-Making: A Right to the City; a Right to the Street' *Journal of Human Rights & Environment,* vol 3, 254–272.

Layard, A 2016, 'Public Space: Property, Lines, Interruptions', *Journal of Law, Property & Society* vol. 2, 1–47.
Lehmann, S 1995, *Privatizing Public Lands,* Oxford University Press, New York.
Lovett J, 'Progressive Property in Action: The Land Reform (Scotland) Act 2003', *Nebraska Law Review* vol. 89, 739–820.
Massey, D 1980, 'The Patterns of Landownership and its Implications for Policy', *Built Environment* vol. 6, 263–271.
Niemann, D 2016, *A Tale of Trees: The Battle to Save Britain's Ancient Woodland*, Short Books, London.
Page, J 2009, 'Grazing Rights and Public Lands in New Zealand and the Western United States: A Comparative Perspective', *Natural Resources Journal* vol. 49, 403–432.
Rankine, J 1892, *The Law of Land-Ownership in Scotland*, William Blackwood & Sons, Edinburgh.
Robbie, J 2015, *Private Water Rights,* Edinburgh Legal Education Trust, Edinburgh.
Rose, C M 2003, 'Romans, Roads, and Romantic Creators: Traditions of Public Property in the Information Age', *Law & Contemporary Problems* vol. 66, 89–110.
Day, S 2017, 'If the Hills Could Sue: Jacinta Ruru on Legal Personality and a Maori Worldview', https://thespinoff.co.nz/atea/atea-otago/27-11-2017/if-the-hills-could-sue-jacinta-ruru-on-legal-personality-and-a-maori-worldview/.
Shore, C and Williams, D (eds.) 2019, *The Shapeshifting Crown: Locating the State in Postcolonial New Zealand, Australia, Canada and the UK,* Cambridge University Press, Cambridge.
Shrubsole, G 2019, *Who Owns England? How We Lost Our Green & Pleasant Land & How to Take it Back,* William Collins, London.
Stegner, W 2008, *Wallace Stegner's West*, Heyday Books, Berkeley.
Walker, D M (ed.) 1981, *The Institutions of the Law of Scotland: Deduced from Its Originals and Collated with the Civil, Canon and Feudal laws, and the Customs of Neighbouring Nations in IV Books by James, Viscount of Stair,* The University Presses of Edinburgh and Glasgow, Edinburgh and Glasgow.
Wonnacott, M. 2006 *Possession of Land*, Cambridge University Press, Cambridge.
Zaretsky, E 2012, *Why America Needs a Left: A Historical Argument,* Polity, New York.

3

OF PUBLIC OWNING

3.1 Introduction

People have an innate sense of what is theirs, and what they must do to 'get the prize' of ownership (Rose 1985, p. 81). For individuals, the common law prescribes a formula, where a physical taking coupled with *animus possidendi* rewards the claimant. Yet, the idea of *public* owning provokes (and demands) very different responses than crude questions of control and intent. Rather than yelling 'this is mine' (ibid.), claims to public ownership encourage us, and those around us, to argue instead 'this is ours'. These are two very different utterances. To shout 'this is mine' sits easily within the individualized paradigm – the mindset we conflate as ownership writ large. Its assertion of dominion is one the law readily recognizes, and enforces. By contrast, the latter claim is ill suited to this private worldview. 'This is ours' tends to be spoken in a softer language, where collective rights and multiple owning have lesser purchase, words less familiar to the modern rhetoric of ownership.

Swimming against this strong rhetorical tide of private owning, Chapter 3 explores our many understandings of the public 'ownership' of public real property. It resorts to well-tested metaphors, images of spectrums, and the settled mechanism of the trust to explain, or at least illustrate, the idea of public owning. It then leaps off-script, considering other iterations of ownership perhaps better aligned to the public domain – the likes of unorganized publics at large, political theories of deep public ownership, or messy non-binaries where public and private are spatially porous.

In terms of structure, the chapter begins by canvassing the 'incidents' of public ownership, an enquiry framed within the conventional rights discourse of the private estate. Next, it asks the owner question, *who* owns public real property? This is a wide-ranging interrogation, one that examines a spectrum of putative owners, from the singular state to the multiple 'us', and from the territorially demarcated to the spatially blended. Last, the chapter ends in disruption. First, by unsettling colonial assumptions about the 'us' in public ownership – a contest of ideas that resonates deeply in the wide-open spaces of public lands. Second, by challenging the *emphasis* of ownership, with a shift from owner-identity to owner-purpose. Here, 'the question of who owns the land is perhaps less important than how and why', where ownership *per se* is not 'reified' but instead the 'owner's' rationality' is the key (Christophers 2018, p. 37), a subtle re-ordering, if you like, of the priorities and rationales of public owning.

Rhetoric and persuasion are implicit to this chapter. The former is key to setting the tone of the public narrative. The latter convinces us (or not) that one model of public ownership is more plausible than others. Carol Rose says that 'property is persuasion', and this chapter agrees, an effective public estate must persuade. To Rose, property may be seen in a variety of ways: as a picture, a metaphor, or narrative (1994). Added to this list, legal geographers see property as performance (Blomley 2013). The many iterations of public ownership explored in this chapter *persuade* us (or not) of their *plausibility* by the indicia they project, their images, stories, symbols, or acts of public doing. Seeing public real property through these 'Rosean theorems' is a blue-sky way to consider the estate afresh. It also reveals that retrofitting 'public' answers to an essentially private enquiry may be a vexed, often flawed process. In seeking out public ownership, perhaps we should be looking for *other*, less conventional indicia of title, the well-trodden grassed pathways, city parks seething with humanity, even gridlocked freeways. And less tangibly, in the shifting paradigms, the new stories that depict the diverse ways we relate to public space – the narratives that persuade us to call it 'ours'.

3.2 Public ownership: a rights-based analysis

This chapter's analysis of public ownership starts conventionally with the (still) dominant perspective that treats ownership as an aggregation or bundle of rights. The concentration of key stick rights in an owner's bundle affirms that ownership is 'the greatest possible interest in a thing which a mature system of law recognizes' (Honore 1961, p. 108). The bundle of sticks metaphor is a pedagogically elegant explanation of private ownership, and its rise to popular use by property academics in the later 19th century occurred in a distinctly private context (Banner 2011). But the metaphor, for all its obvious private appeal, is harder to translate into the language of the public realm. Holistically, a faithful rendition of the publicized bundle would treat 'public property owned by the body politic as nothing but the amalgamation of individual holdings' (Nili 2019). This view, described by Schmuel Nili as the 'private aggregation model', would logically mean that public real property only exists as 'the aggregation of individual resources' (p. 350). Such an explanation entrenches the primacy of the private right, and delivers a metaphoric depiction of the public estate in classically negative terms, defined by what it is not, the collective amalgamation of what are essentially (and otherwise) private rights.

C.B. Macpherson's oft-cited typology of 'private', 'state' and 'common' property (1978) is likewise premised on a strict reading of the individual rights paradigm. In the case of both state and private ownership, there is one exclusive stick-holder, be it a private individual/corporation, or the government. What sets Macpherson's 'common property' apart is that such rights are non-exclusive; that is they are held in common (or aggregated) with others. But as Macpherson insists, the 'point needs some emphasis', rights to 'public parks, city streets, highways' remain *individual* rights (p. 5).

To dig deeper into the granular, this 'private aggregation model' then begs a series of consequent (and problematic) investigations: what sticks belong in the public bundle? The *sina qua non* of private property, the right to exclude, with its gatekeeper explanation 'give me the right to exclude a person from a resource, and you give me property' is the antithesis of public property (Merrill 1998, p. 730). Rather, its inverse right of inclusion seems (at first glance) a more logical fit. Macpherson would mostly agree, since in the case of 'common property', its creation is underscored 'by the guarantee to each individual that he [*sic*] will not be excluded from the use or benefit of something' (ibid.). Yet, in practice, there are many publicly owned spaces from which we are not included. The corporate public property of state agencies is the clear-cut example. We are not free to wander the corridors of the departments of health, education, or environment. And what of public spaces where inclusion is only confirmed upon the payment of an entrance fee, the price of 'belonging' in municipal museums, state art galleries, public swimming pools, fenced botanic gardens, or even over-crowded city parks.[1]

Indeed, public places replete with Rose's 'wide-open synergies' do not universally promise unfettered inclusion. For example, there is no express guarantee of a right of public access in the *National Parks and Wildlife Act 1974* (NSW). Under Section 2A(1)(c), an object of the Act is 'fostering public appreciation, understanding and enjoyment of nature and cultural heritage and their conservation'. This object is preceded in order (and presumably importance) by 'the conservation of nature, natural habitats, ecosystems and ecosystem services' (Sect. 2A(1)(a)), and 'the protection of objects, places or features of cultural value within the landscape' (Sect. 2A(1)(b)). There is no statutory listing of public access. Similarly, in section 30E(1), access is not one of the five overarching Management Principles, although reference is made (again) to the 'promotion of public appreciation and understanding [of a park's] natural and cultural values', and the compatible provision of 'sustainable visitor or tourist use and enjoyment'. By contrast, public access is the default norm in New Zealand's conservation areas,[2] suggesting that inclusion is an inconsistent, and unreliable gatekeeper.

The right to possess is another core private property right, the 'origin of property' no less (Rose 1985).[3] Yet to possess public space is such a singular obsession, one at odds with sharing, the likelier epitome of our public performances in public space. Trying to shoehorn possession into public rights to land leads to awkward semantic contortions. In Scots law, the idea of 'public possession' is a pre-requisite to the finding of a public right of way at common law. Not only must there be a 'fixed route' between 'two public places', but the route must be publicly 'possessed' for twenty years (Anderson 2016, p. 257). Here, 'possession' adopts a lighter footfall; better understood as prescription, where there is peaceful, open and uninterrupted public use devoid of any claim to exclusivity. Property is no stranger to ambiguous terminology, as Chapter 2 posits. But to inscribe possession absent exclusivity is a term of legal art that borders on the oxymoron, at least to modern eyes.

The right to use holds much promise for the public estate. As a private right, it is one of Tony Honore's eleven 'standard incidents of ownership', listed second after possession. The right is described in a mere two paragraphs as 'a cardinal feature of ownership' (p. 116), which may, or may not overlap with the (subsequent) incidents of management and income. In its narrow interpretation, the right refers to the 'personal use and enjoyment of the thing owned' (p. 116). Limitations placed on an owner's use of a thing are implicitly acknowledged as real and substantive. Yet they do not 'detract from [the right's] importance', 'since the standard limitations are, in general, rather precisely defined' while 'the permissible types of use constitute an open list' (p. 116). Therefore, its strength stems from its open-endedness, its almost infinite latitude to embrace diverse acts of use and enjoyment that are not diminished simply because one particular use is proscribed.

Analogously, Simon Douglas explores the legal lacuna of the freehold fee simple through the lens of the equally empty right to use. Douglas argues that use is better described as a 'liberty' - as open-ended as Honore's 'right':

> If a freeholder, for example, is denied planning permission to build a conservatory, then although he [*sic*] has lost an important freedom, nothing follows from this which suggests that he is unable to cook in his kitchen, eat in his dining room, read a book in his lounge, etc. There are still an unlimited number of other things that a freeholder can do. Planning restrictions do not undermine the open-endedness of the freeholder's liberties to use.
>
> *(p. 368)*

Moreover, these liberties are 'exigible', that is, enforceable against the world. A private landowner has rights to use their land in ways that are 'free as against all persons' (p. 368). Yet, instead of expanding on the incidents of the liberty to use, Douglas devotes much of his analysis to finding its jural correlative, likely the 'extremely limited duty' of non-impairment of use. In the end, it is the vibe of the thing that speaks to the heart of this curiously vacant liberty, and its centrality to the fee simple, the 'strong intuitive grasp of what it means to own land' and the concomitant difficulty 'to express this in legal terminology' (p. 364). Scots law also struggles with the blank check quality of the right to use, recognizing that in the abstract, it 'permit(s) the owner to use his [*sic*] property in any manner he sees fit. He may build dens of iniquity or temples of righteousness, sow and reap crops, or do nothing at all if he pleases' (Paisley 2000, p. 125). It is in its *limitations* that the right is best understood, the circumscriptions of geography, the extent of an owner's estate, or the stipulations of contract, statute, or the common law of nuisance (ibid.).

These various observations of the private right to use can be translated to its public analogue. One could argue that it is the sheer number of things that public owners may do that defines the right, not the narrow category of public acts that are, from time to time, proscribed. Similarly, the exercise of the public right is constrained by its contexts, the lie of the public land, the land's public purpose(s), or the real-world exigencies of private law or statute. Take these necessary constraints away, and (quoting Douglas) 'there are still an unlimited number of other things that a [public owner] can do'. Perhaps, the Michigan Supreme Court spoke to the essence of this public right to use when it described children 'building sand castles, throwing stones in the water, and splashing around'.[4] These are but several of an almost limitless plenitude of public rights that members of the public may use and enjoy.

Public rights of use are also prioritized on the basis of 'first in time'. The timing and consequent persuasiveness of each particular claim measures its success, 'reserving' desirable stretches of public sand, or secluded corners of city parks through unequivocal acts of first possession, like the strategic placement of a towel or picnic hamper. Indeed, use claims to public space are increasingly blatant, with sophisticated shelters or large marquees proliferating at the expense of the modest beach umbrella as markers of lengthy duration. No doubt, such brazen acts implicitly heed Richard Epstein's cautionary note that despite the indicia of claim, 'sometimes a long absence results in a gradual displacement' (2002, p. 528). However, first in time is not universal. As Epstein also illustrates, shoveling out a winter car park on Chicago's snow-covered public streets rewards the sweat of the claimant's brow, 'allocating' that car park to the nearby resident-laborer, not the first opportunistic driver who chances upon an empty space. This practice creates a complex system of 'dibs', rationalized by Epstein (ironically) as an example of Harold Demsetz's theory of scarcity underscoring private property rights, and not as a customary ordering of public rights of use and enjoyment. Dibs is the 'Chicago Way', a sorting of public use rights dependent on local norms that disappear when the snow melts (Kass 2015). Yet, away from localized examples, the public right of use and enjoyment remains a paradoxically empty, little-scrutinized right, notwithstanding its rich promise.

So, if inclusion, public possession, or use and enjoyment are deemed unsuitable or unsatisfactorily empty, then what other rights could conceivably belong in the public bundle? Perhaps, new sticks could be created – and added. After all, this divisibility, the flexibility to add or detach 'go-anywhere' rights is the metaphor's supposed shining strength. The difficulty here is twofold. New rights are, notwithstanding the bundle's alleged flexibility, suspect in the eyes of *numerus clausus* adherents who argue the list of property rights is closed (Merrill and Smith 2000). Or, they risk being an exercise in tautology in their replication of a pre-existing right to use. The problem with this rights-based narrative is that it situates the public estate in an alien paradigm, stranded in a mindset where public entitlements are forced to mimic private rights to conform to the propertied discourse. Or, in the (potentially more promising) case of a public right to use and enjoy, there is a hiatus of detail. If our thinking is constrained by orthodoxy, of Hohfieldian paradigms where a public right requires its public jural correlative, then we start on an endless search for binaries – of rights and duties, privileges and no-rights, and so on. Stuart Banner observes of Hohfield that his 'greatest influence was not in the details but rather how his scheme emphasized the nature of property as relations between people' (2011, p. 104). Indeed, Banner argues 'Hohfield's idiosyncratic terminology never really caught on'. Rather it was (quoting Oliver Wendell Holmes) 'a hocus-pocus that for daily purposes seems to me superfluous' (p. 104).

Yet superfluous or not, many property jurists are drawn to the Hohfieldian flame in their search for legal 'straight thinking'. As we saw, binary technicalities dominate Douglas' scrutiny of the private liberty to use. In a rare example of public rights analysis, Thomas Coggin likewise employs Hohfield's 'hocus-pocus' to theorize the nature of entitlement to public space in the modern city (2019). Coggin argues that these entitlements are spatial 'privileges', 'a freedom from the right or claim of another' (Hohfield 1913, p. 60). Coggin's analysis 'spatializes' Hohfield by, *inter alia*, enlivening 'alternative binaries' away from the narrow right/duty duality.[5] The 'simple act of walking on the sidewalk' could therefore be rationalized 'as a privilege which no-one generally has a right to deny (the "no-right")' (p. 66). No doubt, many uses of the urban public square are spatial privileges, as Coggin's refreshing analysis makes clear. Yet, the premise of a privilege depends on others having a no-right, a paradigmatic two-step that one wouldn't necessarily invent if afforded the luxury of a blank slate. This approach also risks trivializing public entitlements as mere 'privileges', and ignores the ancient customary antecedence of certain public rights to land (Sax 1980, Hartog 1985, Clark and Page 2019). In seeking out metaphoric public sticks, one inevitably descends into problematized rabbit holes – the parallel worlds of jural correlatives, or the vacuity of use and enjoyment. At the risk of mixing metaphors, why play in this sandpit in the first place?

3.3 A spectrum of public ownerships

Away from a rights-premised analysis, another way of seeing public ownership lies in picturing its different iterations on a spectrum.[6] Like the preceding analysis, this too is (mostly) a conventional account of property, drawing on traditions of law, equity and trusts to allocate ownerships based on separable legal and beneficial titles. This public spectrum begins at one end with absolute ownership, where the state is the sole legal owner of public real property. It next shifts to a position where public legal and beneficial title is vested in separate, distinct owners. The spectrum ends with another version of absolute ownership, but this time an equitable-only variant, de-coupled from the need for any legal trustee to act on behalf of the many. In substance, this spectrum marks a progressive dilution of legal public ownership, from a bright legal owner at one end, to an invisible (and therefore deleted) legal owner at the other. Each will be examined in turn.

The idea of the state being sole and absolute owner of public real property aligns with the equally simple definition that 'public land is simply land owned by public bodies' (Christophers 2018, p. 6). In this fused 'totality of [public] ownership', there is assumedly no separable equitable estate, the beneficial interest in the land being simply 'absorbed into the legal estate'.[7] This flat understanding of public ownership is analogous to Macpherson's account of 'state property', which 'consists of rights which the state has not only created but kept for itself' (1978, p. 5). As an owner, Macpherson argues, 'the state … is taking and exercising the powers of a corporation' (p. 5). In Scots law, this is equivalent to the sovereign's *regalia minora*. In Roman law it is *res universitatis*, the 'bounded' corporate property of public bodies, 'of municipal theatres and racecourses and other income producing property' (Rose 2003, pp. 106, 108).

There are two key difficulties with the basic 'state as owner' model. The first is its lack of universality. The second is more profound, the existential outcomes that this simple model yields. In black-letter law, there is a wealth of doctrine, case law, and statutory implication that makes it plain that the legal title of many public lands is vested in the state *in trust* for the public. The most celebrated example is the public trust doctrine in the United States,[8] where certain inherently public resources are inalienable because 'trust obligations prevent the government from conveying the trust resource away from public ownership' (Ryan 2015, p. 529). Another is the public forum doctrine where 'the title of streets and parks… have immemorially been held in trust for the use of the public (see Chapter 7)'.[9] Public highways in Australian states and Canadian provinces are likewise imbued with trust-like ownerships, preserving intrinsic public rights to pass and re-pass as an obligation of the state's ownership of the surface rights. This trust relationship arises from both statutory implication and judicial explication.[10] In the United Kingdom, it is expressed as a fiduciary-like duty of the highway authority.[11]

However, the more significant critique of the 'state as owner' model arises not from its patchiness, but rather the risk it poses to the public estate's integrity. This risk arises because of the model's overt simplicity, where one corporate owner is seen to be no different from another. Macpherson highlights this tendency when he writes that 'state property is not an individual right not to be excluded. It is a corporate right to exclude' (p. 5). The logical corollary of the state's power to exclude is that state property 'fit[s] the definition of (corporate) *private* property (emphasis added)' (p. 5). Where a state owner is 'apt to be as jealous of its property' as a private owner, public segues into private, but not the reverse. Another Canadian scholar, Mariana Valverde repeats this phenomenon. In writing of the diverse city governance of Toronto and the 'everyday law on [its] streets' (2013), Valverde observes that 'parks, sidewalks and other spaces experienced as "public" are not actually common property. … Rather, these spaces are the private property of the municipal corporation' (p. 35):

> [They are] owned by "the city" as popular parlance puts it in a phrase that underlines the distance between the municipal corporation as property owner and the municipal corporation as a democratic coming together of citizens.
>
> *(pp. 35–36)*

Indeed, the city's power to regulate its 'public spaces', such as issuing permits for hoardings to be placed on 'its' sidewalks, is seen as an incident of private ownership. The conflation of 'corporate public' with 'corporate private' semantically privatizes a public resource. Contrast this characterization of sidewalks with that of Nicholas Blomley, whose study of the logic of 'pedestrianism' (see Chapter 6) – also in a predominantly Canadian context– reinforces the sidewalk's role as a 'staunch defender of a finite public realm' (2011, p. 32). Blomley does not start his sidewalk analysis from the position of corporate property, but rather, as a distinct public species of the 'genus public highway'. He ends in a very different propertied place, one where the sidewalk is unambiguously and robustly *public*. Finally, to complete this (unintentionally) Canadian review, Sarah Hamill likewise cautions that the 'government-as-owner' model is 'a clear attempt to force all property into a private property model', one that emphasizes the government's use of the land rather than the public's benefit in it' (2012, p. 365).

Next on the spectral axis lie distinct legal and beneficial public ownerships – vested in different entities. Here, the state as legal owner holds public real property in trust for its citizenry, the land's 'true' beneficial owners.[12] A bifurcated or split version of public ownership, this model is, as flagged, famously enacted by the US public trust doctrine. The public trust is said to originate from English common law, received into the thirteen colonies prior to the Revolution. It is a principle that developed thereafter with a distinctly American flavor, 'transformed by American jurists into a brute assertion' (Rose, 1986, p. 729), so much so, that in jurisdictions with similar origins, such as Canada or Australia, the public trust receives scant, if any, judicial attention (Hamill 2012, p. 400).[13]

Originally, the public trust protected public rights in waterways and foreshores, its principal concern being public rights of navigation and fishing, and the 'lands beneath navigable waters or washed by the tides' (Rose 1998b, p. 351). Later, it encompassed more flexible recreational uses, including swimming, bathing and other shore activities (Sax 1970, p. 477; Stevens 1980, pp. 221–223). By the end of the 20th century, it had 'unhooked from its traditional moorings around navigable waters and applied to dry land as well' (Rose 1998b, p. 352).

Discussion of the public trust often begins with its so-described 'lodestar' case, *Illinois Central Railroad Company v Illinois* in 1892.[14] There, the conveyance of prime Chicago lakefront land to a private railroad was held by the US Supreme Court to be invalid and beyond state power. Title to such inherently inalienable (submerged) land was:

> different in character from that which was intended for sale ... It is a title held in trust for the people of the state that they may enjoy the navigation of the waters, carry on commerce over them, and have liberty of fishing therein freed from the obstruction or interferences of private parties.
>
> *(p. 452)*

Its modern incarnation can be traced to Joseph Sax's seminal 1970 journal article, 'The Public Trust Doctrine in Natural Resource Law: An Effective Legal

Intervention'.[15] Sax's scholarship was instrumental in heightening awareness of the doctrine, widening its scope to the protection of environmental and scenic values, and encouraging states to pass environmental laws that entrenched public trust values (Stevens 1980, p. 228; Rose 1998b). As well as being a judicial doctrine, the public trust is embedded in several state constitutions, including Hawai'i, Florida and Pennsylvania, which stipulate the state or commonwealth 'as trustee for the benefit of all of the people' (Ryan 2015, pp. 572–573). Today, the public trust's reach includes wetlands, the reclamation of tidal zones, public access rights across dry sands, and environmental water flows. Others theorize its application to surfing waves or atmospheric carbon sinks (Nazer 2004, Ryan 2019). Two leading cases, *Matthews v Bay Head Improvement Association* and *Mono Lake*[16] illustrate its mechanics.

In *Mono Lake*, the California Supreme Court held that 1940 levels of water extraction (which diverted freshwater flows from Mono Lake to the Los Angeles Aqueduct) were a breach of the state's public trust obligations. As its proponents[17] successfully argued, 'Mono Lake was held in trust by the state for the public, and no organ of the state could give away its water if that would be in destruction of the resource' (Ryan 2015, p. 606). Unsustainable diversions had caused lake levels to drop, exposing acres of dry lakebed, threatening the lake's ecology as salinity levels rose, and exposing the area's population to increased public health risks of airborne alkali particles (pp. 599–601). The court recognized the trust implications of this unfolding crisis, and ordered the California Water Resources Control Board to reduce Los Angeles' prior appropriation rights to comply with the state's public trust obligations. The Board's subsequent Decision 1631 returned some 12% of the city's supply to the seventy square mile saline waters of the lake. As Erin Ryan observes, *Mono Lake* made it clear that the 'public' in the public trust was the citizens of the whole state of California, not just the water rights of Los Angelenos. The citizenry's beneficial ownership was moreover akin to a complicated 'process of public expression', not a mere 'aggregation of private interests' (pp. 632–633). Finally, it was an ownership that required an ongoing duty of oversight, a necessary incident of the state's legal title.

One year later in *Matthews*, public trust values migrated from non-navigable waters to public access rights across privately owned dry sands. Noting that 'beaches are an irreplaceable, unique resource', the New Jersey Supreme Court held that the 'exercise of the public right's to swim and bathe below the high water mark may depend upon a right to pass across the upland beach. Without some means of access, the public right to use the foreshore would be meaningless' (p. 323). Moreover, these rights are not limited to passage alone, and include 'some enjoyment of the dry sand area' (p. 325). The court based its finding on a *flexible* public trust, rejecting alternate bases for public access – prescription, dedication, or custom – as 'archaic judicial responses to a modern social problem' (p. 325). *Matthews*, analogously to *Mono Lake,* also clarified that the public owners of this public trust right are not the localized public of the Bay Head environs, but the public of the sovereign state of New Jersey (p. 632).

Matthews and *Mono Lake* exemplify the public trust's plausibility as a version of public ownership, with the doctrine providing clarity as to the respective roles of state and public, and the extent of the public's ownership. Its success (albeit limited to links with water) may also be credited to the persuasiveness of its advocates. Rose argues, for instance, that Sax did more than 'revive and re-invent' the public trust by simply 'dusting off this venerable phrase,' but added a 'powerful, if controversial, rhetorical element' to the doctrinal discourse (1998b, pp. 351–352). Ryan concurs; the force of Sax's prose made it 'one of those rare academic works that literally changes the world' (2015, p. 602).

Beyond the classic trust, a beneficial-only form of public owning occupies the final spot on the public spectrum. Here, state intervention is superfluous, since the resources concerned are what Rose calls 'inherently public property' (1986), a 'meta-property held in common by those who understand and follow its precepts' (p. 747):

> There lies outside purely private property and government-controlled 'public property' a distinct class of 'inherently public property' which is fully controlled by neither government nor private agents. Since the Middle Ages this category of 'inherently public property' has provided each member of some 'public' with a bundle of rights, neither entirely alienable by state or other collective action, nor necessarily 'managed' in any explicitly organized manner. Aside from individual private property, the nineteenth-century common law of property in both Britain and America, with surprising consistency, recognized two distinguishable types of public property. One of these was property 'owned' and 'managed' by a governmental body. The other however, was collectively 'owned' and 'managed' by society at large, with claims independent of and superior to the claims of any purported governmental manager. It is this latter type I call 'inherently public property'.
>
> *(p. 720)*

In this 'other' version of the public estate, property rights vest in a seemingly implausible 'unorganized public', not a 'governmentally organized public' (p. 721). As an unlikely model of public ownership, it nonetheless enjoys, as Rose suggests, an ancient antecedence. In Chapter 2, for example, the ambiguous place of the foreshore in Roman and (then) Scots law reflects a long-standing ephemerality about its superior title. Likewise, the statutory deeming of that same liminal space as 'lands owned by no-one' in New Zealand in 2011 reflects this historical continuity – where public rights to foreshore use are robust despite the lack of a clear, unitary titleholder.

While this owning public may be 'unorganized', it is not *disorganized*. Rose argues the 'intriguing' capacity for a diffuse public to 'order its affairs authoritatively' stems from an unlikely source of modern law, custom (1986, p. 742). Custom works in a self-policing way, 'the medium through which the public may organize itself, act, and even "speak" with the force of law' (p. 759). As an integral part of the public compact, individuals exercise 'self-restraint and civic regard for the greater good' and as such, enforce custom's precepts through a mutual self-adherence. David Bederman describes custom as those 'informal usages and understandings considered binding by those who practice and share them' (1996, p. 1375). The practice of queuing could be analogized as customary, where places in a public line acquire property-like status, and are regulated and enforced by fellow-participants who 'practice and share' its norms (Gray 2010).

Many uses of the public estate derive from custom. In its arcane English iterations, time immemorial custom supports hardy fisher-folk drying nets on foreshores, mid-summer maypole dancing, or the collection of firewood in ancient woods (Bederman 1996, pp. 1381–1382).[18] 'From Coke to Blackstone and beyond, custom was a central category in English jurisprudence ... a protean term, irreducible to clear or coherent categories' (Hartog 1985, p. 814). Its modern manifestations are however the most fascinating – and vexed. In the settler colonial state, custom must confront the manner of its introduction – the brutal violence of colonization that dispossessed Indigenous peoples and their law. It must also deal with the perception of anachronism, an agrarian relic with little application to the urban context. Perhaps most significantly, custom fuels suspicion because of its invocation of legal pluralism, the challenge to the hegemonic, 'single text' view of the law that 'represses the existence and relative autonomy of competing and conflicting socially constituted visions of legal order' (Hartog 1985, p. 934).

Despite these hurdles, custom lingers, and at times flourishes in unlikely places. Public rights to fish (Hamill 2017), rights to the public forest estate (Clark and Page 2019), or access to the Oregon coast (Bederman 1996) provide three counter-intuitive examples where black-letter law supports public customary rights – rights that happily subsist with little need for any supervening trustee state. Custom is also consistent with the logic that property is 'grounded in relationships of social and material connection', a vesting of title, or sense of ownership that goes beyond 'official actions' such as registering legal titles (Thorpe 2018, pp. 742–746). Where custom 'signals a community's emotional investment in a place' (Rose 1986, p. 759), it tells of a socially enacted understanding of public ownership derived from the ground up. In these successful 'comedies of the commons', the felicitous 'more is the merrier' provides the scaled return on the public's investment, ensuring 'greater value through greater participation' – that in turn protects the public realm by making it less prone to private capture (p. 768).

Seeing public ownership through a spectral lens provides a clear(er) view of the public estate, a perspective less problematized than a rights-premised line of sight. It illustrates where different iterations of public owning lie – along an axis where the variable state shifts from being a bright titleholder at one end, to superfluous at the other. Moreover, the spectrum provides a way in to explore the existential weakness of the 'government as owner' analogy, and conversely, the greater coherence of the trust. It also reminds us of the nagging logic of the unorganized public. In particular, the spectral view demonstrates the great diversity of public owning, and highlights that when it comes to the crude question of public ownership, one size doesn't fit all.

3.4 An a-spatial, non-binary public owning

So far, this study of public ownership has largely concerned territorially bounded public lands. Here, public ownership ostensibly ends at the dividing fence. Yet, 'worlded' experience (Braverman et al. 2014) suggests the position is not so hermetically clear-cut. Public/private ownership is no simple binary; public incorporeal ownerships wash over into private lands, and private interests encroach into public.

Despite such inconvenient facts on the ground, the concept of spatial demarcation is critical to private ownership, with its exclusion-focused theories and well-developed law around boundaries, artificial and natural. So, given the private estate's propensity to atomize ownership, what about the public estate? Are boundaries equally integral to the public estate's sense of ownership? Or, are they less significant? Should a *public* mindset mimic the private's emphasis on the divisiveness of boundaries? Or, should it seek to blend, to adopt a porous, non-binary tone that reflects legal geography's emphasis on the complexities and inter-connectedness of the *where* of property (Braverman et al. 2014)?

In addressing these ephemeral questions, it is necessary to understand why boundaries became so reified (and concrete) in the private estate. Nicholas Blomley proposes that the confluence of cartography and private property in the late 16th/early 17th centuries had profound and lasting consequences. In *Law, Space, and the Geographies of Power* (1994), Blomley analyzes the legacies of common law jurist Edward Coke (1552–1634) and cartographer Christopher Saxton (1542?–1610?), whose careers converged in a 'deeply implicated transition ... a representational project in which space, place and law begin to be cast in an increasingly modern and "liberal" fashion' (p. 63). Blomley argues that Coke's legacy lay in his systemization of the common law; in reducing what was formerly a heterogeneous legal geography of diverse property into a unitary, homogenous map. He did this by 'dis-embedding' the common law from its many localized contexts, replacing it with a 'superstructure' where 'the law can be interpreted only at the highest level of spatial abstraction' (pp. 75–76). 'Law becomes increasingly "territorial" rather than predominantly local' (p. 80). Saxton compounded this peculiar abstract spatiality with the publication of his atlas of county maps of England and Wales in 1579. These maps were advanced in their detail, reflecting the survey's increasing sophistication. But what was lost in this 'modernizing' process was the heterogeneity of the local parish. Caxton's 'project', like Coke's, sought to systemize space:

> Space is no longer mapped from within the places from which it is understood, but (apparently) from without. The sensuous and tactile nature of premodern mapping ... gives way to a rational and purportedly truthful representation of space. Space no longer appears to have a subjective quality, but increasingly appears as an objective and pregiven surface. ... This objectification is a move, I think, of signal importance, entailing a modernist conception of space as something to be measured, contained, divided, manipulated, and – crucially – alienated.
> *(p. 91)*

Blomley's analysis of the rise of the bounded, alienable space of private property begs the question, what came *before* this hardening of the lines of demarcation? Those 'sensuous and tactile' pre-modern maps must have been of necessity blurred, less binary, and true to their messy context. Perhaps this perspective, of looking at space 'from within its places rather than from without', is a natural starting point in thinking anew about the lines of public ownership.

Blomley's later scholarship also picks up on this imagery of public/private porosity. For example, the 'boundary crossing transgression' of residents of Strathcona, Vancouver – who extend their private gardens into adjacent street verges – challenges the idea that the public-private divide in property is 'mutually divisible and collectively exhaustive' (2005, p. 286). Blomley suggests that private gardens on street verges (in particular, an improvised bathtub of flowering perennials placed on the sidewalk) create a property hybrid, 'a different place that was neither purely private nor public but partook of both … a collective sharing by a group of private individuals … involving everybody' (p. 290). The tub garden was in various parts a public 'gift' by nearby residents, yet it also was a product of Lockean labor, an 'informally constituted' hybrid (p. 294). As a performative example of property, informal street gardening shows that 'people live in much more complicated, fluid, hybrid [property] worlds' (p. 294) than the binary world imagined by exclusion theorists.

In 2016, Blomley returns to the same flowering bathtub to further critique exclusion-theorized accounts of private property (such as Katz 2008; or Merrill and Smith 2002). His 'everyday' account of boundaries, as tested in this interstitial space, observes the 'curious oversight' that had to date ignored the 'widespread phenomenon' of the public/private boundary (2016, p. 239). In Strathcona, these public/private demarcations yield an ownership amalgam defined by 'a "sharing" and "extending" … across and through the boundary line' (p. 240), not its 'delineation'. Hence, if a passer-by should hypothetically pick a flower without permission, this amounts not so much to the theft of private property, but 'an affront to the collective intent of the bathtub' (p. 240). Blomley concludes of the 'need to consider the boundaries between public and private property in any account of property boundaries more generally, with the caution that such boundaries may be far from clear-cut in their meanings' (p. 241). Given that most private parcels inevitably abut public real property (streets, sidewalks, or occasionally parks), this analytical need is pressing.

In some cases, clear boundaries serve the public estate well. In the United States, where one-third of the continental landmass is in federal ownership, boundaries 'keep the land public, wild and indivisible'. But in Britain, where '90% of lands are privately owned', 'they kept the public out' (Solnit 2001, pp. 162–163). Hence, recreationalist groups such as the Sierra Club 'fight for boundaries' to preserve the American status quo, while 'British walking activists fight against them' (ibid.). The converse risk of hard boundaries lies in the enclaves they create, disconnected public islands in an erstwhile private sea, an atomization that is the antithesis of ecology's inter-connectedness. 'A natural area can function well only if it is integrating into a larger physical landscape. It needs to contribute to the sound functioning of a bigger nature' (Freyfogle 2007, p. 12).

Moreover, the public fence affords little protection against governments intent on shrinking public acreage for partisan political reasons.[19] In 2017, the Trump administration issued a proclamation that reduced Bears Ears and Grande-Staircase Escalante National Monuments in Utah by nearly two million acres. The unprecedented removal of national monument status over vast tracts of public lands, and the shrinkage of protected boundaries to suit an interpretation of the Antiquities Act that monuments occupy 'the smallest area compatible with protection of its designated objects' (Britton-Purdy 2019, p. 927) illustrate how public boundaries are far from inviolable. As Britton-Purdy argues powerfully, '[g]enerally speaking, public-lands law has been very little theorized; but [in the face of this Proclamation] it needs a theory now' (p. 922).

Public/private boundaries work differently, depending on which side of the fence you find yourself. On the public side, spatial boundaries seem by nature defensive. At best, they hold the line, as public advocacy groups valiantly fight to protect public lands. At worst, they can be manipulated (and shrunk) to suit a cynical re-interpretation of how a century-plus statute operates in the field. Contrast this passive posture with the rhetorical power of the fence's private side, a line well used to excluding, not accommodating. Conversely, where public property rights are functional, not spatial (Banner 2002), rigid boundaries are (logically) less impactful. Incorporeal public rights like conservation easements (Fairfax et al. 2005) or countryside rights of way cut across lines and demonstrate property's plurality – and porosity. Equally, less formal property 'happenings' such as Blomley's flowering bathtubs, also breach borders, yielding property hybrids that reward sharing while simultaneously valuing the individual's sweat of the brow. As Blomley opines, public/private boundaries seem 'far from clear-cut in their meaning'.

Last, if different property types possess different values, then one conceivable effect of rigid boundaries may be to enclose those values within their spatial confines. Thus, if the values of public real property include 'a macro-sociability (a sociable mixing with strangers), democratic egalitarianism, and the solace of wide-open spaces' (Dagan 2012, p. 1443; Page 2019), these values may possibly end at the public/private fence. Yet (again), 'world-ed' experience suggests this is not universal, particularly in so-called livable cities replete with rich public infrastructure, whose citizens enjoy an accrued social capital larger than their public estate's footprint. Such concerns of sociability and the public estate will be further canvassed in Chapter 4.

Private boundaries are generally well defined, arbitrary, and exclusionary in their meaning and intent. Public boundaries are more equivocal. They tend to be porous, sympathetic to context, and as such, less binary. If boundaries enclose ownerships, then the nature of the public boundary may say something commensurate about the nature of the public ownership within.

3.5 Contested public ownerships in the colonial settler state

In the settler colonial state, the identity of the 'public' in public ownership is particularly vexed. Unresolved questions of sovereignty, and debates over culturally appropriate uses of public lands increasingly disrupt colonial narratives – accounts that erase Indigenous ownerships and privilege public ownership as 'particular to white settler subjects' (Anson 2019, p. 49).[20] In this shifting, decolonizing landscape, public real property plays a surprisingly central – and subversive – role; as if its vast emptiness and spaces of solitude evoke an enduring 'land memory' (Penalver 2009), a lingering knowledge that pre-dates the travails of settler colonial expansion – and the public lands system that was one of its key creations (Reis 2019, p. 64).

In settler colonial states, public lands, 'their colonial histories and their neocolonial presents' (Reis 2019, p. 65) inform a certain understanding of public ownership, and a certain type of 'public'. In the United States, Alyosha Goldstein argues that 'settler colonial imperatives and racialized geographies underwrite the public domain' (2018, p. 127), a structural bias which yields a public that is 'always already a particular *settler* public – itself composed of specific antagonisms and divisions – that strives to secure national certainty and security through indigenous dispossession' (p. 138, emphasis added).[21] The converse view is that the public in public lands is emblematic of the indivisible nation-state. Goldstein quotes former US Senator Harry Reid to illustrate the latter, who said on the proclamation of Nevada's Gold Butte National Monument in 2016 that 'threats to our public lands [are] threats to our economy, our environment, and our culture. When we preserve our lands, we preserve America' (p. 139). In this contest of culture and competing histories, the owning public is depicted as either the implicated successor to the settler colonial mantle, or a diverse citizenry amnesic to its colonial past.

In traversing this contested public terrain, the recreational rock climber has (unwittingly) become a modern trope, a symbol of this cultural chasm and flashpoint of competing 'publics'. The rugged recreationalist is likened to the rugged homesteader of the 19th century, who practices 'the kind of erasures historically and contemporarily perpetuated by settler colonial forces', and specifically, 'from those who participated in an agenda of manifest destiny centuries ago to those who participate in mainstream US rock climbing today' (Reis 2019, p. 72). What the colonial settler and the 21st-century rock climber share is the spatiality of the public domain, and a sense of entitlement to its use and exploitation – an expectation derived through the fact of Indigenous dispossession.

In Australia, climbers and Indigenous owners are locked in high-profile disputes over access to bouldering or rock-climbing sites in national parks. In the Grampians National Park in Victoria, the parks authority has banned the sport in new protection zones, citing increases in visitation, destructive bolting and chalking practices, and the trampling of vegetation as forcing its hand to protect the 'cultural and environmental assets' of traditional owners (Ferguson, 2019a). Climbers counter that they have been vilified for the state's neglect in protecting indigenous rock art, and claim a competing cultural entitlement to the Grampians across a 110-year history of climbing (Ferguson, 2019b).

In the Northern Territory, a public ban on climbing Uluru, an iconic rock monolith in the Uluru Kata Djuta National Park came into effect in October 2019. Again, similar cultural claims to public ownership were ventilated. Anangu traditional owners have long argued that climbers show disrespect for their sacred lands and beliefs by clambering across the monolith. An Indigenous park ranger said that closing the climb is 'a strong example of Anangu making decisions for their land':

> It's rather emotional, having elders who picked up this long journey before I was born to close the climb. They're no longer here, but we're carrying their legacy to close their climb. So there's a bit of sadness here, but also happiness knowing … respect is going to be given to given to Anangu's wishes.
>
> *(Allam and Bowers, 2019)*

Other citizens disagree, claiming a right to climb is part of the national culture and ancestry as much as anyone else's (Roberts 2019). The climb is important 'because the rock is a symbol for all of us' (Allam and Bowers 2019).

In the United States, this cultural clash over 'who' is the owning public is analogous, if not as high profile. Again, rock climbers have been intriguing bit players in two recent controversies that implicate public lands. The first involves (the earlier noted) reduction of Bears Ears and Grand Staircase Escalante National Monuments, which provoked a furious reaction from the activist outdoor clothing company, Patagonia. Described as 'a corporate Eden of sorts', and boasting a proud 40-year history of support for grass-roots environmentalism (Gelles 2018), Patagonia accused the Trump administration of 'an assault on public lands'. On its website, Twitter, and in advertisements in the *New York Times,* the company starkly declared 'The President Stole *Your* Land' (emphasis added). Patagonia's political (and later legal) challenge to the Proclamation reflects a corporate ethos deeply rooted in the public domain. Its founder, Yvon Chouinard, was an 'enigmatic mountain climber' whose foray into outdoor retail began when he 'taught himself to blacksmith, and began making and selling climbing gear that was less damaging to the rocks he and his buddies were scaling in Yosemite' (Gelles 2018).

Nonetheless, the company's apparent good motives attract critique. April Anson says that Patagonia's ad 'fences' us in to 'a settler space' (2019, p. 52), one that 'coheres the liberal environmentalist with rural conservative strains of settler identity' (p. 54) and reduces 'complex histories of land theft' to a lament for 'the loss of rock climbing … opportunities for Patagonia's Californian employees' (p. 53). Similar criticisms follow the high-profile ascent of El Capitan by free-climber Alex Honnold in 2018, documented in the film *Free Solo*. Honnold's conquering of the 3,000-foot rock-face minus safety ropes is a tale of the rugged individual pitted against nature. But it is also a narrative that 'fails entirely to acknowledge the first peoples of the Yosemite valley, … and the ways in which National Park designation [make] El Capitan accessible to privileged and well-funded climbers like

Chin and Honnold, [a designation] rooted in a history of colonial violence and displacement' (Reis 2019, pp. 76–77). In effect, erstwhile allies become unlikely adversaries. Patagonia, the company described as 'a group of avid environmentalists who just happen to sell coats' (Gelles 2018) is simultaneously implicit in the perpetuation of colonial violence. The colonial prism yields polarized (and polarizing) understandings of the public ownership of public lands.

Sarah Hamill tells a similar tale of competing publics and colonial dispossession. Hamill's study of the sparse jurisprudence of the public property right to fish – explored through the comparative lens of late 19th century Ireland and early 21st century Canada – reveals places where 'the public in the public right to fish was very different' (2017, p. 54). Across time and space, this little-regarded public right has been employed for political ends. In Ireland, the exercise of the right came to be linked to the nationalist cause, such that by the turn of the 20th century, English courts rarely validated the right in practice – notwithstanding its express statutory legitimacy. Conversely in Canada, the common law public right was a 'sword not a shield' that 'served to preclude' exclusive Indigenous fishing rights (p. 84), courts preferring instead a wider, generic public right to trump Indigenous claims to fisheries. In effect, Hamill argues, public rights in both Canada and Ireland reinforced 'a *de jure* dispossession with a *de facto* continued use' by the dominant settler class (p. 85).

These stories of rock climbers and fisher-folk expose the pressing need to decolonize public ownership in settler states, and find a way though the polarizing debates that beset the 'public' in public ownership. No doubt, the template for paradigmatic change is inherently contextual – and as such idiosyncratic – yet the example of the former Urewera National Park in Aotearoa/New Zealand (see Chapter 2) may be useful. There, the de-gazetted park, through statutory edict, became a merged entity of land and owner. As 'an identity in and of itself', Te Urewera serves to not only 'strengthen and maintain the connection between [the Maori iwi] Tuhoe and Te Urewera', but also, equally, 'to provide for Te Urewera as a place of public use and enjoyment, for recreation, learning and spiritual reflection, and as an inspiration for all'.[22] As Section 3 of its organic Act mandates, Te Urewera is a place for all New Zealanders.

Translated to the American context, Te Urewera epitomizes the challenge of what Goldstein opines is a 'more nationally inclusive national public and the celebration of national commons … without inscribing settler prerogative and naturalizing colonial and racialized dispossession' (p. 140). One senses how profoundly (and quickly) this could shift – if the political winds were favorable. In September 2019, the Outdoors for All Act was introduced in the US Congress, its aim to increase equity in the public outdoors. The Act funds the creation and improvement of outdoor recreation areas in communities lacking ready access to public space. Local nearby open space is seen as critical in connecting communities of color with public lands and national parks, places where a lack of diversity renders them 'a less than welcoming environment' (Pannell 2019). The powerful Sierra Club recognizes the link between public lands and cultural change, advocating that 'along with the rest of our institutions, policies and culture, we must de-colonize the outdoor experience' (ibid.).

In settler states, the narrative of public lands and their owning public is far from settled. In their empty public corners, ancient land memories linger, hauntings that disrupt passing modernity, and its prevailing rhetoric of a particular 'public' ownership. As Anson writes of its public contours:

> Public lands offer a third space of sovereignty: the places where the excesses and contingencies of American colonial rule are made visible. Public lands present a spacious invitation to the practice of commoning, recognizing our shared – and uneven – places within settler colonial capitalism as well as our common desire for a public outside of that system.
>
> *(p. 59)*

3.6 Thinking public ownership differently

This section concludes Chapter 3 by exploring how public ownership may be re-thought. As intimated, this involves a shift in emphasis, away from predictable analyses of owner-identity to embrace alternative enquiries of owner-purpose. It does this primarily by a review of nascent theories of public ownership, drawn from political theory, critical geography, and the law, explanations that lend purpose to public owning. It also visits the websites of groups sympathetic to public property rights, the likes of whoownesengland.org or the highlinenetwork.com in a quest to reveal the subliminal – keywords that may 'bell the cat' on the collective societal purposes public ownership serves.

It is uncommonly refreshing to read others remark on the ubiquity of public property, and how often we fail to register it in everyday life. These are the (paraphrased) opening words of Schmuel' Nilis 'The idea of public property' (2019). Nili's venture into public property (he is a political theorist) is driven by what the author sees as the deteriorating moral conduct of modern democratic leaders.[23] In guarding against 'leaders stealing what belongs to the people' (p. 346), Nili constructs a vision of public property that lies 'at the very heart of political life' (p. 345). He calls this *deep public ownership*, where 'all the resources encompassed within a jurisdiction' are vested in 'the sovereign people' (p. 353). This 'morally plausible' account supposes that 'the property rights of the sovereign people precede rather than stem from specific laws' (ibid.). Indeed, private property is carved from this deep public collective, held by individuals 'in Rousseauian fashion as "trustees" of goods owned by the public' (p. 355). Consistent with feudal/tenurial notions that qualify private property, deep public ownership also underscores that processes such as eminent domain or escheat reflect the state's authority to restore property to its true public owners. In this understanding, public property is both foundational, and politically pre-eminent.

Nili's theory shares common ground with Rose's 'unorganized public', recognizing that the undifferentiated public may be property's ultimate owner – although for Rose, this ownership is confined to 'inherently public property'. Nili's account also aligns (in part) with Roman law's *res publicae*, which grants public property rights to the citizens of nation-states, not the world at large. Its most compelling feature however is that deep public ownership (ironically) makes the *owner* question subsidiary to, and dependent on, the *purpose* question. Nili outlines four key purposive requirements for a plausible account of public property. First, that it 'captures the moral complaint against *de facto* rulers stealing from the people', second, that it's public status is immune to 'uncoordinated' private appropriation ('the collectivist requirement'), third, that it accommodates liberal conceptions of private property, and fourth, that it 'informs broader moral intuitions concerning public affairs' and 'political issues that extend beyond property' (p. 349). This emphasis puts the sovereign state's moral/democratic compact central to the idea of public property. It also defines public property by the overarching purpose(s) it serves. By privileging public purpose, and erecting a principled, morally defensible fence around what is ours, this theory works to de-center and contextualize owner identity.

Critical human geographers have likewise engaged with the rationales of public ownership. Doreen Massey observes that the 'apparently simple term "landownership" can mean very different things', a point that 'applies equally to the public sector' (1980, p. 237). Writing at a time when public ownership was on the cusp of a sustained (and existential) ideological attack, Massey makes two key arguments. First, that public ownership only matters if it means something different from private ownership. Here, the role of the state is vital, enabling a 'different and social form of ownership' to make this distinction viable, one where policy levers ensure that the public landowner's behavior is 'socially conscious' (p. 271). Second, like private ownership, public ownership can take many forms. To illustrate, Massey identifies three broad strands of private ownership in 1980s England, 'former landed property' held by 'venerable owners' such as the landed aristocracy or established Church, 'industrial property', where land is owned as a condition of production, and 'financial property' where ownership is purely speculative. The first gives some inkling of what a 'different and social form of [public] ownership' may look like, with its deep social and relational connotations unrelated to investment choices or economic factors (the land being mostly inherited). 'The kind of asset a piece of land represents to its owner' (p. 266) is a diverse mentality that should pervade public ownership, as much as it does private.

Nearly 40 years later, critical economic geographer Brett Christophers repeats this refrain (2018). Citing Massey as inspiration, Christophers argues that the appropriation of public land in neoliberal Britain ('The New Enclosure') has been an ongoing project since the 1980s, a force little impacted by the changing political hue of central governments. Its inexorability is enabled when the public sees little purpose in the public retention of land. 'Britons have not mourned public ownership since … they have not associated it with public benefit; they did not regard the land as genuinely, meaningfully theirs' (p. 327). Going forward, Christophers sees little point in a public ownership where 'land can only have one type of value – market value' (p. 141). If land is to remain publicly owned, 'at least let the state function as a public owner … rather than requiring it to ape private-sector approaches and values'. Otherwise, he argues, all land should simply be privatized:

> Why? Because public ownership becomes a mere label, a hollow gesture towards a genuinely alternative mode of owning and using land. Public ownership must be allowed to mean something truly different from private ownership for it to have any real worth or significance.
>
> *(ibid.)*

The public purpose thesis has not gone unnoticed by legal thinkers. Antonia Layard says that:

> [w]e absolutely need to keep arguing for public ownership, both to maintain the doctrinal distinctions that do exist … and more importantly still, because public ownership provides opportunities for soft governance and the framing of discursive debates to keep the public interest (however defined) at the forefront of … disposal and management decisions.
>
> *(2016, pp. 42–43)*

Meanwhile, in Canada, Sarah Hamill castigates the judiciary for its 'weak understanding' of what she terms 'common property' (using C.B. Macpherson's typology). This manifests in an interpretation of public ownership premised on the 'baseline' private model, and its corollary, the flawed 'government as owner' template. Such propensity is not only a gross simplification of 'common property *qua* common property' (2012, p. 367), but it sidelines the '*public benefit*' in public ownership (emphasis added).

This emerging multi-disciplinary discourse suggests that if we can first articulate *why* we own public property, then the 'who' question may optimistically resolve itself. Or else, fade to grey. It's as if we cannot unlearn the habits of private property, with its bright focus on the individual owner and their hallowed bundle of rights. Nor can we unhook value from commodity when thinking of land, since 'prizing nothingness is harder than prizing something' (Solnit 2017, p. 50). However, public land NGOs and activist groups already reflect this priority in their virtual faces to the world. The Trust for Public Lands 'creates parks and protects land for people', 'connecting communities to the outdoors and to each other' to 'explore, wonder, discover and play'. The High Line Network imagines the 'next generation of public spaces' and 'innovative infrastructure reuse' in North American cities. The Surfrider Foundation is 'the champion of surf and sand, everyday people who passionately protect our playground – the ocean, waves and beaches that provide us so much enjoyment'. And the blog that became a book, *Who Owns England* (Shrubsole 2019), seeks to save endangered public realty, such as county farms. Each mission statement is defined by its purpose, not the constraints of who *we* may, or may not be.

This chapter has explored public ownership from a diversity of perspectives. In canvassing widely, a number of 'public essences' may be distilled. First, public ownership is poorly conceptualized as a collectively held bundle of individual stick-rights. In this paradigm, public 'rights' are second-rate imitations of their private cousins. Rather, public ownership resonates with the language of trusts; a settlement of 'this is ours' that remains, in its vesting, a work-in-progress. Second, while public ownership is fenced in by boundaries – mostly from the private side of the divide – the public (side of the) fence reflects a public owning that is porous and non-binary in nature. And third, while public ownership may struggle with questions of owner-identity, it is clearer in the purposes it serves. These purposes are wider than one particular 'public' – a classist or racially defined 'this is ours'. Rather, public purposes must serve the interests of all members of the public, howsoever constituted, an enactment of spatial justice especially relevant in the settler colonial state.

As Massey and others argue, public ownership must be different from private ownership to have any meaning, any purpose beyond the 'hollow gesture'. This premise seems a good place to start. This difference will in part come from the outside, in the setting of policy parameters that imbue public ownership with a 'social consciousness'.[24] This difference will also be derived intrinsically, in what we *do* with our beneficial-like public owning. Perhaps, in this second sense, to publicly own is to publicly do. A doing that is not limited by what, from time to time, we cannot do. April Anson says that public lands are a 'verb' (2019, p. 59). Although Anson is referring to activist performances of doing, 'the work … of turning away from the commodity commons and toward the commoning of anticolonial community' (ibid.), her choice of 'verb' reveals an internally plausible – and persuasive – account of public owning. At Mono Lake, California, public trust values ensure that visitors can continue to 'hike, fish, camp, canoe, climb, ski, bird watch, photograph, and otherwise enjoy the ample natural amenities' (Ryan 2015, p. 596). Seeing public ownership as this plenitude of verbs opens a portal into what true public ownership may entail.[25]

Notes

1 As to the former, the Botanic Gardens in Prospect Park, Brooklyn, New York are fenced, and charge an entrance fee. As to the latter, in Dolores Park, San Francisco, California, popular grassed areas could be reserved for a set period by the payment of a fee to the city's Parks Department. This trial was abandoned after public outcry, suggesting a line had been crossed.

2 Section 17(1) of the *Conservation Act 1987* (NZ) provides that – subject to a number of exceptions – 'the entry to and use of conservation areas by the public shall be free of charge.' Section 17(2) permits a 'reasonable' fee to be charged for access 'for the use of facilities (other than paths and tracks).' Section 13 outlines circumstances where conservation areas may be closed, such as public safety, emergency or overriding conservation imperatives. Where closure occurs, the Minister is obliged to inform the public and why, Section 13(2). Even railway lines that cut through conservation areas are open for public access, except for a five-meter strip from the midpoint of the rail line, Section 24L.

3 Similarly, Honore called possession 'the foundation on which the whole superstructure of ownership rests' (1961, p. 113).
4 *Kerrie Hunter Otto v Inn at Watervale, Inc.* SC: 155380, Benzie CC: 14-009969-NO (April 6, 2018).
5 Coggin lists five ways in which Hohfield's thinking is useful in theorizing entitlements to urban public space, de-centering the narrow rights/duty binary being one. The other four are: an opening up of 'alternative binaries' that better explain informal urban relationships; transposing everyday practices on the urban street into Hohfield's legal relations; by placing a focus on not just positive claims but also legitimizing harms to space, and fifth, by opening up an examination of which jural relations are at play, and why space is in fact a legal privilege (2019, pp. 59–61).
6 An earlier version of this public spectrum can be found in Page and Brower (2019).
7 *Corin v Patton* (1990) 169 CLR 540 at 579.
8 *Illinois Central Railroad Company v State of Illinois* 146 U.S. 387 (1892).
9 *Hague v Committee for Industrial Organization*, 207 U.S. 496 (1939) at 515–516.
10 In New South Wales, section 5 of the *Roads Act 1993* states that '(1) A member of the public is entitled, as of right, to pass along a public road (whether on foot, in a vehicle or otherwise) and to drive stock or other animals along the public road. (2) The right conferred by this section *does not derogate from any right of passage that is conferred by the common law* (emphasis added), but those rights are subject to such restrictions as are imposed by or under this or any other Act or law.' In Canada, the Supreme Court held that '[u]nder statutes where the fee simple is vested in them, the municipalities are in a sense owners of the streets. They are not, however, owners in the full sense of the word, and certainly not to the extent that the proprietor owns his land. … It holds them as trustee for the public. The streets remain subject to the right of the public to pass and repass, and that character, of course, is the very essence of the street', *Vancouver v Burchill* [1932] S.C.R. 620, at 625.
11 Section 130 *Highways Act 1980* UK states as a protection of public rights that '[i]t is the duty of the highway authority to assert and protect the rights of the public to the use and enjoyment of any highway …'. See also, Part IX Obstruction of highways and streets.
12 This splitting of (private) ownership into separate legal and equitable estates dates back to the Middle Ages. Equitable ownership first took form through the device of the *use*, popular for its sidestepping of feudal dues, and allowing for interests in land to be alienated by will. In 1535, the *Statute of Uses* purported to 'execute the use' in an attempt to protect Crown revenue. The Crown's attempt to abolish equitable ownership was however short-lived, the use being quickly replaced by the 'use upon a use' (or trust).
13 Sarah Hamill calls it 'the trust analogy' in Canadian law. She argues that it is weaker than the US doctrine, and that it has been effectively de-platformed in favor of the 'government as owner' model since *Batty v City of Toronto* (2011) 108 OR (3d) 571 (the Occupy Toronto case) (Hamill, 2012).
14 *Illinois Central Railroad Company v State of Illinois* 146 U.S. 387, 452 (1892). For a history of this case, see (Ryan 2015, pp. 569–572).
15 The doctrine acts as a restraint on the state in its dealings with public trust lands. 'When a state holds a resource which is available for the free use of the general public, a court will look with considerable skepticism upon *any* governmental conduct which is calculated *either* to reallocate that resource to more restricted uses *or* to subject public uses to the self-interest of private parties' (Sax 1970, p. 490).
16 *Matthews v Bay Head Imp. Ass'n.,* 95 N.J. 306 (1984); *National Audubon Society v Superior Court of Alpine County (Mono Lake)* 658 P.2d 709 (Cal. 1983).

17 Plaintiffs in *Mono Lake* included among others, the National Audubon Society, the Mono Lake Committee (concerned local citizens) and environmental NGOs, Friends of the Earth, CalTrout, and the Sierra Club Legal Defense Fund.
18 William Blackstone defined the unwritten customs of England as rights that that 'ran beyond memory', were 'peaceable, certain and consistent', 'binding', and 'not unreasonable' (Bederman 1996, pp. 1383–98) citing William Blackstone, *Commentaries on the Laws of England 1765*.
19 These include what Britton-Purdy calls 'public-lands populism' and the vested interests of mining and drilling companies (2019).
20 Similarly, Goldstein argues that federal land policy over US public lands has been constitutive of the logic of a 'white settler expectation' of property entitlement, both public and private (2018).
21 Quoting Moapa Tribal council leader Vernon Lee (Goldstein 2018, p. 138).
22 Sections 3 and 4 *Te Urewera Act 2014* (NZ)
23 Nili confirms this core rationale, writing, '[t]his observation motivates my search for a compelling account of public property' (2019, p. 346).
24 In New South Wales, Australia, the state government has a newly created Ministry for Public Space, in what it claims is a world-first. www.nsw.gov.au/your-government/the-premier/media-releases-from-the-premier/new-minister-for-public-spaces-protections-for-public-land-150-million-for-new-parks/.
25 'Why then did indefiniteness [or open-endedness] of use – abstracted from actual numbers or intensity of use – count as the essential measure of "publicness"? (Rose 1986, p. 764).

References

Allam, L & Mike Bowers, B 2019, 'Tourists rush to climb Uluru on the last day before its permanent closure', *The Guardian*, 25 Oct. 2019 at: www.theguardian.com/australia-news/2019/oct/25/uluru-climb-opens-two-hours-late-on-last-day-before-permanent-closure (accessed: 1 December 2019).

Anderson, C 2016, *Property: A Guide to Scots Law,* Thomson Reuters, Edinburgh.

Anson, A 2019, 'The President Stole Your Lands: Public Lands and the Settler Commons', *Western American Literature* vol. 54, 49–62.

Banner, S. 2002, 'Transitions Between Property Regimes', *Journal of Legal Studies,* vol. 39, S359–S371.

Banner, S. 2011, *American Property: A History of How, Why, and What we Own,* Harvard University Press, Cambridge, MA.

Bederman, D 1996, 'The Curious Resurrection of Custom: Beach Access and Judicial Takings', *Columbia Law Review* vol. 96(6), 1375–1455.

Blomley, N 1994, *Law, Space, and the Geographies of Power,* The Guildford Press, New York.

Blomley, N 2005, 'Flowers in the bathtub: boundary crossings at the public–private divide', *Geoforum* vol. 36, 281–296.

Blomley, N 2011, *Rights of Passage Sidewalks and the Regulation of Public Flow*, Routledge, Abingdon.

Blomley, N. 2013, 'Performing Property: Making the World', *Canadian Journal of Law & Jurisprudence*, vol. 26(1), 23–48.

Blomley, N 2016, 'The Boundaries of Property: Complexity, Relationality, and Spatiality' *Law & Society Review*, vol. 50, 224–255.

Braverman, I et al. 2014, *The Expanding Spaces of Law: A Timely Legal Geography,* Stanford University Press, Stanford.
Britton-Purdy, J 2019, 'Whose Lands? Which Public? The Shape of Public-Lands Law and Trump's National Monument Proclamations', *Ecology Law Quarterly*, vol. 45, 921–963.
Coggin, T 2019, 'Judicial Imaginations of Everyday Space: A Hohfiedlian Critique of Spatial Relationships in US Jurisprudence', SJD Thesis, Fordham University, New York.
Christophers, B 2018, *The New Enclosure: The Appropriation of Public lands in Neoliberal Britain,* Verso Books, London.
Clark, C & Page, J 2019, 'Of protest, the commons and customary public rights: an ancient tale of the lawful forest', *UNSW Law Journal,* vol. 42, 26–59.
Dagan, H. 2012, 'Pluralism and Perfectionism in Private Law', *Columbia Law Review*, vol. 112, 1409–1446.
Douglas, S 2013, 'The Content of a Freehold: A "Right to Use" Land', in N Hopkins (ed.), *Modern Studies in Property Law,* Hart Publishing, Oxford.
Epstein, R 2002, 'The Allocation of the Commons: Parking on Public Roads', *Journal of Legal Studies*, vol. 31, S515–S544.
Fairfax, S et al 2005, *Buying Nature: The Limits of Land Acquisition as a Conservation Strategy*, 1780–2004, MIT Press. Cambridge.
Ferguson, J. 2019a, 'Indigenous owners used to kick out climbers in Grampians', *The Australian*, May 15, 2019 at www.theaustralian.com.au/nation/politics/indigenous-owners-used-to-kick-out-climbers-in-grampians/news-story/4cb8bcdf266eb751ae363251fc722d8a (accessed 2 December 2019).
Ferguson, J. 2019b, 'Grampians climbing ban came soon after complaint', *The Australian*, September 14, 2019. Available at www.theaustralian.com.au/nation/politics/grampians-climbing-ban-came-soon-after-complaint/news-story/74f5dbd24248e2a14276856cf8e017e6 (accessed 2 December 2019).
Freyfogle, E 2007, *Agrarianism and the Good Society: Land, Culture, Conflict and Hope*, University of Kentucky Press, Lexington.
Gelles, D 2018, 'Patagonia v Trump', *The New York Times*, May 5, 2018, at www.nytimes.com/2018/05/05/business/patagonia-trump-bears-ears.html?searchResultPosition=1 (accessed 1 November 2019).
Goldstein, A 2018, 'By Force of Expectation: Colonization: Public Lands, and the Property Equation', *UCLA Law Review Discourse*, vol. 65, 124–140.
Gray, K. 2010, 'Property in a Queue', in G. Alexander & E. Penalver (eds.), *Property and Community,* Oxford University Press, New York.
Hamill, S 2012, 'Private Rights to Public Property: The Evolution of Common Property in Canada', *McGill Law Journal*, vol. 58, 365–403.
Hamill, S 2017, 'The Public Right to Fish and the Triumph of Colonial Dispossession in Ireland and Canada' *UBC Law Review,* vol. 50, 53–94.
Hartog, H. 1985, 'Pigs and Positivism', *Wisconsin Law Review*, 899–935.
Honore, A M 1961, 'Ownership' in A G Guest (ed.) *Oxford Essays on Jurisprudence*, Oxford University Press, Oxford.
Kass, J 2015, 'Dibs on parking spaces after snow is the Chicago Way' *Chicago Tribune*, February 4, 2015 at www.chicagotribune.com/columns/john-kass/ct-chicago-snowstorm-dibs-kass-met-0204-20150204-column.html (accessed 12 December 2019).
Katz, L 2008, 'Exclusion and Exclusivity in Property Law'. *University* of *Toronto Law Journal*, vol. 58, 275–315.
Macpherson, C B 1978, 'The Meaning of Property' in C B Macpherson (ed.) *Property: Mainstream and Critical Positions*, University of Toronto Press, Toronto.

Massey, D 1980, 'The Patterns of Landownership and its Implications for Policy', *Built Environment,* vol. 6, 263–271.
Merrill, T.W. 1998, 'Property and the Right to Exclude', *Nebraska Law Review,* vol. 77, pp. 730–755.
Merrill, T W & Smith, H E 2000, 'Optimal Standardization in the Law of Property: The *Numerus Clausus* Principle', *Yale Law Journal,* vol. 100, 1–70.
Nazer, D 2004, 'The Tragicomedy of the Surfers' Commons', *Deakin Law Review,* vol. 9, pp. 655–713.
Nili, S. 2019, 'The Idea of Public Property', *Ethics,* vol. 129, 344–369.
Page, J & Brower, A 2017, 'The Four Dimensions of Public Property" in R. Hickey & H. Conway (eds.) *Modern Studies in Property Law,* Hart Publishing, Oxford.
Page, J. 2019, 'Property, values, and the empirics of place', *Griffith Law Review,* vol. 28(1), 1–22.
Paisley, R 2000, *Land Law,* W. Green/Sweet & Maxwell, Edinburgh.
Pannell, J 2019, 'Celebrating Outdoors for All', September 26, 2019, available at www.sierraclub.org/articles/2019/09/celebrating-outdoors-for-all (accessed 1 October 2019).
Penalver, E 2009, 'Land Virtues', *Cornell Law Review,* vol. 94, 821–888.
Reis, A 2019, "#Equity Outdoors: Public Land and the Decolonial Mediascape', *Western American Literature,* vol. 54, 63–78.
Roberts, G 2019, 'Climbers scramble for last chance at Uluru', *The West Australian,* Oct. 11, 2019 at https://thewest.com.au/entertainment/art/climbers-scramble-for-last-chance-at-uluru-ng-s-1972898 (accessed 3 December 2019).
Rose, C M 1985, 'Possession as the Origin of Property', *University of Chicago Law Review,* vol. 52, no. 1, 73–88.
Rose, C M 1986, 'The Comedy of the Commons: Custom, Commerce, and Inherently Public Property', *University Chicago Law Review,* vol. 53, no. 3, 711–781.
Rose, C M 1994, 'Seeing Property' in C M Rose (ed.) *Property and Persuasion Essays on the History, Theory, and Rhetoric of Ownership,* Westview Press, Boulder, CO.
Rose, C M 1998a, 'The Several Futures of Property: Of Cyberspace and Folk Tales, Emission Trades and Ecosystems', *Minnesota Law Review,* vol. 83, 129–182.
Rose, C.M. 1998b, 'Joseph Sax and the Idea of the Public Trust', *Ecology Law Quarterly,* vol. 25, 351–362.
Rose, C M 2003, 'Romans, Roads and Romantic Creators: Traditions of Public Property in the Information Age', *Law & Contemporary Problems,* vol. 66, 89–110.
Ryan, E 2015, 'The Public Trust Doctrine, Private Water Allocation, and Mono Lake: The Historic Saga of *National Audubon Society v Superior Court*', *Environmental Law,* vol. 45, 561–640.
Ryan, E 2019, 'From Mono Lake to the Atmospheric Trust: Navigating the Public and Private Interests in Public Trust Resource Commons', *George Washington Journal of Energy & Environmental Law,* vol. 10.
Sax, J 1970, 'The Public Trust Doctrine in Natural Resource Law: Effective Judicial Intervention', *Michigan Law Review,* vol. 68, 471–566.
Sax, J 1980, 'Liberating the Public Trust Doctrine from its Historical Shackles', *U.C. Davis Law Review,* vol. 14, 185–194.
Shrubsole, G 2019, *Who Owns England? How We Lost Our Green & Pleasant Land & How to Take it Back,* William Collins, London.
Solnit, R 2001, *Wanderlust: A History of Walking,* Penguin Books, New York.
Solnit, R 2017, *A Field Guide to Getting Lost,* Cannongate Books, Edinburgh.

Stevens, J 1980, 'The Public Trust: A Sovereign's Ancient Prerogative Becomes the People's Environmental Right', *University of California Davis Law Review*, vol. 14, pp. 195–232.

Thorpe, A 2018, 'Pop-Up Property: Enacting Ownership from San Francisco to Sydney', *Law & Society Review*, vol. 52, 740–772.

Valverde, M 2013, *Everyday Law on the Street: City Governance in an Age of Diversity*, University of Chicago Press, Chicago.

4

OF SOCIABILITY, HUMAN FLOURISHING, AND THE WELL-LIVED PUBLIC LIFE

4.1 Introduction

American jurists Thomas Merrill and Henry Smith say that academic discussions of property generally fall into one of two paradigms; its reduction to a bundle of rights, or the identification of 'some overarching meta-principle that is thought to be served by the institution of property' (2019, p. 1).[1] Given such bald choices, this chapter takes the latter path, exploring how the meta-principle of the *well-lived life* may be served by – and through – the institution of *public* real property. A citizen's well-lived life is a complex notion, but it is enabled and enhanced by similar factors. These include, amongst others, the promotion of sociability, the ideal of human flourishing, and the pursuit of happiness. Property scholarship has to varying degrees, from the profound to the passing, engaged with each of these social goods. This chapter is an explicitly *propertied* interrogation of sociability, propriety and happiness, as it seeks answers to its central thesis, to what extent is the well-lived life (and its co-constitutive elements) an organizing principle of the public estate.

Sociability is an oft-cited value of property, albeit an outlier to the law and economics orthodoxy (Rose 2006; Page 2019). In terms of the public estate, it underlies Carol Rose's vision of 'inherently public property' (1986). Conversely, propriety and human flourishing are tenets of progressive property, a theory that enjoyed considerable traction in the first decade of this century. And happiness, and its pursuit, is a republican virtue that figures famously in the United States Constitution. All share the characteristic of abstruseness; yet each contributes to the ephemerality of a well-lived life – in meaningful, sometimes visceral ways. In considering what makes citizens sociable, propitious, and happy, this chapter recognizes that public realty is integral to the mix, providing the metaphysical context and physical infrastructure that 'add valuable options of human flourishing that significantly broaden people's choices' (Dagan 2012, p. 1425).

Chapter 4's structure adopts the above order. It opens with sociability, which already has skin in the public property game, thanks to Rose's seminal work. Next, it considers propriety and human flourishing, and their oblique references to the public estate. It then shifts to happiness, seemingly the least objective (and property-like) of analytical tools. Yet, happiness has been variously promoted as a 'legal science' (Bronsteen et al. 2015), and in the context of urban design, 'great public space' is described as 'almost happiness itself' (Montgomery 2013). The chapter ends in a critique of its chosen meta-principle, challenging its universality at a number of levels, while also observing the modern migration of sociability to the private commons, and the *un*happiness that public real property, from time to time, engenders.

Whatever their qualifications, public spaces are intuitively sociable. On any given day, they provide the spatial capacity and civic infrastructure for citizens to enjoy (or at least pursue the potential of) well-lived lives. Think of chance encounters on sidewalks (Jacobs 1961), the raw energy of packed summer beaches, or dance parties by the Bryant Park fountain in New York City, and one can almost touch this exuberant sociability. Indeed, one can 'see' a public life lived well (Rose 1994). Like the vast reservoir of possible public uses remarked upon in Chapter 3, the almost infinite capacity of public property to cater for a well-lived life is alluring. It is a bright and shining beacon, an appealing vision of the public estate that may be too good to be true.

4.2 Sociability

Rose has long held the view that 'property is one of our most sociable institutions' (2006, p. 3). Explicitly, she links sociability to *public* property in at least two pieces of scholarship, her landmark 1986 journal article 'The Comedy of the Commons: Commerce, Custom, and Inherently Public Property', and again, later in 2006, in 'Property and Language: The Ghost of the Fifth Panel'. In this literature, she argues that sociability is critical to public property for (at least) two differing reasons. The first is its exponential capacity to make returns on scale, public investments that secure and protect public lands from private capture. The second is one of narrative, the sociable stories that persuade us of, and validate, our propertied relationships to public space.

Indeed, more widely, Rose exhibits an unassuaged interest in the public estate, writing extensively on and around the topic. In 1994, for instance, she remarked how 'public and private property law can interact with physical circumstance in a way that lends the larger landscape a kind of special visibility' (p. 268). And again in 2005, Rose observes that notwithstanding its lack of definition, or absence of prominent scholarly advocates, 'the concept of the public as beneficial owner is by no means untenable as a matter of property theory or practice. It has been around a long time' (2005, pp. 1014, 1017).[2] Rose's is a rare voice in public real property discourse.

In 'The Comedy of the Commons', Rose likens sociability to a scaled return on investment. The greater the public engagement (in their exercise of public rights), the greater is the public buy-in, and the higher its value to individuals participating in the sociable activity. This is the 'felicitous' merry-go-round where 'the more is the merrier' and 'the better for all' (pp. 767–768). Not only does increased sociability reinforce 'solidarity and the fellow-feeling of the whole community' (p. 768), it also protects the public estate from private encroachment. This is because the very public-ness of its popular exercise creates the 'rent' or value that protects it from private capture. The best and highest use of certain land – to borrow the grim language of economics – may be its sociable public use.

Sociability is easily imagined where the public right in question is festive, where it's all about games of cricket on village greens or celebrations of the summer solstice, an agrarian, rose-tinted vision of the public estate. But in imagining the everyday uses of mundane public realty, of highways, or sidewalks, sociability likewise delivers a business-like return on the public investment. This is because, Rose argues, trade and commerce is likewise an inherently sociable activity. After all, 'commerce requires the interaction of persons, and this [interaction] requires access to certain physical locations' (p. 770). It also has a lasting sociability beyond the individual transaction, 'inculcat[ing] rules, understandings and standards of behavior enforced by reciprocity of advantage' (p. 776). Again, this is a scaled return, the greater we use these public corridors in the pursuit of commerce, the greater their public value as they efficiently 'allow us to get along with each other' (ibid.), and entrench societal cohesion.

Finally, Rose looks to 'historic change in public property doctrine' (p. 779) as evidence of sociability's ongoing significance, and relevance. By the end of the 20th century (in the United States at least), recreation had surpassed commerce as the primary determinant of public lands use. Recreation, like commerce, is a 'socializing institution … carried on in a social setting [that] clearly improves with scale' (ibid.). To this end, the best and highest use of 'unique recreational sites' is retention in public hands, since 'all of us benefit from the greater sociability of our fellow citizens' and the 'democratic give-and-take' that comes from public interaction (pp. 779 and 780). In both work and play, Rose concludes, sociability and socializing are the publicly created rents that forge and maintain a robust public realm.[3]

Twenty years later, in 2006, Rose again makes the link between property and sociability, but this time in terms of narrative theory, not the comedic outcomes of the more the merrier. Highlighting what she regards as a key aspect of her scholarship, namely the close relationship between property and language, Rose doubles down. Property, she says, is 'a highly sociable institution, dependent on symbolic gestures that link claimants and audiences. … In a sense, property and language *are simply property itself*' (p. 28, emphasis added). Such symbols or gestures are property's 'texts', its 'expressive endeavors' that signal the type of property claimed. Claimants succeed or fail depending on the persuasiveness of their storied pitch, and importantly, whether the relevant target audience 'gets it' (p. 6). In a related context, narrative is also employed as a 'post-hoc explanation' that validates the propertied claim, and provides the story that underlies the logical leap from implausible to plausible (1990).[4]

In the case of public real property, Rose uses imagery of *the good life* as its potent 'text' or 'expressive endeavor'. In describing a street scene painted by 14th-century Siena frescoist Ambrogio Lorenzetti, Rose observes the artist's 'particular knack' in depicting the sociable good life:

> [T]he good life was just outside the window, in the streets of late medieval Siena, where one could find 'bustling shops, circle dances, constructions sites, farmers, [a] pet monkey and [an] acrobatic cat'. ... On this street there is public access, but private property too, People stop to chat with one another and with the street vendors. They laugh at the pet monkey's antics, drop into a shop and buy something, or have a seat and watch the other passers-by.
>
> *(2006, pp. 18–19)*

Fast-forward to the early 21st century, and similar scenes of the modern public square convey the continuing significance of this 'sociability with a diversity of strangers' (Brill 2002, p. 48). These are the narratives of the public good life, performed by and through the diverse acts of strangers; of salsa dancing in Bryant Park, selfies at the Bean in Chicago's Millennium Park, shared intimacies in public art galleries, and so on, and so on. In an earlier work, Rose calls this 'seeing property as narrative', where pictures or images tell a *story* of people's collective relationships to land, 'enlist[ing] the visual imagination to make the audience understand property relationships and the social relationships that underlie them' (1994, p. 289).

So, why is this public life; its narratives, images, and above all, its intuitive sociability, so enmeshed with the public estate? Rose has given us two powerful reasons: sociability is the value that protects the public estate from private capture; and it tells the persuasive, plausible narratives that property (as a wider institution) needs. But there are others.

One is the *freedom* that the public estate offers us to be sociable, Jeremy Waldron's pithy observation that 'everything that is done has to be done somewhere. No one is free to perform an action unless there is somewhere he [sic] is free to perform it' (1992, p. 296). Anecdotally, a lot of socialization occurs on public realty, the diverse platforms where we are freest to gather, meet, and perform. Lee Fennell describes urban public lands as 'interaction spaces' whose value derives from their 'non-excludability' (2014, pp. 1373 and 1380). This ostensible freedom from exclusion facilitates a host of social goods, including 'knowledge exchange, social capital accumulation, and various other agglomeration benefits that accrue to individuals in close proximity to one another' (Foster and Iaione 2016, p. 297).

Freedom of entry and egress also means (in theory at least) that public realty acts as 'a social leveler, an equalizer of power inequities, at least temporarily and locationally' (Brill, 2002, p. 54). Amnon Lehavi, whose work explores the social links between New York's 'local public commons' and nearby adjacent communities, draws on similar rationales. He writes of *egalitarianism*, public-ness and democracy, and 'mixed non-utilitarian values' such as 'vertical equity, social integration or preservation of human dignity' (p. 147) to explain why sociable public spaces ground diverse expressions of communitarianism (pp. 120–125). This attribute is separately explored in Chapter 7.

Freedom also translates into the personal autonomy that public spaces enable, by allowing us to escape from the social controls of (private) home or work. Public acreage may act as so-called 'third spaces', or community-shared 'living rooms' (Beatley 2009, p. 335) in which social interactions flourish. Importantly, third spaces cultivate social capital, and like Rose's 'the more the merrier', the greater the investment in time in third spaces, the greater the social capital return.[5] Community gardens or allotments exemplify 'third spaces' away from work and home, public terrain that provides urban food production, the cooling of urban heat island effects, and importantly, the enhancement of urban conviviality through social interaction (Capon and Thomson 2011, pp. 370–371; Frumkin and Fox 2011, p. 237).

Finally (albeit not exhaustively), another rationale lies in the myriad ways in which public realty exposes us to the *anonymous frisson* of public life. This is variously described as the 'solace of the public crowd' (Jamison 2019) or the 'marvel of the stranger' (Brill 2002, p. 54). Such feelings are not always predictable or comfortable, but they are replete with the wonder of unfamiliarity, of chance encounters in 'streets full of splendid strangers' (Jamison 2019), or what Brill calls 'a celebration of possibility' (2002, p. 54).[6] In this way, the public estate is also educative, providing 'an alternative venue for alternative social learning [such that] public life becomes more attractive, more informative, more theatrical' (Brill, 2002, p. 54).

All this sociability, howsoever rationalized, is exponentially expansive as Rose predicts. Not only in terms of the (seemingly) limitless range of sociable activities possible on public acreage, but also spatially beyond public boundaries. Harking back to the idea of porous public borders (Chapter 3), the public domain's sociability often escapes its territorial confines. From a doctrinal perspective, this spillover is unsurprising, since 'legal institutions are likely to be narrower than social spheres' (Dagan 2012, p. 1425). The sociable after-effects of public space linger into our private spaces, and rekindle as we anticipate the promise of return visits. In (easier to measure) fiscal terms, the drift of the public domain's non-economic values to surrounding private property leads to an accumulation of wealth, a curious metamorphosis of public sociability into private capital. In talking of so-called 'positive externalities', Lehavi notes:

> Successful public spaces may often entail significant advantages for residents who do not actively use the public space. Positive spillover effects stemming from a public space typically include an increase in adjacent real estate prices and a boost to economic and commercial activity.
>
> *(2013, p. 121)*

It is not only nearby properties, but whole neighborhoods that may change because of the presence of hyper-successful public lands. New York City's iconic High Line has transformed the West Chelsea neighborhood around the elevated parkland, becoming 'a catalyst for some of the most rapid gentrification in the city's history' (Moss 2012). Before the High Line, real estate values were 8% below the city's average. In the immediate years after its opening, values increased by 103% (ibid.), and the socio-economic character of the area changed. Luxury apartments replaced local service businesses, and hordes of tourists descended into the park, drowning out local amenity. The High Line is much criticized as a 'Trojan horse' for gentrification, for its lack of diversity, its failings as a 'democratic public space' (Reichl 2016), and its poor engagement with local residents. Contrast this to Chicago's 606, another elevated (and disused) rail line-turned park that avoided the excesses of 'High Lineification' (Marshall 2017). The 606 is a 'utilitarian, neighborhood-serving rail trail' with little 'city-wide significance' (ibid.), but abundant in local sociability. These two examples reveal not so much sociability's absence or abundance, but a focus on *whose* sociability. They also illustrate the porous and multi-directional flow of private and public values between adjoining public and private lands, as seen through the prism of sociability.

The epiphany that is Rose's comedy of the commons shines a light on the importance of sociability to the public estate, and its theoretical and performative groundings. In the public outside, sociability pervades all. People purposefully going about their business, tourists following the crowds, parents kicking balls with their kids, or impromptu dance lessons in grassy quadrangles, all these and more are the manifestations of sociability in the public domain. Simultaneously a 'celebration of possibility' and daily repetition of the mundane and the ordinary, the sociability of public realty – in all its ephemerality and diversity – makes our lives better lived. Indeed, it is this particular consequence of sociability, its capacity to enhance human flourishing, that forms the subject of the next discussion.

4.3 Propriety and human flourishing

The recent theory of progressive property 'aims at realizing the ideal of human flourishing' (Alexander and Penalver 2012, p. 80). Arguably, an offshoot of 'property as propriety', progressive theory is a countervailing account of property that contests ascendant justifications based on exclusion, information costs, or disaggregated bundles of rights. Progressive theory provides a principled depiction of property, strongly imbued with Aristotelian ideals of 'faring well (well-being) and doing well (virtue)' (p. 87). Its chief proponents are American jurists, notably Gregory Alexander, Eduardo Penalver, Joseph Singer and Laura Underkuffler, who articulated an overarching 'Statement of Progressive Property' in 2009.[7] Its critics counter that its indeterminacy is its Achilles heel, a well-meaning meta-principle that reduces property as a 'means to realizing *any* particular theory of the good' (Merrill and Smith 2019, emphasis added), or an open-ended conversation (Baron 2010).

Pre-dating progressive theory is the 'property as commodity/property as propriety' dichotomy. In the 1990s, Rose articulated 'property as propriety' as the counter to 'property for preference satisfaction' (1994, p. 65). Propriety is a 'weaker but still very stubborn idea' that portrays a far older institutional vision of property as 'the foundation of decency and good order' (p. 64) and bulwark for 'each person's role in the commonwealth' (p. 51). Alexander argues analogously that this dichotomy represents a little-understood tension in the Anglo-American common law of property. On one side, (what Alexander terms as) *commodity* views property as the means to satisfy individual preferences, pursue private agendas, and acquire wealth. As a fulsome account of property however, Alexander says it is unsatisfying, and 'only half-right' (1997, p. 2). The other half of the duality is propriety, a 'prior normative vision of how society and the polity that governs it should be structured' (ibid.). As an understanding of property that 'rings oddly in modern ears'; propriety defies the modern myopic assumption that property serves exclusively private ends. Rather, the proprietarian account serves public and communitarian ends. Here, property is the 'material foundation for creating and maintaining the proper social order' (p. 1). In substance, propriety and human flourishing are two sides of the one coin. In 2009, for instance, Alexander writes that propriety creates the civic milieu in which citizens lead fulfilling, sociable, well-lived lives, and the ideal of human flourishing is enacted (p. 763).

Human flourishing is thus integral to, and implicitly weaved throughout propriety and progressive theory. But neither theory joins the dots when it comes to explicitly linking public real property with the well-lived life. Indeed, in failing to draw any distinction between private and public property, each reinforces the corrosive synonymy that treats property and private property as one and the same. However, in seeking to broaden the institution, and imbue it with virtues, these theories do implicate the public realm in several indirect, unremarked (and probably unintended) respects. First, like Rose, they recognize that property is inherently social, where 'dependency and inter-dependency are inescapable aspects of well-lived lives' – such that it's 'quite literally impossible for a person to flourish without others' (p. 87). The pursuit of human flourishing thus becomes 'an unavoidably cooperative rather than pursuit or purely personal project' (ibid.), one that must inevitably escape from private space into public, and in so doing, bringing public real property into its orbit.

Second, property is said to 'implicate plural and incommensurable values' (Alexander et al., 2009, p. 743). Many values are individual, but others are social, the likes of 'environmental stewardship, civic responsibility, and aggregate wealth' (ibid.). Away from the satisfaction of personal preferences, values that enhance the common or public-wealth, or reflect communitarian obligation, are more likely the values of the public estate (Page, 2019). And third, flourishing requires both 'basic material goods and a *communal infrastructure*' (Alexander and Penalver 2012, p. 87, emphasis added). Here, public real property comes closest to explicit acknowledgment, as part of a community's 'aggregate material resources [which] plausibly, though indirectly, affect the ability of its members to flourish' (p. 97). Communal infrastructure is what we imagine it to be, the roads, sidewalks, parks and civic amenities that form the backbone of the public estate.[8]

Despite its good intentions, the problem with progressive theory, or property as propriety, is that it continues to 'ring oddly to modern ears'. Human flourishing fails to relate to our lived or majoritarian experiences of property, where exclusion and the market dominate. Human flourishing also suffers because it is harder to measure. Rebecca Solnit writes of driving through public and private landscapes in the western United States, comparing lands she can access, to those off-limits. There, she observes that 'prizing nothingness is harder than prizing something' (2017, p. 50).[9] It is difficult to prize lands that are not 'useful for growing or grazing', like public lands of 'trees and steepness' (ibid.). Places of nothingness. Faced with such stark value choices, perhaps the best way we can prize the public realm is to prize it for its human flourishing? This requires, as Chapter 3 argues, a re-privileging of public purpose, recognition that public lands are optimally (perhaps exclusively) places of propriety. A realm that in Rose's words, unequivocally founds 'good order' and secures an individual's 'place in the commonwealth'.

Joseph Sax might agree with these propositions. In *Mountains Without Handrails: Reflections on the National Parks* (1980), Sax writes of American national parks, and the philosophies that underpinned their early history (see also Chapter 7). Sax identifies one little-documented justification for retaining wilderness in public ownership – in a subject otherwise devoid of 'little serious or sustained writing' (p. 18). It is the ideal of the citizen's 'contemplative faculty', attributed to Frederick Law Olmstead, best known for another great public space, Central Park in New York. Sax says that Olmsted was instrumental in the protection of California's Mariposa Grove in the mid-19th century. Olmsted's guiding principle there was not preserving scenery for scenery's sake, but rather, protecting the giant sequoias for their capacity 'to stimulate powerful, searching responses in people' (1980, p. 19). This was a 'political duty', the provision of land for 'the ordinary citizen … to exercise and educate the contemplative faculty', and to escape the drudgery and toil of their workaday lives (p. 21). His was a 'prescription for parks as an important institution in a society unwilling to write off the ordinary citizen' (ibid.). Notwithstanding what Sax calls Olmsted's 'strange archaic vocabulary', this call to public ideals invokes the very essence of well-lived lives and human flourishing, and the *capacity* for public lands to further these altruistic ends. If, as Sax argues, this was a guiding principle at the dawn of the national park era, then these iconic pieces of the public mosaic remain, in part, for their capacity to enable human flourishing.

Unlike sociability – which figures large in public property scholarship – the property theory of human flourishing intersects with the public estate in oblique ways. One must divine the public realm, almost read between the lines to discern its presence in this most well-meaning of property's meta-principles. At one level, this is surprising; given the capacious – and obvious – role communal infrastructure can play to make our lives well-lived. Or, the public values that public real property espouses. But, of course, at the abstract level, where property doctrinally and theoretically inhabits, this is not surprising at all.

4.4 Public happiness

Happiness is the third plank to this chapter's scrutiny of the public estate's centrality to the citizen's well-lived life. Unlike sociability or human flourishing, happiness is not a theoretical construct or doctrine of property. Rather, it is connected (sequentially) to property by a two-stepped process. First, is the recent literature that validates happiness as a subject of proper legal enquiry, a 'legal science' capable of application to legal space. Second is the complementary and equally recent studies that explore the intersection of urban design and happiness. While urban design sits outside property's black-letter remit, the discipline nonetheless implicates public realty. This is because property is central to the shaping of our communities. Cities, towns and suburbs are blends of property types, unique mosaics of private, common and *public* real estate that yield commensurately bespoke communities – each distinctive in their propertied design (Page 2019). In a similar vein, Theodore Steinberg observes that 'property permeates everywhere' (1995), an institutional ubiquity that extends to public acreage, while Waldron's truism says much the same. 'Everything that is done has to be done somewhere' (1992) is an intuition born of property's complex design rules of exclusion and inclusion, and the interplay of private and public lands. Applying this conjunctive logic, this section hypothesizes that public real property can be, on its sometimes-happy occasions, a verifiable form of happiness itself.

In *Happiness and the Law*, John Bronsteen et al. (2015) observe how 'the study of happiness is the next step in the evolution from the traditional economic analysis of the law to a behavioral approach' (pp. 4–5). This evolution of the science of happiness has been underway for some time. Currently, happiness data includes 'hedonic psychology measures', which scientifically validate and objectify an individual's 'subjective well-being' (Montgomery 2013, p. 31), or the index of the 'well-being analysis', the inverse of the widely used cost-benefit analysis. The full extent of happiness economics is beyond this book's scope, but what make its emergence interesting are its empirical implications, the capacity for happiness to be objectively measured, and conceivably mapped to place. Importantly, in legal terms, this objectification 'opens the door to a more complete and accurate picture of how law interacts with human life' (Bronsteen et al. 2015, p. 183). This is in effect the authors' point, that 'data about the positivity of life' should be incorporated into our laws, and consequently 'the sooner it is, the better our laws will be' (p. 5).

Assumedly therefore, the happiness that emanates from happy public real property is capable of measurement and objective benchmarking. And with this newfound data and the insights it provides, comes the 'ultimate purpose of the law, to make people's lives better' (p. 183). Or, in the case of the laws of the public estate, the ability to make its disparate laws clearer, more coherent, logically organized, and better able to protect public acreage. Such is the theory, dependent as it is on the measurable capacities of the science of happiness.

But are public spaces happiness personified? Charles Montgomery's 2013 study of the intersection of happiness and urban design suggests yes; that vibrant and easily accessible public spaces add to the happiness quotient. More broadly, the public estate informs and influences a range of happiness factors: the shape of cities, their dispersed or concentrated design, the architectural relationship of private space to public, the privileging of public over private transport, and the availability and ease of access to public resources. Conscious policy decisions about urban design impact on a community's social capital – and its citizen's consequent happiness.

Montgomery begins his study of urban happiness in Bogota, Colombia, where a democratically elected mayor, Enrique Penalosa unveiled a radical agenda, seizing neglected private estates to create networks of new green open space, and investing in critical public infrastructure such as cycle ways and libraries (2013, p. 235). His legacy was a happier city, an end that did not require ever-greater accumulations of private wealth, but paradoxically simpler needs:

> We need to walk, just as birds need to fly. We need to be around other people. We need beauty. We need contact with nature. And most of all, we need not to be excluded. We need to feel some sort of equality.
>
> *(p. 6)*

Penalosa's prescription for happiness constitutes a running sheet of public real property. Conversely, what had caused prior misery to its citizens were the excesses of private property. Bogota's was an urban history of privatization of public spaces and resources, where 'cars and mobile vendors had taken over public plazas and sidewalks' and 'people had walled or fenced in what were once public parks' – such that 'common civic space was disregarded and degraded' (ibid.).

What makes a city happy, Montgomery reasons, is its design, and the consequent interplay of private and public that its property patterns yield, a mosaic that either mediates or inhibits relationships with others.[10] Montgomery reduces public space to folksy terms, 'happiness is a house with many rooms, *but at its core* is a hearth around which we gather with family, friends, the community, and sometimes even strangers to find the best part of ourselves' (pp. 38–39, emphasis added). This hearth of happiness is typically the public domain in older inner-city areas. But where there is no central hearth, we see all too familiar legal geographies of dispersal, the multitude of cul de sacs and sprawlscapes of 'infinitely repeated form' that multiply 'at the edge of the urban blast radius' (p. 47).

In his circular logic, Montgomery sees public space and happiness as self-reinforcing and self-referential. 'Great public space is a kind of magical good. It never ceases to yield happiness. It's almost happiness itself' (p. 6). Here, in this thinking, the 'humble sidewalk, park and bike path' is elevated to 'a psycho-spiritual realm' (p. 7), a loop-back of happiness that either entrenches a well-lived life by the richness of the public realm, or impoverishes it by its absence.[11]

There is an apparent, self-evident link between public real property and happiness, and more broadly, the citizen's well-lived life. As a putative organizing principle of the public estate, the well-lived life is exuberant in its warm and fuzzy appeal. And in its nitty-gritty, the concrete and steel and grass and greenery of public infrastructure, there is an undeniable materiality to living life well. Yet, in unpacking what the well-lived life may mean, its constituent elements tell a more complex, less even story. Sociability is a propertied concept with rich public property antecedence. The scholarship of Rose is testament to this. By contrast, the broader ideal of human flourishing, as expressed in progressive theory at least, offers little in the way of any direct relationship with public property. This may simply reflect flourishing's 'incommensurability'. But there is scant theoretical heft to work with here, only an inferential reading between the lines. And in the narrower pursuit of happiness, Montgomery draws a compelling link between urban public space and happy citizens, a link with empirical promise. But is happiness *per se* desirable all of the time?

The difficulty of the meta-principle of the public well-lived life, for all its ostensible application, is the holes one can find in it. The remainder of this chapter is spent on critiquing the universality of the well-lived life as an explanation of public real property. As the next section underscores, no meta-principle is perfect.

4.5 The (im)perfect well-lived life

There are inconsistencies and flaws in the meta-narrative of the comedic, endlessly sociable, flourishing-enhancing commons. These include that an increasing lot of sociability happens on private land; that the public domain does not always engender human flourishing, let alone happiness; that some people's sociability is more equal than others; and (more broadly, of course) that private sociability is likewise a social good. While the well-lived life may be the public estate's cheerful expressive endeavor, this is not always faithful to what happens on the ground. This concluding discussion addresses the pragmatic and the contextual, the not always sunny, or uneven sides of sociability, happiness, and human flourishing.

The first objection is factual. A lot of public sociability has migrated from the public estate to so-called private commons, to shopping malls, corporate high streets, entertainment centers, casinos, sporting stadiums, theme parks, or the lunchtime plazas of downtown commercial buildings. These privately owned, publicly accessible spaces attract the acronym of POPs (privately owned public spaces).[12] In modern everyday life, the public estate no longer enjoys a monopoly on sociability, as POPs increasingly come to dominate our spatial leisure or down time.

Even, in the public domain, private interests, left unchecked, engage in a kind of spatial reverse takeover, as public parks or city squares choke on private concessions, mobile food carts, or closed-off fashion shoots. Or, national parks lose famous place names to trademark claims, or square feet of public parkland can be hired for a fee.[13] At the end of the day, the net effect is the same, whether our sociability becomes an overwhelmingly private affair, public lands are privatized by stealth, or the two estates merge seamlessly into a (privately dominant) hybrid.

Here, imitation is the sincerest form of flattery. Successful private commons attract paying patrons by mimicking the features of public real property. A sense of openness, the façade of inclusivity, the aura of sociability, are copied or adapted to further private ends. David Ulin ascribes the success of the Grove shopping and entertainment precinct in Los Angeles to its mimicry of great public streets, an 'ersatz space [where] real things happen' in a city ranked a lowly 33rd in a national survey of walkable access to parkland (pp. 76–78). Developer/owner Rick Caruso is open about its chosen design:

> Its why we don't have gates. … If we're going to build a great street, it needs to do everything a street would do, which means you don't have gates. You keep it open. The more we do that, the more you become part of the fabric of the city.
>
> *(Caruso, quoted in Ulin, 2015, p. 78)*

The quasi-public formula works. In 2013, the Grove was said to be more popular (and sociable) than Disneyland, attracting 18 million visitors per year with its 'main street of dreams' (Tyrnauer, 2013), loved trolley car, and nearby Farmer's Markets. If this 'ersatz space' makes up for a dearth of genuine public infrastructure, does it matter? After all, as Ulin observes, the Grove is where the LA public could (re) learn 'sidewalking', 'the serendipitous encounter, the random meeting, the flow of the crowd, the friend you haven't seen in years, … a part of the way cities work' (p. 78).

However, it should matter where the space purports to be 'public'. The reasons *why* form a compelling refutation of the argument that the slow death of public sociability is of little moment. And inversely, why sociability and the well-lived life remain critical to the public estate.[14] Private spaces, unlike public property, are premised on rules of exclusion. Despite appearances, many POPs are tightly controlled, surveilled and policed. From codes of conduct regulating behavior and clothing standards, to the suppression of protest and dissent (Christophers 2018, pp. 314–321, and Chapter 7), privately owned public spaces take a very different slant on what is 'acceptable' public sociability.[15] Their diversity is likewise skewed. As Ulin notes of the Grove, 'the diversity it attracts … is determined by the mercantile nature of the experience; no one is there who doesn't have money to spend' (p. 78).[16] This mercantilism in turn underscores how private commons are designed foremost for materialist consumption. Other, richer expressions of public life, even if condoned, are peripheral to the core business, and run the risk of confection or commoditization (Layard, 2016, p. 44, writing of public art). As Brett Christophers surmises of once-public lands in central London, 'private-public places – privately owned, but professing to offer public space – [are] sterile, uniform places, which inhibit genuine public access and lack the diversity and humanity of traditional street life' (p. 315, quoting Anna Minton).

Such arguments, of course, do not negate the importance of sociability to our enjoyment of the private domain, where property-related values such as personhood, solitude, and privacy are best advanced in the hearth of the domestic home. Sociability can be sliced in public and private ways, such that sociability 'with a handful of trusted intimates' (Ellickson, 2008) is equally as intrinsic to human flourishing as the convivial sociability of a diversity of strangers. The risk lies beyond the domestic hearth or private workplace, where private property encroaches into the public, and seeks to supersede and replace it.

The second counter-argument is that some public spaces are distinctly unsociable. Nor is the well-lived life the unidirectional outcome of the public estate. One can easily be carried away by the romanticism of sociable public real property – and forget the grinding despair of the ubiquitous motorway or interstate, ribbons of *public* concrete that shuttle millions of carbon-emitting commuters from far-flung suburbs to distant work, and home again. Or, the failed parks and city squares that ignore design principles of thinkers like William Whyte and his 'social life of small urban spaces' (1980) to become forlorn, windswept zones of dysfunction and crime. This is the public estate's blind spot, the less-spoken ways in which it negates the well-lived life through its very materiality. It is convenient to shift the blame for our dreary urban landscapes, those 'geographies of nowhere' (Kunstler 1993), or dispersed sprawlscapes of 'endlessly repeated form' (Montgomery 2013) to the cumulative evils of private property and the motor vehicle. Yet, some public parks are no-go zones. And, freeways and highways *are* public acreage, perhaps the 'only true public realm' (Layard 2016) that despite their public-ness, engineer social ills. It was not always thus. Once the public highway was a place of sociable multiple-use, shared spaces of commerce, foot traffic, even childhood play in its quieter backstreets (Schwarz, 2015, p. 10). Our highway statutes imply as much. Yet the era of 'motordom' has transformed the highway into an unsociable thoroughfare of unhindered vehicular passage (Montgomery 2013, pp. 69–77). In short, public real property is not a universal, unidirectional enabler of the well-lived life. Sometimes, it actively works against it.

Another flaw turns on the question of *whose* sociability? Not everyone enjoys equal access to public acreage, and therefore, applying Waldron's spatial logic, not everyone's sociability is equal. The privileging of certain group's sociability can be seen in literature that observes a middle-class dominance of the English right to roam (Monbiot, 2020), racialized critiques of New York's uber-successful High Line (Reichl 2016), the higher proportion of 'municipal public parks in white, affluent neighborhoods' (Lehavi 2013, p. 122), or the difficulties of public gardening while Black. In Detroit, Michigan, African-American Marc Peeples had been building garden beds in Hunt Park, a public park in the city's east, when three white women – who reportedly had their own plans for the green space – sought his 'eviction' through allegations of criminal conduct (Perkins 2019). In March 2018, for example, police were called because Peeples was allegedly carrying a gun. Instead, Peeples was found to be raking leaves. The women's accusations escalated to include claims of violent threats and even pedophilia, ultimately resulting in Peeples' arrest. Acquitted on the basis that the claims were fabricated and largely motivated by race, Peeples eventually returned to the sociable tilling of his self-made garden allotments, now named Liberated Farms. His only 'crime' was to be gardening while Black, a case that highlights the structural inequalities of sociable opportunity, the dynamics of spatial injustice, and the implications of *belonging* and *not belonging* on public acreage, a topic explored next in Chapter 5.

Finally, is the more always the merrier, as Rose propounds? Can we love public realty to death, a perverse kind of suffocating sociability? This is, after all, a variation on Garrett Hardin's tragedy of the commons, where the unregulated consumption of open-access resources leads to their ruin (1968). One can easily envisage scenarios where over-use diminishes public amenity, leading to restrictions on visitor numbers, the imposition of entrance fees, or other prohibitions. This is the line crossed where sociability shifts to congestion. Lee Fennell notes that '[r]esources such as urban parks that appear nonrival (plenteous) at one level of use can become rival (congestible) above that level' (2014, p. 1388). Similarly, Nicholas Blomley makes the commonsense observation that public resources such as sidewalks are finite (2011). But Hardin's tragedy is an overtly polemical tale, one that ignores a counter-history of successful commons regimes (Ostrom 1990). Plus tales of congestion overlook the capacity for thoughtful design to successfully regulate our comedic love affair with great public spaces. This consideration is less a refutation of sociability, than a cautionary or logistical note.

Sociability, flourishing, and the pursuit of happiness intersect with the public estate in pragmatic and qualified ways. Public realty is not a non-stop, ever-expanding comedy. Property theories and public lands don't always neatly align. But in advancing a less-than-perfect well-lived life, the public estate is probably the best property show in town. The private estate is happy to promote good times, but its promotion comes at a price, and on conditions. With the public estate, however, sociability is freer, less conditional. There is an underlying genius in Rose's comedy of the commons. There is likewise much to recommend her compelling narrative of the textual good life, sociable stories that loop back to our frequently convivial experiences of the public domain. For these dual epiphanies alone, and the physical public infrastructure that enables them, public real property and the well-lived life share a rich and common ground.

Notes

1 Examples of meta-principles include 'autonomy, efficiency, equality or individual flourishing' (Merrill and Smith, 2019). Merrill and Smith are critical of both aspects of this simple binary. In terms of the meta-principle approach, they argue that issues are made to fit the meta-principle narrative, and 'reduce … property to being a means to realizing any particular theory of the good' (p. 2).

2 Other Rose articles that touch upon public property include: 'Property as Storytelling: Perspectives: Game Theory, Narrative Theory, Feminist Theory' (1990), 'Energy and Efficiency in the Context of Common Law Water Rights' (1990), 'Joseph Sax and the Idea of the Public Trust' (1998), 'The Several Futures of Property: Of Cyberspace and Folk Tales, Emission Trades and Ecosystems' (1999), and 'Romans, Roads, and Romantic Creators: Traditions of Public Property in the Information Age' (2003).

3 Lee Fennell similarly writes of urban 'interaction spaces' as common pool resources that create public *value* through popular sociable use (2014, p. 1373).

4 One example where propertied narrative abounds is in the rule against perpetuities. There, 'magic gravel pits' and 'fertile octogenarians' are employed as stories that leap over gaps of logic in the doctrine's complexity. In terms of public real property, there are analogous tales of 'time immemorial' in the doctrine of prescription.

5 'Conversely the more time people spend away from the public eye at home, the more disinvestment there is in community social capital' (Eicher and Kawaski 2011, p.122).

6 Brill says that public life should not be confused with community life. In a debate that mirrors the confusion between common and public property, Brill differentiates the two through the lens of sociability. 'Public life is sociability with a diversity of strangers, Community life is sociability with people you know somewhat' (2012, p. 48). These are the family, friends, neighbors, and 'nodding acquaintances' that inhabit our immediate communities. While this mark of distinction is helpful, it is not always a true statement for public real property, since the public realm is as much omnipresent in our nearby lives as it is in our more 'distant' public lives.

7 See, in particular, 'A Statement of Progressive Property' (2009) 94 *Cornell Law Review* 743.

8 Likewise, Point 5 of 'A Statement of Progressive Property' explains, '[p]roperty enables and shapes community life.' Indeed, its better angels render 'relationships within communities liberating and ennobling … and establish the *framework* for a kind of social life appropriate to a free and democratic society' (Alexander et al. 2009, p. 744, emphasis added).

9 Solnit is describing the vast open spaces of deserts or 'the public lands of trees and steepness', spaces in the western United States that remained public because they were deemed useless for private cropping or homesteading (2017, pp. 49–50).

10 '[T]here is a clear connection between … social deficit and the shape of cities' (p. 55). However, Montgomery also lists other reasons; the dominance of the private car, dispersed geographies of sprawl, long commuting times, and little opportunities to walk and socialize. Yet, in their way, all continue to speak to the pervasiveness of property.

11 Happiness and urban design also enjoy strong synergies with 'property as belonging' (see Chapter 5).

12 For example, as at August 2018, New York City has 551 POPs. A special webpage on NYC Planning is devoted to POPs. There, it is explained that POPs differ from City parks simply because 'they are provided on private property and maintained by private owners' (www1.nyc.gov/site/planning/plans/pops/pops-resources.page).

13 In California, place names to iconic sites in Yosemite National Park were lost to private operators, while in San Francisco, the popular Dolores Park trialed (briefly) a system whereby patrons could reserve marked lawn areas for a fee of up to $260. After public outcry, the city's Parks Department abandoned the trial. N Woolf & J Wong, 'San Francisco retracts program to pay to reserve park's lawn areas after outrage', *The Guardian*, 25 May 2016 at www.theguardian.com/us-news/2016/may/24/san-francisco-dolores-park-reservation-policy-retracted; Honig, 2017, pp. 96–97.

14 Massey says these 'new enclosures' need to be 'witnessed with alarm.' Reasons for concern include the 'vesting of control over these spaces in[to] the hands of non-democratically elected owners', and the exclusion of certain people such as '"unemployed" loiterers' deemed not to be 'prospective shoppers' (Massey 2005, p. 152).

15 Antonia Layard writes of the 'increasing rolling up of [English] city centres into large privately owned enclaves … enclosed in a single plan, city cores are accessible only to "visitors" not citizens. Lawfully accessible only under licence as actual or potential

consumers, in many city centres visitors are now unable to walk a dog, play a guitar, take a photograph, or smoke a cigarette in places otherwise understood to be, and presented as being, in the public realm' (2012, p. 260). See also the literature of shopping malls, such as Gray and Gray (1999) and Layard (2010).

16 This lack of diversity is mirrored in the concerns of the 'legitimate' public, who find that 'sociability, civility and commerce can once again flourish in an atmosphere of safety and security' in sanitized private-public places, far from 'public places in the cities … gradually appropriated by drug dealers, homeless people and so forth, driving away other citizens' (Lehavi 2013, p. 124).

References

Alexander, G 1997, *Commodity & Propriety: Competing Visions of Property in American Thought 1776–1970*, University of Chicago Press, Chicago.

Alexander, G. 2009 'The Social-Obligation Norm in American Property Law', *Cornell Law Review*, vol. 94, 745–819.

Alexander, G et al. 2009, 'A Statement of Progressive Property', *Cornell Law Review,* vol. 49, 743–744.

Alexander, G and Penalver, E 2012, *An Introduction to Property Theory*, Cambridge University Press, New York.

Baron, J 2010, 'The Contested Commitments of Property', *Hastings Law Journal*, vol. 61, 917–967.

Beatley, T 2009, 'Planning for Sustainability in European Cities', in S. Wheeler and T. Beatley (eds.), *The Sustainable Urban Development Reader*. Routledge, Abingdon.

Blomley, N 2011, *Rights of Passage Sidewalks and the Regulation of Public Flow*, Routledge, Abingdon.

Brill, M 2002, 'Problems with Mistaking Community Life for Public Life', *Places,* vol. 14, no. 2, 48–55.

Bronsteen, J. et al. 2015, *Happiness and the Law*. University of Chicago Press, Chicago.

Capon, A and Thompson, S 2011, 'Built Environments of the Future', in A Dannenberg et al. (eds.), *Making Healthy Places Designing and Building for Health, Well-being and Sustainability,* Island Press, Washington, DC.

Christophers, B 2018, *The New Enclosure: The Appropriation of Public lands in Neoliberal Britain,* Verso Books, London.

Dagan, H 2012, 'Pluralism and Perfectionism in Private Law', *Columbia Law Review*, vol. 112, 1409–1446.

Eicher, C and Kawachi, I 2011, 'Social Capital and Community Design', in A Dannenberg et al. (eds.), *Making Healthy Places Designing and Building for Health, Well-being and Sustainability,* Island Press, Washington, DC.

Ellickson, R 2008, *The Household: Informal Order Around the Hearth*, Princeton University Press, Princeton.

Fennell, L 2014, 'Agglomerama' *Brigham Young University Law Review*, no. 6, 1373–1414.

Foster S R and Iaione C 2016, 'The City as Commons', *Yale Law & Policy Review*, vol. 34, 281–349.

Frumkin, H and Fox, J, 2011, 'Contact with Nature' in A Dannenberg et al. (eds.), *Making Healthy Places Designing and Building for Health, Well-being and Sustainability,* Island Press, Washington, DC.

Gray, K and Gray, S 1999, 'Civil Rights, Civil Wrongs and Quasi-Public Space', *European Human Rights Law Review,* vol. 4, 46–102.

Hardin, G 1968, 'The Tragedy of the Commons', *Science,* vol. 162, no. 3859, 1243–1248.
Honig, B. 2017, *Public Things: Democracy in Disrepair,* Fordham University Press, New York.
Jacobs, J 1961, *The Death and Life of Great American Cities,* Random House, New York.
Jamison, L. 2019. 'The Photographs That Made Me Feel Less Alone', *The Atlantic,* Dec. 2019 available at www.theatlantic.com/magazine/archive/2019/12/garry-winogrand-leslie-jamison/600805/ (accessed 15 May 2019).
Kuntsler, J H 1993, *The Geography of Nowhere: The Rise and Decline of America's Man-Made Landscape,* Simon & Schuster, New York.
Layard, A 2010, 'Shopping in the Public Realm: A Law of Place', *Journal of Law & Society,* vol. 37, 412–441.
Layard A 2012, 'Property Paradigms and Place Making: A Right to the City, a Right to the Street', *Journal of Human Rights & the Environment,* vol. 3, 254–272.
Layard, A 2016, 'Public Space: Property, Lines, Interruptions', *Journal of Law, Property & Society,* vol. 2, 1–47.
Lehavi, A 2013, *The Construction of Property Norms, Institutions, Challenges,* Cambridge University Press, Cambridge.
Marshall, C 2017, 'Want to join New York's High Line crowd? Don't listen to Joanna Lumley', *The Guardian,* 15 Aug. 2017 available at www.theguardian.com/cities/2017/aug/15/new-york-high-line-crowd-london-garden-bridge-urban-design (accessed 26 May 2019).
Massey, D 2005, *For Place,* SAGE Publications, London.
Merrill, T W & Smith, H E. 2019, 'The Architecture of Property' in H Dagan and B Zipursky (eds.), *Research Handbook on Private Law Theories,* Edward Elgar, Cheltenham.
Monbiot, G 2020, 'Lockdown Is Nothing New: We've Been Kept Off the Land for Centuries', *The Guardian,* 22 April 2020, available at www.theguardian.com/commentisfree/2020/apr/22/lockdown-coronavirus-crisis-right-to-roam (accessed 24 April 2020).
Moss, J 2012, 'Disney World on the Hudson', *New York Times,* 21 Aug. 2012 available at www.nytimes.com/2012/08/22/opinion/in-the-shadows-of-the-high-line.html (accessed 10 August 2019).
Montgomery, C 2013, *Happy City: Transforming Our Lives Through Urban Design,* Farrar, Straus and Giroux, New York.
Ostrom, E 1990, *Governing the Commons: The Evolution of Institutions for Collective Action,* Cambridge University Press, New York.
Page, J. 2019, 'Property, Values, and the Empirics of Place', *Griffith Law Review,* vol. 28, no. 1, 1–22.
Perkins T 2019, 'Detroit Man Sues Three White Women Who Called Police on Him for "Gardening while Black"', *Detroit Metro Times,* 4 Mar. 2019, available at http://metrotimes.com/table-and-bar/archives/2019/03/04/detroit-man-sues-three-white-women-who-called-police-on-him-for-gardening-while-black (accessed 10 August 2019).
Reichl, A 2016, 'The High Line and the Ideal of Democratic Public Space', *Urban Geography* vol. 37, 904–925.
Rose, C M 1986, 'The Comedy of the Commons: Custom, Commerce, and Inherently Public Property', *University of Chicago Law Review,* vol. 53, no. 3, 711–781.
Rose, C M 1990, 'Property as Storytelling: Perspectives from Game Theory, Narrative Theory, Feminist Theory', *Yale Journal of Law & the Humanities,* vol. 2, 37–57.
Rose, C.M. 1994, 'Seeing Property' in C M Rose (ed.) *Property and Persuasion Essays on the History, Theory, and Rhetoric of Ownership,* Westview Press, Boulder, CO.
Rose, C M 2005, 'Book Review: Property in All the Wrong Places', *Yale Law Journal,* vol. 114, 991–1019.

Rose, C M 2006,'Property and Language, or the Ghost of the Fifth Panel', *Yale Journal of Law and the Humanities*, vol. 18, 1–28.

Sax, J 1980, *Mountains Without Handrails, Reflections on the National Parks*, University of Michigan Press, Ann Arbor.

Schwarz, S 2015, *Street Smart: The Rise of Cities and the Fall of Cars*, Public Affairs, New York.

Solnit, R 2017, *A Field Guide to Getting Lost*, Canongate Books, Edinburgh.

Speck, J 2013, *Walkable City, How Downtown Can Save America One Step at a Time*, Farrar, Straus and Giroux, New York.

Steinberg, T 1995, *Slide Mountain, or The Folly of Owning Nature,* University of California Press, Berkeley.

Tyrnauer, M 2013, 'Main Street of Dreams', *Vanity Fair*, March 2013, available at www.vanityfair.com/culture/2013/03/rick-caruso-the-grove-la (accessed 15 May 2019).

Ulin, D 2015, *Sidewalking: Coming to Terms with Los Angeles*. University of California Press, Oakland.

Waldron, J. 1992,'Homeless and the Issue of Freedom', *UCLA Law Review*, vol. 39, 295–324.

Whyte, W H 1980, *The Social Life of Small Urban Spaces,* The Conservation Foundation, New York.

5

OF PUBLIC BELONGING

5.1 Introduction

Chapter 4 examined how public real property contributes to well-lived lives. This chapter builds on that enquiry to interrogate *belonging*, an analogous, partly overlapping concept that is likewise intrinsic to living well. Yet, belonging represents something more; an intuitive, deeply contextual affinity to space, place and community that transcends (sometimes fleeting) feelings of happiness or sociability. In choosing *belonging* as an organizing principle, this chapter seeks to identify and analyze how the public domain, in its own particular and unique ways, anchors us to physical and social spaces, and engenders relations of belonging, sense of place and attachment to community.

Chapter 5's structure is in part abstract and part material. The abstract rests in theory, a lengthier survey of the recent writings of property as belonging, property and place, and property and community scholars. The consequent aspect, the material, looks at how this thinking relates to context, relational literature and anecdote that transposes theory to praxis through the intervention of public real property. Here, the focus is predominately urban, a series of brief case examples that explore how the creative use or re-use of urban public space fosters place making and ties to community. In so observing, this chapter does not claim that public real property is solely determinative of belonging.[1] But by example and theory, it does join certain dots, noting the happy coincidence that a robust public estate helps, rather than hinders, relations of belonging – coincidences that should be seen as more than mere happenstance.

Belonging is a useful – albeit unlikely – lens through which to view public real property. As Sarah Keenan explains, a focus on 'belonging rather than exclusion brings into view spatial factors that tend to be otherwise overlooked in exclusion-focused theorizations of property' (2015, p. 72). Keenan's focus on relations of belonging shifts property analysis away from the positional (the subject) to the spatial (the context). In so doing, it encompasses the physical, social and conceptual spaces of belonging to present a 'fuller picture' (p. 10), one outside the private estate's narrow terms of reference. This is a totality that enlivens the wider diversity of property (Page 2017), and logically engages the public domain. Likewise, as Davina Cooper argues, property relations of belonging extend not only to 'belonging' in the standard subject/object sense,[2] but (importantly) belonging in the part/whole sense, the belonging that arises when the property relationship makes one feel part of an inclusive, greater whole. This is a belonging that again envisages a fuller understanding of property, a perspective that opens up a 'black box of unofficial property interests' beyond simple subject/object relations dependent on rules of exclusion and their enforcement by the state. As Cooper argues, opening up this 'black box' enables us to see property as constitutive of community, and to appreciate the significance of contextual norms of inclusion that private-centric theories 'miss or misrecognize' (2007, p. 659).

Public belonging is also useful for the *utopian* perspectives it yields (Cooper 2013, p. 32). Or, the ways in which different property relations can be *subversive* of the private hegemony (Keenan 2015). That being said, belonging is not perfect; by necessary implication, it infers that some people belong, and others do not. Indeed, non-belonging is superficially like exclusion, where 'some will smoothly fit because they are "in place" and proper, while others will be "out of place" and improper' (p. 14). Nor is it an exclusively *public* explanation of property, since we also belong through our relationships with private spaces, our loved homes or gardens, or through longstanding ties to common property, the likes of life memberships of community associations or sporting clubs.

However, belonging, place and community – concepts that this chapter loosely coalesces under its headline title – provide an alternative and valuable means to consider our relationships with public real property. Theirs is a transformative perspective; enabling, dynamic, spatial, contextual, connective, disruptive, sometimes even utopian, divergent viewpoints anchored by and through the materiality and idea of public real property.

5.2 Public property and belonging

Analyzing public property through the lens of belonging is earlier described as 'unlikely' because neither Keenan nor Cooper single out the public estate for preferential treatment. Cooper's key focus is on how 'conceptually potent, innovative sites' (like the self-governing Summerhill School, or a queer Toronto bathhouse) may 'revitalize radical politics', or 'engage in the work of civil repair', goals oblivious to the utopia's particular property status (2013, p. 9). Indeed, Cooper's principal study of property as belonging takes place on the privately owned grounds of Summerhill School in Sussex. Similarly, Keenan's sparse references to the public estate do not make a special case for a greater public belonging. Drawing on critical geographer Doreen Massey[3], Keenan argues similar injustices pervade public space as much as they inform private. She writes, 'even spaces designated as "public" are produced by power relations that are conflicting and unequal and are thus more accessible to some people than others' (2015, p. 60):

> Public property tends to hold up some bodies more than others – women and transgendered people are less likely to be able to walk through a public park at night; those from non-English speaking backgrounds are less likely to find books they need at a local public library; indigenous people are less likely to enjoy the public holiday held to commemorate the founding of the colonial state.
>
> *(p. 92)*

Yet, despite such major flaws, belonging promises an alternative way to conceptualize public real property, a methodology that (sympathetically) de-centers exclusion, centers space and place, and underscores the co-constitutive relationship of the subject and their surroundings. In so orienting, belonging has the potential to carve out a conceptual niche for the public realm, a territory that exclusionary-premised theories of the private estate struggle to conceive of, and develop.

Belonging is said to be a 'conceptually ambiguous term', variously meaning 'a relationship to place that "fits" or is "at home"', 'the location of an object or person in its "proper place"', or 'the process of creating a sense of identification with, or connection to cultures, people, places and material objects' (Keenan 2015, p. 12).[4] Keenan argues that belonging is 'a necessarily relational term', the 'state of fitting smoothly, or without trouble, into a conceptual category or a material position' (ibid.). Belonging and property are logically related because 'spaces where subjects belong are spaces of property' (p. 14). In this convergence, property is characterized as 'a spatially contingent relation of belonging', and 'a relationship held up by space' (p. 65). The propertied subject is de-centered in this worldview, becoming 'inseparable from the conceptual, social and physical space that surrounds her' (p. 8). Belonging is also mutually constitutive; the emplaced subject 'taking space with her as she moves' (p. 16), while (re-)shaping the spaces in which she is physically embedded (p. 87).

Cooper regards belonging as 'the first, and most important, aspect of property practice' (2007, p. 629),[5] a core element that lies at the 'definitional and normative level' of both subject/object and part/whole orientations of property (ibid.). In its latter iteration, belonging particularly describes the 'relationship of connection of part to whole', variegated social relations that implicate 'collective identity/community', reveal a 'complex tapestry' of legal pluralism beneath the rhetoric of private ownership, and form a 'particularly constitutive relationship' (pp. 627, 629 and 630).[6] Here, property is a 'set of networked relations on which the subject is embedded', not simple propositions about a subject's 'mastery or control over an object' (p. 636). Translated to Summerhill School,[7] belonging gives a fuller picture of school life. While conventional property analysis may capture the head-teacher's title to the school grounds, or students' property in their personal effects, it would 'miss a lot of what goes on':

> It would miss the legal orders recognized and enforced by the school (but disregarded by the state); it would miss the overlapping character of property rights, powers, and freedoms as rights variously granted by state, school, and community custom meet and fold over each other; and it would miss the ways relations of property and governance blur into each other. Approaching property at Summerhill in conventional terms would give us, in short, a disappointingly thin picture of school life.
>
> *(2013, p. 161)*

The same could be said of the public estate. What we see presently is a 'disappointingly thin picture'. Property 'misses a lot of what goes on'. Yet, by centering the spatial, contextualizing the subject, and viewing property as relationships of belonging held up by space, we clear conceptual room for public real property in the wider institution. The spatial recognizes the public acreage that forms (part of) the fabric of urban and rural landscapes, the parks, roads, sidewalks, subways, and civic and cultural *spaces* where we connect and belong. Context emplaces the subject *in situ*, no longer stuck in an abstract jural plane, but integrated constitutively into public as well as private terrain. And seeing property as relations of belonging puts exclusion in proportionate focus, and as such, better recognizes the totality of what is going on, people's relationships with land beyond private boundaries. As will be exemplified later, public spaces connect individual 'parts' to communitarian 'wholes' in ways best understood through this part/whole view of property as belonging.

Another of belonging's great strengths lies in its capacity to subvert the dominant paradigm, to disrupt a singular view of property that is exclusive, commoditized, and by default, private. This lies at the heart of Keenan's *subversive* potential of property. The synonymy of property and private property is so hardwired that it impugns any ready acceptance of the public as property. Belonging offers the radical capacity to act as circuit breaker to this reflex, to produce a different 'space that holds up "alternative" relations of belonging' (p. 94). The disruption it yields is not immediate, most likely it is incremental, forcing hegemonic space 'to adapt, however slightly' (p. 96). Such a notion is closely aligned to performative understandings of property, where quietly defiant acts of public claim to contested space shift the dial, howsoever slightly, and imperceptibly in the moment.

Lastly, belonging also allows us to catch momentary glimpses of an imagined *other,* a utopian-like vision of property. As Cooper argues, only non-private property offers the richness of this possibility. 'Understanding property not through private ownership but through squatting, common or public lands is utopian' (2013, p. 32). The struggle for spatial justice, seen, for example in the Diggers' short-lived settlements of the 17th century, is likewise replete with utopian sentiment. Spatial protest is often directed against a loss of belonging, and the lament for what could have been otherwise, an *other* way of relating to land. The links between protest and public realty are explored in detail in Chapter 7:

Despite belonging's appeal, its corollary – non-belonging – marks a demonstrable downside. As seen in Chapter 4, attempts to remove Marc Peeples from a Detroit park for the 'crime' of gardening while Black, differ little, in first blush at least, from the operational effects of private property's rules of exclusion. In the eyes of his accusers, Peeples did not 'fit'. He was seen as not being in his 'proper place' in the public parklands. Aligning with Jeremy Waldron's seminal thinking on the fundamentals of location and property, Peeples' freedom to act (here, to engage in public gardening) depends on him having a spatially defined place – to belong: 'There are some places where one is simply not allowed to be' (1992, p. 296). However, as Waldron further elaborates, there are distinctions between private lands, and what he terms 'collective property', or its subset of 'common property':

> A place is common property if part of the point of putting it under collective control is to allow anyone in the society to make use of it without having to secure the permission of anybody else … [places] that are relatively open at most times to a fairly indeterminate range of uses by anyone. In the broadest terms, they are places where anyone may be. (pp. 296–297)

Nomenclature aside, Waldron's analysis of private versus public property goes to the essence of exclusion, non-belonging, and the distinctions therein. On private land, one is simply not allowed to be, and the state may be compelled to intervene to enforce the owner's exclusionary edict. But on public realty, anyone may relatively be (and belong). Ultimately, Peeples was allowed to be in Hunt Park. He could belong there and till its soil, and the state could not lawfully preclude him from belonging, despite others' opposing perceptions of proper place. Exclusion is usually a bright line, albeit subject to legal qualifications like the implied license to enter, or racial accommodations laws (Singer 1995). Belonging and non-belonging are perceived as societal 'matters of balance and emphasis' (p. 298), but importantly, belonging is set against a baseline expectation that public lands are where we (normally) are allowed to be. In writing of the plight of the homeless in 1990s America, Waldron says, '[w]hen all else is privately owned, the sidewalks are their salvation' (p. 301). At the end of the (qualified) day, public real property is where we belong. There is no such promise with private property.

Belonging is a radical conceptualization of property. It emphasizes connection, space and relationship in ways beyond the ken of the commoditized mainstream (Cooper 2013, p. 183). By and large, it is the antithesis of modern private property. As is its oppositional wont, belonging opens up theoretical room for the *other* in property, including a normalization of public real property. How belonging plays out on the ground, of theory becoming praxis is explored later through several studies of urban public belonging. For the moment, however, this chapter continues with related theory, next the vexed role of place in property.

5.3 Public property, place and space

Place is largely the province of geographers. Lawyers, for institutional reasons, are chary of it, or simply ignore it. Yet, as Nicholas Blomley suggests (tongue in cheek), and quoting David Harvey, 'geography may be too important to be left to geographers alone' (1994, p. i).[8] Taking up this suggestion, this section delves (in the briefest of ways) into critical geography, as well as canvassing the law's sparser insights, to survey place and space, and their intersections with the public estate. Much of this crossover falls into the field of legal geography.[9]

There is, of course, a distinction between space and place. On occasions, this book has played fast and loose in its less than discriminate use of these terms – provoking Wesley Hohfield's ire that terminological looseness is the root of conceptual confusion. No longer, it is hoped. *Space* is conventionally thought of as blank or inert, the smooth surface upon which place is inscribed. As Keenan opines, 'legal judgments, executive powers, legislation and legal commentaries tend to treat space as something to be planned over, built on, cultivated, bought, sold and/or protected; a blank canvas ... to be smoothly acted upon' (2015, p. 21) Once so planned, alienated, built over, or cultivated, property leaves an indelible 'land memory' of its impact (Penalver 2009), carving space into atomized cadastral parcels. Yet curiously, and despite the lasting land memories it inflicts, property treats its 'subjects as if they live lives free from context' (Keenan 2015, p. 22).

Critical geographers challenge this apolitical, static view of space. Doreen Massey describes space as a shifting, unfixed concept, subject to forces of 'dynamic, heterogeneous simultaneity', or, in a nod to its storytelling capacity, a 'simultaneity of stories-so-far' (2005, p. 9). As already ventilated, space likewise has implicit power dynamics (and imbalances), such that it must be viewed 'through lenses conditioned by society' (Stedman 2016, p. 899). Interestingly, Tim Cresswell describes spatial claims as explicitly 'normative', where something or someone belongs in proper place, and not another (1996). Space can also be read like a text, 'we can thus talk of a hierarchy of readings, with favored, normal, accepted readings and discouraged, heretical, abnormal readings— dominant readings and subordinate readings' (p. 13).

In critical legal theory, space may also take diverse and multiple forms; as physical, social and conceptual *spaces of belonging* (Keenan 2015, p. 11) These comprise tangible spaces that are physically or naturally built, spaces that are socially and culturally constructed, and spaces that are 'the realm of abstract ideas and designs about how the physical and social world does or should operate' (ibid.). Space is lastly malleable, shaped by the propertied subjects who pass through it and take space with them, such that each is constitutive of the other (Barr 2016; Keenan 2015).

Place emerges from within the wider reference system of space. Preferring critical geography's dynamic, heterogeneous view of space, Keenan says that '[p]lace is thus a point or moment within the much larger and ever-evolving dimension of space' (p. 42). As a particular convergence or event, place is but transient and temporal, not an abstract 'site of permanence'. Place is also simultaneously defined by internal conflicts and multiple identities, such that it is of the 'here and now' only, and 'constantly in a state of becoming' (p. 44). Cresswell, a geographer in the critical tradition, describes place as 'never established', but rather operating 'through constant and reiterative practice … made and remade on a daily basis' (2004, pp. 38–39).[10]

Antonia Layard is a rare legal jurist who engages with law and place. In the context of asserting a right to the city (as both space and place), Layard argues that existing legal frameworks require 'a change of mindset', and 'a reconsideration of our understandings of property, particularly our sense of *public property*' (2012, p. 258, emphasis added). Layard envisages a 'right' to the city implemented at the local scale, as a 'communal right' not an 'individual entitlement.' Importantly, however, its conceptualization requires an engagement with 'place rather than property, acknowledging the two as *distinct*' (ibid., emphasis added). Where property is depicted through the private lens, place inevitably becomes distinct from, and disenfranchised in property discourse. This is unsurprising, given the evidence on the ground where 'the pursuit of profit through the deployment of property rights reduces the city [to a] collection of properties', not a place (pp. 259, 261–262). Property's impediment to engaging with place lies, in Layard's view, with English law, in its failure to recognize a legal category of public space and its erstwhile problematizing of vague, ill-defined concepts such as 'city' or 'public' property. Resolve that quandary, perhaps through re-orienting 'property paradigms [to] a localist context', as Layard posits, and place making may be possible (p. 272).

Legal geographers likewise join the dots between property, space and place. Preeminent in recognizing the geographies of property in land is Nicholas Blomley. Blomley's work critiques the 'pervasive' liberal view of space as 'a stable set of coordinates, detached from social and political processes' (2010, p. 204; also 1994), and its consequent viewing of place as 'a neutral category, understood as a contained zone' (ibid.). Blomley argues instead that space is 'relational, produced through diverse, networked processes [that are] not "outside" social and political life, but folded into and produced through forms of interaction and relationality' (p. 205). Space is thus deeply implicated in property, in its 'enactments, politics, and enforcement' (ibid.), such that spatial claims to territory constantly re-make place (p. 213). While Blomley's critique is chiefly of private property, and its individuated, detached processes of spatialization, his work also explores property's other, more diverse enactments. These include collectivist claims to abandoned inner-city buildings (2004), performances of public gardening (2005, 2016), or the governance of public sidewalks (2011). Such claims enact relational, deeply contextual performances of property that remake space in public, collective, and at times, hybridized forms of private and public (2013).

Public real property, as Layard hints, has intrinsic synergies with critical geographical conceptualizations of place and space. Certainly, it is more empathetic than its a-contextual private twin. Public realty occupies both natural and built 'physical' and 'social' *spaces*. As subjects pass through it, the public realm is constantly made and re-made, as public *places* of the 'here and now'. Its articulation as Massey's 'simultaneity of stories-so-far' is especially resonant in the settler colonial state, where the narratives of public lands are conflicting (see Chapter 3), and the calls for their de-colonization grow ever louder. Such subtle shifts portend how the present subordinate could become the new dominant propertied reading of postcolonial public lands.

Yet, the central implication that flows from this brief canvassing of property, and space and place, is the need to uncouple the former from an exclusively private-centric understanding, the conclusion that Layard reaches. Equally pertinent is the desirability to escape from a universalizing spatial view that is atomized, context-free, and individuated. To (again) use Cresswell's narrative of subordinate and dominant readings, property's changed spatial text should be the 'discouraged', 'heretical', or 'abnormal' one – public narratives with an altogether different 'simultaneity of stories'. As currently articulated, such a paradigm shift seems beyond private property. By logical analysis, and the implied inference of theorists such as Layard, this may be a task better attuned to the public estate.[11]

5.4 Public property and community

Community is a 'contested', ill-fitting term in property theory (Page 2017, p. 187). It is described as 'fluid, often elusive' (Lehavi 2009, p. 45), or 'maddeningly ambiguous' (Alexander and Penalver 2010, p. xxix). Its cheer-squad in property theory is led by progressive theorists, principally American professors Gregory Alexander, Eduardo Penalver, Laura Underkuffler and Joe Singer, who collectively penned 'A Statement of Progressive Property' in 2009. Like propriety in Chapter 4, progressive theory's embrace of community has little to say, directly or explicitly, about public real property. Rather, progressive theory is a school of thought entrenched in liberal property traditions, a school with little regard for the public estate. Unlike the radicalness of belonging, or the inter-disciplinary scope of place, progressive notions of community are premised on viewing communitarian obligation as a virtuous, values-laden corollary of the *private* right (emphasis added).

Yet, this is not the full story of community. As the facts on the ground dictate, communities are more than a collection of private properties where owners ostensibly owe duties.[12] Rather they are patchworks, variegated blends of private, public and common lands that yield infinitely variable, bespoke patterns of diverse property (Page 2019).[13] Much of this discussion here (that is, of community's links with public real property) turns on inference and implication. These are the inferences drawn from progressive property that hint of a role for the public domain. Or, the implications that flow from a progressive articulation of community that is 'thicker' and less optional than conventional liberal thinking. This section also draws on Eduardo Penalver's progressive argument that property acts as entrance to community (2005), an analysis that likewise leaves the door ajar for the public estate. It closes by moving from implication to explication, with Amnon Lehavi and Jeremy Waldron's separate studies of community and public space.

Progressive theory undoubtedly 'thickens' the idea of community in property. It sits at the end of a liberal spectrum that is most pre-disposed to community.

Compare this to libertarian positions where community does not exist – and presumably community infrastructure is not even on the radar:

> There is no social entity with a good that undergoes some sacrifice for its own good. There are only individual people, different individual people, with their own individual lives. Using one of these people for the benefit of others uses him, and benefits the others. Nothing more.
>
> *(Nozick 1974, pp. 32–33)*

Liberal conceptions improve on this crude, 'there is nothing more' thesis, but what is imagined is a pale, anemic version of community. Here, property-owning individuals voluntarily opt in or out of community, their departures cost and implication-free. In this worldview, community is instrumentalist. Its only value lies in the satisfaction of individual preferences. Community 'is never … an end in itself' (Alexander and Penalver, 2010, p. xix). This freedom to enter or exit at will is not available to all, however. Some communities are highly sought-after places, such that only the affluent have the option to 'vote with their feet' (Page 2019). In such communities, the public estate is subsidiary to private privilege, although curiously its public wealth may cross-capitalize private property through the latter's geographic proximity to public acreage (like the gentrified neighborhoods abutting New York's High Line in Chapter 4, or elite beachside real estate). One case study of a community with overt private values (and significant privilege) demonstrates how high levels of private wealth sit alongside a commensurately impoverished public domain, a suburb where exclusive residences are next door to pot-holed roads, and neglected parklands (Page 2019). The dynamics here are unclear, but their effects are demonstrable.

Progressive property challenges this optional voluntariness of liberal community. It does so by recognizing that the communitarian obligation implicated by ownership is 'thicker', that it demands reciprocity over lengthy timeframes, and that it values long-term obligation in non-fiscal terms (Dagan 2010). In so recognizing, progressive property gives an oblique nod to what is (at least) one measure of the public domain, its amorphous common or public wealth. In the landmark 2009 'Statement of Progressive Property', the public estate receives similarly sideways acknowledgment. Listing community as one of its five key tenets, the Statement reads:

> Property enables and shapes community life. Property law can render relationships within communities either exploitative and humiliating or liberating and ennobling. Property law should establish the framework for a kind of social life appropriate to a free and democratic society.
>
> *(p. 744)*

The propertied framework envisaged for a 'social life appropriate to a free and democratic society' would necessarily involve a component of public infrastructure.

Public assets like sidewalks, public transit, public libraries, or parks. The words 'social' and 'democratic' tend to bell this cat, a form of public 'code', as Chapters 4 and 7 respectively expound. Public real property is also replete with the inherent capacity to 'shape' community life and 'ennoble' its citizens to flourish, through cooperative endeavors that speak to an enlivening of 'civic responsibility' and the accumulation of 'aggregate wealth' (p. 743). Given the language adopted, it seems inconceivable that private property could do such specialized heavy lifting alone.

Penalver pre-dates this 2009 high-water mark of progressive property with his analysis of property as entrance to community (2005). Penalver argues that the 'power of exit conferred by property ownership' has tended to be 'over-stated' (p. 1892). Exit implies the freedom of property owners to avoid communitarian responsibilities. In its most 'ambitious' form, exit translates into 'the power to reside in self-sufficient isolation within one's property' (p. 1891).[14] By contrast, property as entrance views property as a means of 'joining individuals to each other in community' (p. 1894), or 'tying them together into social groups' (p. 1938). Here, the vision of community is 'richer' and 'stickier.' Community tends to be given rather than chosen, and it is characterized by 'relatively high costs of exit' (p. 1891).

Like his progressive colleagues, Penalver's vision of property as entrance is a private one. But also like them, his analysis casts a wide net, catching in its expansive ambit things beyond the owner's fence line. Thus, (private) ownership provides anchoring, 'a stake in their communities, broadly understood, [that] can reduce mobility and induce them to engage more fully in community life …' (p. 1940). One consequence of decreased mobility is 'that property owners are more likely than others to engage in informal and formal social interactions … [and] stronger and more numerous social attachments' (pp. 1948–1949). The higher costs of exit arising from these durable attachments lead to communities that are more robust, enriching, and deeply satisfying (p. 1955). In short, property facilitates entrance to community.

It is not a big stretch to bring public real property into Penalver's tent. Residents who make substantial capital investments in the suburb, town or city in which they live or work often enrich their lives by joining community groups. Groups that play social sport in public parks, practice yoga on beach foreshores, plant trees on degraded riverbanks, or find shared cultural interests in the 'friends' groups of public libraries, museums, art galleries, and so on. In these diverse contexts, it is as much public property as private that acts as entrance to community.

Indeed, the significance of public property is heightened for the generation of young, mostly white millennials, precluded by high real estate prices from buying into global cities from Sydney to New York, or at least into areas close to their employment or preferred services. For this demographic, the public estate is the optimal (perhaps only) way that property acts as entrance; given the insecurity and unsettling mobility of private leasehold and the exorbitant costs of fee simple. Amelia Thorpe remarks on this phenomenon, and the significance of millennials claiming an informal sense of 'ownership' in circumstances where they cannot (or no longer aspire) to claim a slice of formal (private) title (2018a, pp. 31–32). In an empirical study in Montreal, Thorpe observes 'the very low rates of homeownership in the city to explain very high rates of engagement in activities in public space' (p. 36). This is ours supplants this is mine, and connects this generation to place and community in an *other*, more publicly visible, but perhaps more ancient relational way of belonging.

Like Thorpe, Amnon Lehavi writes explicitly of public property acting as entrance to community, although this terminology is never employed. Lehavi's study explores the social interactions between urban residents and nearby 'local public commons' in New York City (2004, 2009, 2013). Local public commons are city-owned neighborhood parks, playgrounds or public squares which serve 'relatively local group of residents on a regular basis' (2004, p. 2). In many cases, they were open spaces the city could no longer afford to maintain, and whose 'management' was assumed as part of a:

> grassroots initiative taken by groups of previously unorganized residents who had realized the instrumental role that successful public spaces play … as well as the adverse flip-side of neglected and derelict public spaces [in] harboring crime, disorder and socioeconomic decline.
>
> *(2009, p. 59–60)*

Here, not only were many of these local public commons 'saved', but they fostered informal (and often enduring) social interactions between neighbors whose only commonality was proximity to the local park or square. These place-based relationships created what Lehavi calls 'spontaneous communities', which ranged across a complex hierarchy from informal 'friends' groups, to incorporated tax-exempt non-profit organizations, and formal fee-paying management structures. Analogous also, are the many publicly authorized or conditional commons that have sprung up as community food gardens in vacant or abandoned city lots (2013, pp. 125–134). In all of these diverse examples, public lands have acted as entrance to community for otherwise unconnected residents. Like communities everywhere, these spontaneous experiences have not always been positive, with bitter disputes about 'outsiders' enjoying certain local commons, or internal wrangles triggered by a plethora of factors, including the original activists retiring or leaving the neighborhood.

Jeremy Waldron also writes of (public) property and community. His scholarship on their 'intersecting logics' is interesting because of his concern with (what he terms) *public space* as property, and the freedom of citizens, irrespective of their status or fortune in life 'to be' in public space (2010). The first concern is necessarily one of property; the second goes to community, and its related issue, *whose* community. America's urban homeless is the fulcrum through which these two logics are thrown into sharp focus, namely the loss of freedom occasioned by the homeless having no space, public or private, to discharge 'basic life-activities' such as sleeping, washing or urinating.

Waldron's thoughts on public space originate from a propertied premise, the wide-ranging right of private owners to exclude *anyone* from their land. Translate this logic to public space however, and the rules change:

> But we may not be entitled to treat public spaces this way, inasmuch as public spaces are conceived of as being available for everyone's use. True, we are entitled in principle to regulate these places by placing restrictions on what *anyone* does there: we can say that *no one* is allowed to build a fire in the park. But when we regulate basic life-activities like sleeping, the impact of this regulation is so qualitatively different in the case of the homeless from its impact on the person who has a home to return to.
>
> (*p. 179*)

In other words, public property is qualitatively different. Its regulation should be measured against a particularly public baseline – where public space is open to all. It serves what Waldron calls a 'common sense of community', one derived from 'a sharing of common citizenship … and a common place of residence – this city' (pp. 184–185). Membership of this civic community can entail 'a large number of people who are strangers to each other', people who may not 'belong to the same clubs or professional milieus … [people] who may not like each other, or understand each other' (pp. 185–186), but nonetheless share an 'authentic' bond. In this 'true' community, one sub-group's view on proper behavior should not prevail against the wider community good. Waldron's ideals are later tempered with pragmatism, conceding that '"true community" is not always as nice as it looks' (p. 188), and that 'actually-existing communities are already exclusionary and inauthentic' (ibid.).

Here, Waldron touches on the complexities of community. Many communities can be 'stifling or oppressive' places (Blomley 2002, p. 220), locales beset by classist elitism, apathy, or worse, by bigotry, racism, or homophobia. By contrast, other communities are possessed of what Massey terms 'a progressive sense of place' (1980). Waldron also highlights the uniqueness of public property as *property*, and how private rules and regulations may be a poor conceptual fit in public space.

As seen, property struggles with concepts such as belonging, place, and community. The root cause of this disconnect is property's overweening private myopia. Widen one's perception of property however, and the terrain shifts with its greater diversity. This is particularly exemplified by literature such as Lehavi's that captures how public property anchors an entrance to community for otherwise unconnected residents. Taking a diverse, wider view has capacious potential. No longer would belonging be at the peremptory whim of the private owner. No longer would community or place be something outside the bounded fence. And Waldron's simple understanding of 'public space' as territorial zones where people can (more or less) 'be' – highlights the uniqueness of public real property. To be and to belong are closely connected. The former is the etymological root of the latter, a deeply intuitive concept enlivened by the relative freedoms of the public estate.

5.5 Belonging relationally in public space and place

This section represents a change in direction. It seeks to turn (what has been so far) a predominantly theoretical analysis – into a grounded one. From a narrative that outlines why private property lacks empathy for belonging, community, or sense of place, to a series of examples that demonstrates (to adapt the words of Blomley) how 'performing [public] property [re]makes the world' (2013). Specifically, this section's work is to explore – through three brief case studies – how the public estate acts as the determinant relational space in Cooper's part/whole sense of belonging.

These vignettes range from a quirky yet global example of DIY urbanism, to the dedication of a new public square in a small Australian city, and closing with a Depression-era public works program that gifted Sydney's coastal suburbs with a string of public ocean pools. They run from the local to the global, the scholarly to the anecdotal, and the unsanctioned to the authorized. What these public examples all share however is a creative use or (re)use of public real property that brings people together, and in so doing, fosters a discernible sense of belonging, place and community.

The first example concerns the phenomenon of (PARK)ing Day, an online social movement of sorts, where each year on the third Friday of September, citizens 're-claim the streets' (or specifically, street-side public car spaces) by transforming them into temporary pop-up parks. These DIY parklets are replete with a park's 'constituent elements', instant turf, (transportable) benches, and potted trees and greenery (Thorpe 2018b, p. 748). Importantly, participants legitimize their transient occupation by paying the parking meter for the allotted time. But instead of parking a stationary vehicle, participants 'park' a pop-up green space that is open to all.

PARK(ing) Day first sprang from an idea by three American urban designers, John Bela, Blaine Merker and Matthew Passmore, who were looking for 'unscripted fragments' of land as sites of urban renewal experimentation (Schneider 2017). The original pop-up park was installed on a 'drab' and 'gray' San Francisco street in 2005. It attracted massive social media attention and generated a global phenomenon in the years that followed. But importantly, on the day itself, its proponents claimed that it 'created an opportunity for social interaction that wasn't there before', as passers-by sat on the temporary bench, ate their lunch, and socialized in what was otherwise a blank, uninviting urban space (ibid.). However, it is Amelia Thorpe's further (and highly original) empirical study of (PARK)ing Day in inner-city Sydney (2018b) that shifted the day's implications from city livability to one with understated significance for property theory, public ownership and belonging.

Thorpe's central argument is that claims to the 'ownership' of public parking spaces are most successful 'when they are grounded in relationships of social and material connection to the site in question' (2018b, p. 742). Hence, PARK(ing) Days staged in neighborhoods where participants had a history of connection (through employment, residence, social networks or community ties) were more likely to go unchallenged by authorities, while sites selected with little or no personal connection were often directed to move on, or failed to generate local support. In other words, the legitimization of a claim to public space was dependent on 'socially and materially connected forms of ownership' (p. 743) asserted through social ties, claims embedded to known context, and performances that understood local dynamics.

Paying the meter also helped, since it gave the occupation a façade of formalism, and provided participants the (legally flawed) comfort of a lease. The payment also probed the ambiguities of council parking ordinances.[15] But in truth, 'the lease provided a gimmick rather than [any] firm legal footing' (p. 760). Rather, the lawful footing that 'stuck' was the sense of public ownership generated by a 'feeling of belonging or connection embedded in wider social and material relationships' (p. 767). As Thorpe observes of public owning:

> Ownership is a type of social practice, one that both reflects and forms social structures. People feel ownership over places where they have established both social and material connections: places they have spent time being physically present and, importantly, engaging with others.
>
> *(pp. 760–761)*

As well as the importance of authentic social belonging as a predictor of success, another key ingredient is that the use of the appropriated parking space must be sufficiently 'public'. An interesting counter-example in Thorpe's study involved members from an architectural firm who set up a space 'for more private (and apparently commercial use)' such that they 'appeared to have made the space "theirs" to the exclusion of others' (p. 765). However well intentioned, such a use crossed a propertied line from the public to the quasi-private domain.

PARK(ing) Day is a polite, playful event that involves no centrally unifying message 'other than rethinking the way public space is allocated' (ibid.). Its participants do not engage in oppositional politics, civil protest, or law breaking, the stuff of Chapter 7. Rather they engage in technically borderline 'activities not in defiance of the law' (p. 759). Or indeed, as Thorpe argues, PARK(ing) Day's real provocation stems from the fact that its 'assertion of legality works *with* rather than against social consensus' (pp. 768–769). Yet, through this prism of re-imagining the public square, if only for the moment, PARK(ing) Day reveals the significance of public belonging, the fleeting sense of part connection to a greater whole generated by the most unlikely and unloved slices of public real estate.[16]

The second example of public belonging is a personal narrative. It represents a first-hand impression of the author's experiences (as part of a small group that lobbied governments and engaged in community fund raising),[17] which culminated in the creation of a new public open space in the declining downtown of a small Australian city. This aspirational project, and its subsequent green town square, known simply as 'The Quad', is located in Lismore, New South Wales. It forms part of an emerging cultural/arts precinct, a turfed, open rectangle surrounded by a public art gallery, a public library, a public conservatorium of music, and a public car park. As one would guess, The Quad (an abbreviation of the word 'quadrangle', based on the site's historic use as the central playground of the city's first state high school) is unequivocally public real estate. It is literally enclosed on all sides by public lands. It hosts much of Lismore's key cultural infrastructure. Adjoining it are public roads, footpaths, a stand of century-old street fig trees, and public sporting ovals and passive recreational space. Attempts by the local council to attract private investors to the site (a mooted apartment hotel) have floundered. Private uses of the green (such as farmers markets) have not materialized. It is defiantly public in the way Blomley depicts the defiantly public sidewalk (2011).

The Quad had traumatic beginnings. Before its re-development, the site was derelict and unwelcoming, a poorly formed bitumen car park dominated by an abandoned 1960s era school building to the north (C Block – the high school's former Science classrooms). Its genesis lay in the idea to re-purpose C Block for Lismore's regional art gallery. However worthy the goal, the argument for a new art gallery in a struggling regional city had many vocal detractors. Indeed, the proposal did not gain majority support in the local council until an open square component was added to 'sell' it to skeptical ratepayers and councillors.[18] The Quad's momentum quietly snowballed thereafter. But as it neared completion in March 2017, a one in 100-year flood devastated the site (and Lismore's downtown). Repairs delayed its opening for six months.

In many ways the re-birth of the Quad became symbolic of the city's halting post-flood recovery.[19] The opening celebrations were cathartic, a rare moment of positivity amidst much loss and gloom. Crowds estimated at 5,000 to 6,000 wandered through the new gallery's art spaces, and stayed to party, dance and socialize on the small green till late that evening. For months later, the Quad dominated social conversations and social media buzz. Literally (at night), the Quad was the only bright shining light amidst the darkness of nearby vacant shops.

The Quad gave Lismore's residents the town square it lacked, a physical green space that has evolved into a social space, and a meeting place that is re-made constantly as a diverse public passes through. But more significantly, this small patch of public realty has successfully connected citizens to their small city in the part/whole sense of belonging. It hosts a plenitude of formal and informal gatherings; a fairly unremarkable 'comedy of the commons' where quotidian uses; quiet reading, family picnics, ball games, walking the dog, and more unfold daily. Meanwhile, organized events likewise strengthen community bonds; exhibition openings regularly spill out onto the grass, interactive public art installations appear and go, 'a washing machine converted into a set of coin-operated speakers beside an open-air dance floor' (Thorpe 2018a, p. 29) sparks impromptu dance parties, monthly public lectures provoke, a one-year flood anniversary commemorated community healing, and winter solstice, feminist, LGBTIQ and Indigenous events have found a new home. The Quad also has plenty of Massey's 'progressive sense of place', as a regular site of left protest, climate change school strikes, rallies for marriage equality, and so on. Now over two years old, the Quad is so well loved that the council has been forced to upgrade the turf and drainage systems to cope with its high use. It has cemented its civic centrality through being a public space of belonging, a focal point for Cooper's 'variegated social networks' (2013, p. 627) that implicate community through the medium of public realty, and give new voice and material form to Lismore's post-flood collective identity. It reflects its online claim to be 'where space meets community':

> A one of a kind cultural precinct and public space adopted by the community as their own creative Playground. Dedicated to showcase a dynamic program of cross-disciplinary acts, the Quad generates a unique phenomenon of collaboration and intersectionality, where people come together united by the power of community and creativity.[20]

Public belonging ends with an under-studied and under-recognized component of the public estate[21], the ocean rock pool. Defined as 'unheated, unchlorinated public seawater pools sited on rocky seafronts [where] waves can wash in over the pool walls' (McDermott 2012), ocean pools proliferated along the New South Wales coast from Australian Federation at the dawn of the 20th century, through to the late 1940s. In particular, there was a spike of ocean pools built during the Depression era as unemployment relief public works projects. Elsewhere in Australia, ocean pools are surprisingly rare. The ocean pool is especially iconic to Sydney, described as one of the city's 'defining characteristics, along with the Opera House and the Harbour Bridge, though not as well known' (Bonner 2008).

Ocean pools are remarkable pieces of public infrastructure. Open year-round, and typically free of charge to enter into and swim, each ocean pool has its own idiosyncratic character that symbolizes the community in which it is emplaced. As social commentator and satirist Benjamin Law writes of these 'sacred public spaces':

> For a spiritual experience, it's all about the ocean baths. On good days, you can swim alongside schools of fish in Wylie's Baths in Coogee. There's a reason people rave about Bondi Icebergs, with its sauna overlooking the violent churn of the surf below. And though I'll never get a visit, I love the idea of Coogee's McIver's Ladies Baths, the last remaining women's-only seawater pool in Australia. Apparently it's particularly popular with nuns, Muslim women and lesbians: I like thinking about the unexpected friendships that have been made there.
>
> *(Law 2018)*

Geographically, ocean pools occupy a liminal space on the urban edge, tidal zones that 'aren't part of the land but … never fully claimed by the surf' (Larkin 2020). Their popularity stems from their 'turquiose sanctuary' (ibid.), as swimming spots hewn from natural rock, buttressed by block walls and washed by the surf, yet free from the risk of ocean rips or sharks, spaces that are 'safe enough encounters with the wild' (McDermott 2012, p. 2).

Architect Nicole Larkin is the author of an emerging research project into public ocean pools, titled 'The Wild Edge'. She argues that 'if our surroundings speak to us of who we are, ocean pools tell of our love affair with the water's edge' (2020). For Sydney-siders, whose love affair with the ocean pool is legend, their sense of belonging is not only connected with the sea. These 'sacred public spaces' also speak to a residual affinity for egalitarianism, a paradox given the city's modern-day obsession with real estate booms and land as commodity. What public ocean pools enact is both an idea and a practice shared at another liminal edge, a performance of community set along the thin strip of public domain that separates Australia's most expensive private real estate from the Pacific Ocean. Australians may 'cling to the edge of the continent' as novelist Anna Funder says, but for those wealthy enough, we cling to the very outermost edges through a combination of privilege or the good fortunes of inheritance – and the exclusionary powers of private property. What public assets like the ocean pool do is to provide spaces of public belonging, the physical and social terrain where the citizen may 'be' to freely float or swim laps. Ocean pools also speak to another lingering (and related) communitarian sentiment, nostalgia for a time when public real property was imbued with public purpose, not the market values of the private estate:

> [A time when governments] invest[ed] in infrastructure like this – spaces whose value lies in their ability to foster community for generations and generate enjoyment, rather than profit. Most of them are still free. Ocean pools are not just monuments to ingenuity and the beauty of the Australian coast, but to different ways of thinking about public space.
>
> *(Tovey 2020)*

Sydney's ocean pools, the Quad, and pop-up parks are three unlikely species of the genus public real property. PARK(ing) Day is a global moment of one day's duration. The Quad tells a personal anecdote that could be anywhere in its local ordinariness. The critical property take on the public ocean pool is a theorization in progress. Yet for all their differences, whether in scale, duration, or maturation, each provides its own unique and identifiable public space of belonging, a connection that gives the public citizenry a sense of the whole through affinity to the part.

Contrast this putative public jurisprudence to the developed literature of private property, and its remarkable capacity for alienation. Alienation is a propertied term with two different but related meanings. The first refers to property's quality of transferability, its capacity to be sold, mortgaged, devised, and so on. The second refers to property's estrangement from place. Private property is a hyper-alienator in both senses of the word. As a commodity, private property is highly tradable. As a landscape outcome, the a-contextual nature of private property militates against its place making capacities. What it yields, rather, is atomized cadastral spaces prepackaged for alienation (Blomley 1994). Or inner-city suburbs beset by 'late-stage gentrification', where generations of belonging have been discarded in favor of the homogenizing gains of private wealth and capital gain (Moskowitz 2018).

Private property tends to placeless-ness. Nicole Graham calls this paradigm 'lawscapes' (2011), the consequence of 'removing the physical "thing" from the property relation and replacing with an abstract "right"' (p. 134). The 'property relation' Graham refers to is that of private property, and the de-physicalized paradigm it yields is the antithesis of belonging. Such placeless-ness has been observed in a multitude of non-law, place-related literature that implicates by inference the distorting effects of private property. For example, Joel Garreau's *Edge City* (1991), James Howard Kunstler's 'geographies of nowhere' (1993), Robert Putnam's *Bowling Alone* (2000), Charles Montgomery's (un) *Happy City* (2013), or Suzannah Lessard's *The Absent Hand* (2019). Lessard calls such landscapes 'atopias', urban geographies that defy traditional understandings of city or metropolis. Rather, atopias are the 'subversive opposite of place as we had known it' (p. 236), disruptive to, and disorienting of, any rudimentary sense of belonging. Lessard writes of her search for the (curiously missing) town of King of Prussia, Pennsylvania, transformed from a discrete rural locality into a jarring, nowhere 'edge city':

> Along the way, I developed a bilingual vocabulary for what I found in King of Prussia as compared with the characteristics of the former world. Where the old landscape is relational, the new one is schizoid, with elements right next to one another that don't relate at all. Where older landscapes are defined by what is special about a given place, the new pieces of King of Prussia could be anywhere – were part of ubiquity, as I was coming to call it. Our old landscape … was co-extensive. King of Prussia was a mixture of several archipelagos, like the pieces of jigsaw puzzles thrown into a box.
>
> *(p. 200)*

Tim Dee writes similarly of this tide of encroaching ubiquity and its impact on belonging, where 'the *place-ness* of place [is] under threat … specificities have been dulled, local habitations and names globalised, the instress or haecceity of every street or field driven from common memory' (2018, p. 3). In his analysis of place, Dee distinguishes between private and public property. The former carves out 'intricate mazes' and 'landscapes of social and economic exclusions' (p. 52). The latter is different. His ambition to 'dis-own' his private wood in rural England by removing its fences and declaring a 'parish wood' yielded an immediate dividend of public belonging:

> For the first time in half a century villagers came to enjoy the wood. … There were new customs established too. On Ascension Day children from the village school tramped over the fields, and in a clearing among the freshly leafed beeches sang hymns to new life and the mysteries of transubstantiation. In summer, after exams were over, there were secular rites and woodland sleepovers.
>
> *(p. 143)*

5.6 Conclusion

Intrinsic to property as belonging (as it is broadly defined in this chapter) is the fundament that space is pre-eminent. Space holds up property. Space permits place to materialize. Unlike subject-premised theories of private property, belonging is centered on the positional, the grounded terrain that is both within and (importantly) without private boundaries. Like the quaintly pastoral belonging of Tim Dee's 'parish wood' and its narratives of connection, entrance to community, and place-affinity that private accounts of property 'miss or misrecognize'.

This chapter has ranged across theory and relational example to argue that belonging explains and contextualizes the public estate in authentic ways. It is not an exclusive, all-encompassing explanation. After all, *all* property is belonging. But it is an enabling one. Belonging's narratives have an empathy for things public, and a capaciousness for place, community life, and (be)ing. Of course, private belonging is equally important for its own ends: personhood, autonomy, privacy, or self-actualization. But private belonging is contingent on the owner's agenda-setting powers (Katz 2008). With public belonging, by contrast, the 'owner's' agenda is diffuse and imbued with notions of the public good, howsoever defined or contested. Public real property is a qualitatively different space and place where in Waldron's words, we are relatively free to 'be' – and belong.

Notes

1 Nor does it say that the legal geography of rural spaces does not likewise engender a sense of belonging, as epitomized by the work of US legal geographer Lisa Pruitt.

2 'This subject–object relationship provides the standard legal definition of ownership of property, centered on fungibility, mastery, and commodification. Subject–object … highlight[s] the centrality of an instrumental, hierarchical relationship between the agent and the severable thing or space' (Cooper 2007, p. 629). Such as 'this book belongs to me.'

3 Massey is critical of over-romanticizing public spaces, writing,

> the tendency to romaticise public space as an emptiness which enables free and equal speech does not take on board the need to theorise space and place as the product of social relations which are most likely conflicting and unequal. … [I]ts public nature needs to be held up to scrutiny which is rarely devoted to it. From the greatest public square to the smallest public park these places are a product of, and internally dislocated by, heterogeneous and sometimes conflicting social identities/relations
>
> *(2005, p. 152).*

4 Keenan cites as various sources, Cooper (1998), Grabham (2009), and May (2013) (2015, p. 12).

5 The others are in order after 'belonging', 'codification, recognition, definition, and power' (Cooper 2007, pp. 628, 630–632).

6 In 2013, Cooper calls this type of belonging 'proper attachment' (p. 163).

7 Summerhill is described on its website as the 'original, alternative "free" school', or the world's 'oldest children's democracy' (www.summerhillschool.co.uk).

8 In the interests of balance, Blomley likewise quotes Lawrence Friedman who says that the 'law … is too important to be left to lawyers'.

9 Irus Braverman et al. contend that legal geography is 'less a "field" than braided lines of inquiry that have emerged out of the confluence of various intellectual interests, … a truly inter-disciplinary intellectual project' (2014, p. 1).
10 The concept of *topophilia* is important to place and belonging.

> The term 'topophilia' was developed by [Yi-Fu] Tuan to refer to the 'affective bond between people and place'. Tuan defined place through a comparison with space. He develops a sense of space as an open arena of action and movement while place is about stopping and resting and becoming involved. While space is amenable to the abstraction of spatial science and economic rationality, place is amenable to … things such as value and belonging. … Place is a product of pause and a chance of attachment.
>
> *(Cresswell 2004, p. 20)*

11 Of course, de-colonized narratives in settler colonial states need to equally draw on Indigenous property law, which views Law and Country as indivisible wholes, such that the land is the law, and the law is the land (for example, Watson 2014). This is a vast subject beyond this book's scope. Ultimately, what is needed is a pluralist interpretation of property and place that draws on Indigenous and non-Indigenous traditions alike.
12 Layard describes cities as 'places more than a collection of privately owned properties' (Layard 2012, pp. 256–257).
13 Lehavi writes similarly that 'the lives of communities necessarily involve the full range of property regimes, including private, public, common, open access, and mixtures of these forms. … This richness is not only a matter of fact, but also has normative merit' (2009, p. 45).
14 Singer, in a related vein, calls this the 'castle' view of private ownership (2006).
15 Antonia Layard has also analyzed (English) highway statutes for their capacity to accommodate multiple shared uses like children's games, or street parties (2012, pp. 263–268).
16 PARK(ing) Day is in the genre of likeminded DIY urbanist interventions: guerilla gardening, yarn bombing, street art, street libraries, urban infrastructure repair, pocket parks, the community garden movement or urban exploration (Thorpe, 2018b). Even single-event happenings such as Blomley's boundary-crossing flowering bathtubs qualify (2005). These activities all share a relational yearning for grounded essentialism, of getting some figurative or real 'earth under the nails' in performing public claims to public space (Farran 2013).
17 The group is the Friends of the Lismore Regional Gallery, an incorporated association under the *Incorporation of Associations Act 1994* (NSW).
18 A majority of Lismore City councilors appeared to oppose what was seen as a costly and unfunded project. However, the 'swing vote' that changed this dynamic was that of an Italian-born councilor who was sold on the idea of a new city 'piazza'. By 5–4, council voted to support the application for federal funding.
19 Another poignant symbol revolved around the death of a prominent swamp eucalypt, killed by floodwaters. As the tree slowly died, and despite the best efforts of council arborists, social media was filled with grief over the loss of a major landscape feature of the Quad, and what had become, in effect, a local example of the 'phenomenal' tree (Davies 2015).
20 www.lismorequad.org.au/cp_themes/default/home.asp.
21 The ocean pool has been extensively studied from the angle of coastal engineering, and more recently architecture (see, for example, Nicole Larkin's study of NSW ocean pools, 'The Wild Edge'), but it has not been the subject of critical property thinking.

References

Alexander, G et al. 2009, 'A Statement of Progressive Property', *Cornell Law Review*, vol. 49, 743–744.

Alexander, G and Penalver, E 2010, 'Introduction' in G. Alexander and E. Penalver (eds.), *Property and Community*, Oxford University Press, New York.

Blomley, N 1994, *Law, Space, and the Geographies of Power*, The Guildford Press, New York.

Blomley, N 2002, 'From "What?" To "So What?" Law and Geography in Retrospect', in C Harrison and J Holder (eds.), *Law and Geography: Current Legal Issues*, Oxford University Press, Oxford.

Blomley, N 2004, *Unsettling the City: Urban Land and the Politics of Property*, Routledge, New York.

Blomley N 2005, 'Flowers in the Bathtub: Boundary Crossings at the Public-Private Divide', *GeoForum*, vol. 36, 281–296.

Blomley, N 2010, 'Cuts, Flows, and the Geographies of Property', *Law, Culture and the Humanities*, vol. 7, no. 2, 203–216.

Blomley, N 2011, *Rights of Passage Sidewalks and the Regulation of Public Flow*, Routledge, Abingdon.

Blomley, N 2013, 'Performing Property: Making the World', *Canadian Journal of Law & Jurisprudence*, vol. 26, no. 1, 23–48.

Blomley, N 2016, 'The Boundaries of Property: Complexity, Relationality, and Spatiality' *Law & Society Review*, vol. 50, 224–255.

Bonner, R 2008, 'Sydney's Rock Pools' *New York Times*, February 24, 2008, available at: www.nytimes.com/2008/02/24/travel/24sydneypools.html?searchResultPosition=1 (accessed 13 October 2020).

Braverman, I et al. 2014, *The Expanding Spaces of Law: A Timely Legal Geography*, Stanford University Press, Stanford.

Cooper, D 1998, *Governing Out of Order: Space, Law and the Politics of Belonging*, Rivers Oram Press, London.

Cooper, D 2007, 'Opening up Ownership: Community Belonging, Belongings, and the Productive Life of Property', *Law & Social Inquiry*, vol. 32, 625–664.

Cooper, D 2013, *Everyday Utopias: The Conceptual Life of Promising Spaces*, Duke University Press, Durham, NC.

Cresswell, T 1996, *In Place/Out of Place: Geography, Ideology and Transgression*, University of Minnesota Press, Minneapolis, MN.

Cresswell, T 2004, *Place: A Short Introduction*, Wiley Blackwell, London.

Dagan, H 2010, 'Reimagining Takings Law', in G Alexander & E Penalver (eds.), 'The Marginality of Property', in *Property and Community*, Oxford University Press, New York.

Davies, M 2015, 'The Consciousness of Trees', *Law & Literature*, vol. 27, 217–235.

Dee, T 2018, *Ground Work: Writings on Place and People*, Jonathan Cape, London.

Farran, S 2013, 'Earth Under the Nails: The Extraordinary Return to the Land' in N Hopkins (ed,), *Modern Studies in Property Law*, Hart Publishing, Oxford.

Garreau, J 1991, *Edge City: Life on the New Frontier*, Anchor Books, New York.

Grabham E 2009, "*Flagging the Skin: Corporeal Nationalism and the Properties of Belonging*', *Body & Society*, vol. 15, no. 1, 63–82.

Graham, N 2011, *Lawscape: Property, Environment, Law*, Routledge, Abingdon.

Katz, L 2008, 'Exclusion and Exclusivity in Property Law' *University of Toronto Law Journal*, vol. 58, pp. 275–315.

Keenan, S 2015, *Subversive Property: Law and the Production of Spaces of Belonging*, Routledge, Abingdon.

Kuntsler, J H 1993, *The Geography of Nowhere: The Rise and Decline of America's Man-Made Landscape,* Simon & Schuster, New York.
Larkin, N 2020, 'Australians love ocean pools-but they are increasingly under threat' *The Guardian*, 20 January 2020, available at www.theguardian.com/lifeandstyle/2020/jan/21/australians-love-ocean-pools-but-they-are-increasingly-under-threat (accessed 15 February 2020).
Law, B 2018, 'The best in the world: a love letter to Australia's public pools' *The Guardian* 13 April 2018, available at www.theguardian.com/cities/2018/apr/13/best-world-love-letter-australia-public-pools-sydney-swimming (accessed 15 February 2020).
Layard, A 2012, 'Property Paradigms and Place-Making: A Right to the City; a Right to the Street', *Journal of Human Rights and the Environment*, vol. 3, 254–272.
Lehavi, A 2004, 'Property Rights and Local Public Goods: Toward a Better Future for Urban Communities', *The Urban Lawyer*, vol. 36, 1–98.
Lehavi, A 2009, 'How Property Can Create, Maintain, or Destroy Community', *Intellectual Inquiries in Law*, vol. 10, 43–76.
Lehavi, A 2013, *The Construction of Property Norms, Institutions, Challenges*, Cambridge University Press, Cambridge.
Lessard, S 2019, *The Absent Hand: Reimagining Our American Landscape*, Counterpoint, Berkeley.
McDermott, M. 2012, Wet, wild and convivial: Past, present and future contributions of Australia's ocean pools to surf, beach, pool and body cultures and recreational coasts, PhD thesis, Edith Cowan University.
May, V 2013, *Connecting Self to Society: Belonging in a Changing World*, Palgrave Macmillan, Basingstoke.
Massey, D 1980, 'The Pattern of Landownership and Its Implications for Policy', *Built Environment,* vol. 6, 263–271.
Massey, D 2005, *For Place,* SAGE Publications, London.
Montgomery, C 2013, *Happy City: Transforming Our Lives Through Urban Design*, Farrar, Straus and Giroux, New York.
Moskowitz, P E 2018, *How To Kill A City: Gentrification, Inequality, and the Fight for the Neighborhood*, Bold Type Books, New York.
Nozick, R 1974, *Anarchy, State, and Utopia*, Basic Books, New York.
Page, J 2017, *Property Diversity and Its Implications*, Routledge, Abingdon.
Page, J 2019, 'Property, values, and the empirics of place', *Griffith Law Review*, vol. 28, no. 1, 1–22.
Penalver, E 2005, 'Property as Entrance', *Virginia Law Review*, vol. 91, 1889–1972.
Penalver, E 2009, 'Land Virtues', *Cornell Law Review*, vol. 94, 821–88.
Putnam, R 2001, *Bowling Alone: The Collapse and Revival of American Community*, Simon & Schuster, New York.
Schneider, B 2017, 'How Park(ing) Day Went Global', September 15, 2017. Available at www.citylab.com/life/2017/09/from-parking-to-parklet/539952/ (accessed 2 February 2020).
Singer, J 1995, 'No Right to Exclude: Public Accommodations and Private Property', *Northwestern University Law Review*, vol. 90, 1283–1481.
Singer, J 2006, 'The Ownership Society and Takings of Property: Castles, Investments, and Just Obligations', *Harvard Environmental Law Review*, vol. 30, 309–338.
Stedman, R 2016, 'Subjectivity and Social-Ecological Systems: A Rigidity Trap (and Sense of Place as a Way Out)', *Sustainability Science,* vol. 11, 891–901.
Thorpe, A 2018a, 'Hegel's Hipsters: Claiming Ownership in the Contemporary City', *Social & Legal Studies*, vol. 27, 25–41.

Thorpe, A 2018b, 'Pop-Up Property: Enacting Ownership from San Francisco to Sydney', *Law & Society Review*, vol. 52, 740–772.

Tovey, J. 2020 'For Those Who Love the Sea but Fear It Too, Ocean Pools Are a Revelation' *The Guardian*, 29 January 2020. Available at www.theguardian.com/lifeandstyle/2020/jan/30/for-those-who-love-the-sea-but-fear-it-too-ocean-pools-are-a-revelation (accessed 15 February 2020).

Waldron, J 1992, 'Homeless and the Issue of Freedom', *UCLA Law Review*, vol. 39, 295–324.

Waldron, J 2010, 'Community and Property: For Those Who Have Neither', *Theoretical Inquiries in Law*, vol. 10, 161–192.

Watson, I 2014, *Aboriginal Peoples, Colonialism and International Law: Raw Law*, Routledge, Abingdon.

6

OF PUBLIC CONNECTION

6.1 Introduction

This chapter explores the significance of *connection* to the public realm. Connection may mean the sense of *belonging* explored in Chapter 5, the 'connection' that transpires through an affinity or attachment to place. However, connection has another, altogether more prosaic meaning, 'the action of linking one thing with another.'[1] The first interpretation is intuitive, an emotive type of connection. The latter, by contrast is instrumentalist, the material or concrete connection that joins A to B. What is common between these two alternate yet symmetrical senses of connection is how each informs and underlies public real property.

Connection also depends on *movement*. In its prosaic interpretation, movement constructs the link joining A to B. It is the connective *flow* of public real property; the pedestrian logic of the sidewalk, the thoroughfare of the public highway, the physicalized ingress and egress and passing and re-passing that marks out the public realm. In its intuitive understanding, moving *in situ* orients and frames context. For example, Rebecca Solnit observes that public walking 'links up reading the map with living one's life, the personal microcosm with the public macrocosm; it makes sense of the maze all around' (2001, p. 176). David Ulin similarly argues that sidewalk walking is 'a way of keeping the city bounded … a mechanism to rewrite the landscape in terms I could understand' (2015, p. 41). Contextualizing the 'personal microcosm within the public macrocosm', or 're-writing landscapes in personal terms' are concepts that require an ability to explore and familiarize, movements enabled through the networks of public realty that permeate and enliven our surroundings. In sum, movement is the physical and metaphysical glue that connects people to public context.

This chapter's interest in movement arises from its centrality to the public estate. Movement has normative consequences; the simple, unconscious practices of placing one foot in front of the other, practices that regulate public space and shape collective behaviors. Movement is also a surprising feature of enforceable public real rights, statutory and doctrinal. Movement similarly informs a nascent body of specifically public property theory. Spatially, movement's imprint is apparent in the propertied landscape, the variable patterns of public real estate that in their layout and design render each city and town distinctive and bespoke; and livable, or less so. And, of course, to close the loop, movement enables connection, the gravamen of this chapter.

In the law and theory of public real property, the bipedal human pedestrian is a convenient trope, a useful lens to explore the implications of movement, and the connectivity that this movement engenders. In her peripatetic ways, the walker forges connections across the public realm, creating norms, laws and justificatory theories as she goes. Indeed, the pedestrian trope explains public real property in surprisingly clear-cut ways. Of course, a trope is but a figurative or metaphorical use of a word, and this imposes its own limitations. Equally, modernity may sideline the otiose pedestrian, such that grinding freeway gridlock supersedes cheery countryside ramblings, and movement seems stymied.

Nonetheless, cautionary notes aside, it is through such pedestrianized eyes that this chapter progresses. First, the literature of walking – its philosophies, joys, and whimsical musings – opens the gate to this enquiry, revealing in its profound moments how movement intersects with the public estate. Walking is said to be 'the mingling of the errand and the epiphany' (Solnit 2001, p. 178), and in this latter respect, its literature delivers up an epiphanous first-cut of a public jurisprudence, and the norms that underscore it. Second, the pedestrian is a theorist, a deep thinker who situates ideas to public context, and rationalizes them while walking. Lastly, the pedestrian is common to what is otherwise an eclectic array of black-letter public real rights; justiciable laws that randomly dot the common law landscape. In exploring the pedestrian's literature, norms, theories and laws, the terrain of public real property takes a certain definable shape, a lie of the land intersected by countless trails of connection.

6.2 The literary pedestrian, and her normative ways

The literature of walking is rich. It describes a catholic array of walker-types: the contemplative stroller, the harried commuter, the *flaneur*, or literary narrator-walker,[2] amongst others. Its settings are likewise expansive, the pastoral countryside, crowded inner city, mountain wilderness, or desert emptiness. The literature attributes infinite qualities to the act of walking, from religious pilgrimage to psycho-spiritual soulfulness: encompassing joys, serenities and eternities (Gros 2015), together with the mundane practicalities of passage. Walking is healthful, political, even primordial, as urban hunter-gathers walk opportunistically, foraging for food or supplies (Solnit 2001, p. 174). We can walk in different styles, from purposeful striding, through sauntering,[3] to aimless meandering. Yet, notwithstanding a vastness of type, purpose and context, the literature of walking is premised on one (almost) universal truth, that walking is 'about being outside, in public space' (Gros 2015, p. 10).[4]

Walking interacts with public real property because a lot of walking happens there, in the public 'outside'. In parks, along beaches, lake foreshores, or on city sidewalks, pedestrians perambulate on public real estate. The literature of walking is likewise set in this public context. And in their ceaseless public perambulation, as captured in this literature, pedestrians frame, observe, and at times enforce collective rules and customs. These are the unspoken *norms* that regulate walking behavior, de-clutter the pedestrian's theorizing curiosity, preface her lawful interactions with public real property, and smooth her connections.

In the literature of walking, pedestrianism's diverse norms find written expression. Jeff Zupan, described as 'probably the best known anthropologist of walking' (Schwarz 2015, p. 147) documents the 'proper shy distance' between pedestrians on sidewalks[5], the numbers of walkers who will swap sides of the street to walk in the sun or shade, or 'how long they will form a mass while crossing a street and how soon they will disperse into lanes afterward' (ibid.). At a more basic micro-level, norms ensure smooth flow. In the United Kingdom, walkers keep to the left (except on tube escalators), in the United States we stay politely to the right, although in Australia, we increasingly opt for either. At the macro-level, however, the pedestrian's micro-motivations are subsumed within an overarching norm of connectivity. Pedestrian behavior seeks out connection, in the two senses that this chapter argues. Where the connection desired is functional, trans-boundary protocols encourage a 'sewing together of the land'. Where the connection is emotive, the literature describes walking's centrality to a very personal quest for sense of place. Each is considered in following turn.

Around boundary lines, pedestrians intuitively know the rules; private property's signals are recognizable, both explicitly (through fences, signs or locked gates) and subtly (by not straying far from the path). Hence, common-law walkers typically need little overt guidance. Even where the indicia of public real property are faint, and private boundary lines discomfortingly ambivalent, the walker does the best she can, or is schooled in its subtle ways.[6] Being constantly alert to the extent of the public realm, pedestrians do largely 'keep out', and 'do not trespass'. But that is a happily lawful consequence, not the driving rationale. In walking literature, the pedestrian's primary urge seems one of keeping moving, of finding ways through. This 'dimension of firmness, of endurance, of keeping going', is in the words of philosopher Frederic Gros 'essential, [since] walking calls for gentle but continuous effort' (p. 201). The pedestrian's instinct to persist, and the arbitrariness of trespass share a contested space, a simmering ender that flares from time when the two cannot reconcile. As Solnit explains, '[w]alking focuses not on the boundary lines of ownership that break the land into pieces but on the paths that function as a kind of circulatory system connecting the whole organism. Walking is in this way, the antithesis of owning. It postulates a mobile, empty-handed, shareable experience of the land' (2001, p. 162). In the uncluttered emptiness of a New Mexico desert,

Solnit observes the universalizing effects of boundary protocol, and this instinctive urge to keep going, a tenacity to connect:

> With the morning sun on my left, I went south along a path that crossed a road to become a fainter road itself, with tufts of grass in the center. … Drifting across the vast space, silent except for wind and footsteps, I felt uncluttered and unhurried for the first time in a while, already on desert time. My road reached the dead end of a private property boundary, so I circled around guessing I could find another path back to the rock cluster, flirting with being lost.
>
> *(ibid.)*

The relationship between norms and law is close (Ellickson 1991). In the case of the pedestrian, the urge to connect can have justiciable implication, as the doctrine of prescription illustrates. Prescription subverts private boundaries, allowing an acquisition of public title though open, peaceful, public trespass of long duration. In the United States, access to wet sands over dry is often acquired through prescriptive, or quasi-prescriptive means, a matter of law explored later in this chapter.

Where connection is stymied, the pedestrian is strategic in her response. Any dispute by necessity involves the practicalities of property boundaries, but at its heart, the argument takes shape over non-connection. In England and Scotland, long-running political protest over the loss of historic countryside connection culminated in legislated rights to roam in the early 2000s. Walkers now step across stiles or pass through kissing-gates to qualifiedly move through private countryside, exercising their very public real right. In the United States, walkers preserve connection by vigilantly protecting the boundaries of an extensive public estate, one where one-third of the continental landmass is in public hands. 'Thus, the Sierra Club fought for boundaries, while British walking activists fight against them, but the boundaries in America are to keep the land public, wild and indivisible, to keep private enterprise out, while in Britain, they kept the public out' (Solnit 2001, p. 163). In the New Zealand high country, long-held conventions of open-air access remain stubbornly resistant to the exclusionary excesses of private freehold or Crown pastoral tenure. The loss of high-country connection in some South Island locations, where conservation lands become carelessly landlocked, or the quality of access is moot, remains an open policy sore awaiting remedy.[7]

Like water finding its level, the walker skirts around private boundaries, mostly observing (where connection remains functional), intermittently transgressing (where the trespass is harmless or the route enhanced), but patiently challenging (where exclusion is egregious). The pedestrian's behavioral norms reveal a sophisticated nuance about property's boundaries, where they lie, and how far they can be negotiated, if at all. As more recent rights to roam illustrate, this sophistication also extends to the nuanced difference between spatial and functional, legal facts known to law students in the language of corporeal versus incorporeal estates in land, but a terminology peripheral to a lay behavior whose first order is seeking connection.

What powers this connective urge is an unswerving understanding that public real property acts, or should act, as a baseline physical network – an inter-linked map of sidewalks, lanes, roads, parks, paths and more. Public real property enables pedestrians to traverse the A to B landscape, from home to work to private leisure, but also the journey from private space to sociable public space.[8] The common link is the medium of public realty, the landed interests on which the pedestrian trope walks. 'Walking [may] sew together the land that [private] ownership tears apart', but only because the public estate enables it. Henry David Thoreau in his iconic essay 'Walking', recognized that 'the best part of the land is not private property, [where] the landscape is not owned and the walker enjoys comparative freedom.'[9] Thoreau saw the risk of 'fences multiplying' across the landscape, and his call to arms was to 'improve our opportunities' (1862). This same intensity is seen in the modern urban walker, whose connective urge flourishes on Jane Jacobs' tightly turned, sidewalk-dominated small city blocks,[10] or Los Angeles' pedestrian-friendly Great Streets (Schwarz 2015, pp. 129–131), but struggles with suburban cul de sacs and their private dead-ends. Pedestrian norms recognize the limits and the possibilities of the spatial and functional, and likewise understand that property lines not only divide, but also connect.

Where the urge to connect is not practical but emotive, one that seeks micro-sense of the macro-landscape, walking literature gravitates to grounded, terrestrial language and the role that public real property plays as place maker. And the tenacity to connect in this intuitive sense remains as strong as its practical other half. To give two examples of urban walkers on the public sidewalk or street:

> Walking, if nothing else, slowed my pace. I could make connections, or fail to make connections, could assess the city on my own terms, contemplate how my impressions (such as they were) did or did not cohere. I could speak a language in which I was fluent – that of the sidewalk, of the walker in the city - and apply it to a territory written in a different tongue. I could start to find a place, a narrative …
>
> *(Ulin 2015, p. 25)*

Or:

> For me walking has to do with exploration, a way of accommodating myself, of feeling at home. When I find myself in a new place I explore it on foot. It's the way I get to know that place. Maybe it's a way of marking territory, of beating the bounds. Setting foot in a street makes it yours in a way that driving never does.
>
> *(Nicholson 2009, p. 12)*

The literature of psychogeography speaks to similar evocations, with its aimless *flaneur* who intuitively connects to her urban environment (Berry 2017; Richardson 2015). Psychogeography lies at the intersection of psychology and geography; a term coined by French situationist Guy Debord in the 1950s. In psychogeography, 'to drift is essential … it better *connects* walkers to the city [through a slow, patient] interrogation of space and history' (Lyons 2017). And of course, the drifting is a publicly enacted one. Thus, in Vanessa Berry's *Mirror Sydney, An Atlas of Reflections* (2017), the musing pedestrian interrogates her city via its public corridors – wandering its obscure or overlooked footpaths, viaducts, tunnels, parks and creek banks as she delves into the harbor city's multi-layered, at times marginalized histories and narratives.

Indeed, Frederic Gros in *A Philosophy of Walking* implies that walking is exclusively a public act or performance, one where its private analogue is (an almost) fraudulent, and decidedly anemic variant, 'hardly walking at all, but intermittent comings and goings, incessant dallying' set in enclosed gardens of 'constructed social distinction' and 'collusive shrubberies' (p. 210). In fulsome detail, Gros describes a number of core qualities or attributes of an 'outside' public walking which cements a pedestrian's connection to context. For example, *slowness* aligns to uniformity of step, a steadiness that is not a measure of pace or speed, but an assured consistency. 'It is one of the secrets of walking, a slow approach to landscapes that gradually renders them familiar. When you are walking, it isn't so much that we are drawing nearer, more that the things out there become more and more insistent in our body' (pp. 37–38). In language reminiscent of Mariana Valverde, Gros says that slowness stretches time and 'deepens space' (Valverde 2014). In this attenuated spatio-temporal dimension, the slow pedestrian connects. The pedestrian also wallows in a *solitude* that is companionable, not lonely. Her company is the landscape, a dialogue birthed underfoot, 'where slowly the road, the feel of the ground, the shape of the hills, the height of the trees, all come back to you; they are acquaintances' (p. 56). Walking is also often done in *silence*, a state where language's clamor dissipates, and 'the absolute simplicity of presence' is retrieved (p. 67). 'In the silence of the walk, when you end up losing the use of words because by then you are doing nothing but walk … in that silence you hear better' (p. 62). And finally, walking is an *eternity of consonance,* a harmony of actions that absorbs the pedestrian into the landscape, enabling a 'radical potential of taking notice':

> Walking interminably, taking in through your pores the height of the mountains when you are confronting them at length, breathing in the shape of the hills for hours at a time during a slow descent. The body becomes steeped in the earth it treads. And thus, gradually, it stops being in the landscape, it *becomes* the landscape.
>
> *(Berry 2017, p. 210)*

The literature of walking is a playful, ruminating body of work. It is gentle, soulful, and thrives in the profound connections between the walker and her context.

Typically, the connection is the intuitive, emotive type; the placed-ness the walker feels to her surroundings. Less obvious is the practical connections the walker must construct, the ways around private lines and through public ways, and the related behaviors that make this traverse relatively smooth and seamless. Walking literature reveals a synchronicity of connection in the public outside.

6.3 The theorizing pedestrian

Norms segue to theory by their making room for deep thinking. In the case of walking norms, they make room by de-cluttering the pedestrian's mind – relegating the minutiae of bipedal mechanics and protocols to the reflexive background, and catalyzing a faculty to think. Of course, not every pedestrian freed from pedestrian protocols takes this creative opportunity. Legal theories of public real property tend to be the musings of the *contemplative* walker, often (but not universally) found in pastoral or natural surroundings, contexts conducive to reflection.

This section reviews recent *legal* theorizations of public real property. While not exhaustive, the sample is representative of a small field. In line with this book, its focus is legal. It does not engage, for instance, with the rich sociological or political theories of public space. And in keeping with this chapter's trope, the following theoretical accounts are viewed through the pedestrian's eyes, and her pursuit of connection.

This discursive path is short and recent. It starts in the last decades of the twentieth century, with Joseph Sax's *Mountains Without Handrails*, an erudite reflection on US national parks, and the theoretical justifications posited for preserving scenery through public lands. Next, it considers Kevin Gray's millennial analysis that 'pedestrian democracy' is laying the foundations of a 'geography of hope' (2010). Gray unpacks the societal implications of a revamped public right to roam, and offers in that process, important altruistic justifications for public real property. Nicholas Blomley's 2011 study of the humble sidewalk, *Rights of Passage: Sidewalks and the Regulation of Public Flow*, identifies another logic he terms 'pedestrianism'. Blomley theorizes that unimpeded flow lies at the heart of sidewalk law, a remorselessly prosaic rationale that exemplifies that the wider public estate may be rationalized in similarly unadorned ways. The theoretical excursus concludes with Antonia Layard's 2016 journal article, 'Public Space: Property, Lines, Interruptions', and its links to Olivia Barr's monograph of the same year, *A Jurisprudence of movement, walking, the common law and unsettling place*.

Each work is unique in that it directly relates to, or its subject concerns public real property. In the case of Gray and Blomley, the literature drills down to the theoretical underpinnings of public rights of passage, in the first instance incorporeal, and in the second, corporeal. With Sax, its concern is the public national park estate. In the combined case of Layard and Barr, the focus is on a jurisprudence of movement as it impacts a contested public realm. In all these works of theory, the pedestrian is a pre-eminent figure, busily making connections as she moves through.

In *Mountains Without Handrails*, Joseph Sax argues (in what could be a metaphor for the wider public estate) that there is scant theoretical corroboration, 'little serious or sustained writing … aside from scattered hints here and there' (p. 18), which explains *why* the US national park system was established when it was. As already canvassed in Chapter 4, Sax offers up one exceptional document, an 1865 report from landscape architect Frederick Law Olmsted that 'explicitly addressed itself to this question.' Writing of the giant sequoias at Mariposa in the Yosemite Valley, Olmstead argued preserving scenery was not 'self-justifying.' Rather, the burning question was 'why the government should take upon itself the burden of scenic preservation' (p. 19).[11] Olmstead's answer, his 'distinctive hypothesis' was one of scenic beauty's unique capacity to invoke the people's 'contemplative faculty' (p. 20). Olmstead saw the preservation of public lands as national parks a political duty of government, a democratic obligation to set aside 'nature parks as public places' to 'exercise and educate the contemplative faculty' of working people. Sax calls Olmsted a 'republican idealist' (p. 24), an American democrat who scorned the condescension of European elites, and their perceived disdain for the ordinary citizen. It was critical to the democratic compact, in Olmsted's view, that working people had places to forget their daily routines and tasks, to disengage 'from the confinement of duty and achievement', and to reflect and contemplate on the bigger pictures. Olmsted also imbued national parks with an aesthetic, a value that preserves natural scenery free from the 'distractions that impede [this] independent and personal response to experience' (p. 22)[12] The contemplative visitor has to be removed from his everyday sensibilities, 'to leave him on his own, to react distinctively in his own way and at his own *pace*' (p. 24) (emphasis added).

To reach this reflective pace, to put Olmsted's ideal into practice, requires passage on foot. Sax cites another 'largely ignored body of literature – produced not by scholars, but by the participants themselves' (p. 27), which captures the essence of Olmsted's 'reflective, independent qualities'. These are the writings of the outdoors enthusiast, the backpacker, angler, recreational hunter,[13] or mountaineer who pensively walks into Thoreau's 'wildness', eschewing the comforts of the insular 'motorized' or 'pre-packaged tourist' to reach transcendent experience. It is her crude action of putting one foot after another, of wading through a creek's shoals, the stealth of shadowing a quarry, of stepping through a hiker's foot-sore, blistered feet, that transform mere physical exertion into 'a concentrated immersion … a special kind of observation' (pp. 40–41).

Importantly, and especially important from the perspective of public real property, Sax distinguishes the national park from what could be otherwise 'a generalized interest in nature' (p. 42). It is the former's special role as:

> an institution within a developed and industrialized society, in contrast to those traditions in which nature is … an alternative to society. The setting of the national park provides an opportunity for respite, contrast, contemplation, and affirmation of values for those who live most of their lives in the workaday world.
>
> *(ibid.)*

In other words, national parks are places of the world. As a societal institution, the public national park may allow us to escape from our everyday selves, but we do not escape beyond our world to a false utopia 'of perfect harmony, forever free of conflict and besetting human passions' (Davies 2016, p. 37). *Public* parks represent 'an important institution in a society unwilling to write off the ordinary citizen as an automaton' (Sax 1980, p. 21). Indeed, the 'contemplative recreationist' is Sax's trope, a figure that reaches back into history to re-kindle and remind us of a core theoretical truth seemingly lost over time, and obfuscated by what Sax terms Olmsted's 'archaic vocabulary' and strange 19th-century 'pseudoscientific proofs'. Sax's take home message is that national parks are deeply symbolic, profoundly democratic parcels of public realty.

Democratic themes continue with Kevin Gray's 'Pedestrian Democracy and the Geography of Hope' (2010), a publication that coincided with the imminent enactment of the Marine and Coastal Access Act in 2009, wherein rights of recreational access, first legislated under the Countryside and Rights of Way Act 2000 (CRoW), were extended to the 'coastal margin' along the English coast (Sects. 309 and 300). Gray sought to locate the 'moral, social and legal ecology of scenic natural landscape', and to discover why 'pedestrian democracy', the 'self-determining, self-empowering, self-fulfilling entitlement of the citizen to walk or climb over natural terrain' is 'both necessary and important in the 21st century' (p. 45). This 'right of foot traverse' (p. 47) is the prism through which Gray theorizes and constructs a moral and social framework for public real property rights.

Gray's work is optimistic, signaling that the advent of CRoW transforms the right of access to the natural environment from an 'optional experiential bonus' to a 'prudential necessity' (p. 52). This paradigm shift arises from 'a complex web of factors and perceptions relating to environmental responsibility, public health, personal and psychological well-being, aesthetic sensibility, historic memory, sense of place, citizenship, human right, distributive equity and social inclusion' (ibid.). Gray categorizes this list into four sub-headings, theoretical organizing principles that justify the modern democratic pedestrian as she purposefully and publicly recreates through (what is in the CRoW case, mostly private) property.

The first 'relates to themes of citizenship, civic equality and distributive equity' (p. 53). It especially touches on egalitarianism, the public counterweight to the relentlessly appropriating and exclusionary tendencies of private property. In English terms, this sentiment is traditionally couched in the language of class, historical grievances arising from working people's loss of access to the countryside (Shrubsole, 2019; Sprankling et al. 2006). In colonies such as New Zealand, English class discourse was transported across the globe, seen in 19th-century Acclimatisation Societies and their success in keeping natural resources such as fish and wild game in public hands.[14] Such past resonates with the present, where public real property remains a force for egalitarian participation in a society of ostensible equals, a more or less level-playing field for both Mancur Olson's *many* and the *few*. As Gray observes in the early 2000s, CRoW 'mobilized the rhetoric of civic integration' with its appeal to under-represented minorities and the socially disadvantaged' (p. 54). This sentiment was evidenced in the parliamentary second reading speeches that preceded the CRoW bill. This theme constantly recurs in property, a decade later in the United States, it takes shape as Joseph Singer's re-invention of the 'democratic estate' as a contemporary rationale for the estates model (2009, p. 1051).[15]

The second grouping, rationales that enhance 'personal well-being and psycho-social connection' and an 'awareness of the therapeutic or regenerative value of the walk through nature' (p. 55) recognizes the physical and mental well-being that comes from outdoors exercise. This is not 'only recreation, but re-creation' (p. 57), transformative experiences that range from the religious pilgrimage to its psycho-spiritual analogue, treks where 'external landscapes become the counter-part of … inner [ones]' (p. 56). In the western United States, the changing use of public lands, seen in the decline of traditional grazing, forestry or mining activities, and the rise of recreation and the conjoined pursuit of solitude, aligns to an urban-izing western constituency (Fairfax 1981), and its quest for connection with empty public spaces.[16]

The third is prosaic, justifications concerned with public health, its escal-ating costs to national budgets, and illnesses caused by physical inactivity. This is the anathema of the fit and active pedestrian, the scourge of torpor. The fourth recognizes the ecological reality that everything is connected to everything else. In Gray's view, this 'link between ecological consciousness and ecological con-science is ultimately the most important statutory recognition of pedestrian democracy' (p. 62), one where human connections with wilder places imbues profound understandings of stewardship and land health, and fundamentally re-orient relationships with land.

Gray injects theories of public wealth (democracy, egalitarianism), public health (physical and mental) and environmental good to explain the public real right of open-air recreation. Nicholas Blomley's sidewalk pedestrian, by contrast, is far less a romantic construct. Blomley locates another *locus* of public real rights, the sidewalk, but reaches a starkly different theoretical justification for public rights, rejecting the 'civic humanist' worldview that the sidewalk is primarily a polit-ical or civic space. Rather, the sidewalk's overriding rationale is *pedestrianism*, 'the orderly movement of pedestrians from point A to point B' (2011, p. 3). Focusing on political protest or rights-based claims to free speech or expression overlooks the sidewalk's chief function, the promotion and facilitation of pedestrian flow and circulation.

Orderly flow faithfully reflects the sidewalk's common law origins as an iter-ation of the public highway. As Blomley puts it, 'in law, a sidewalk is a species of the genus highway' (p. 74). Indeed, it is an especially common law view, developed from English notions of the public highway, 'a way over which there exists a public right of passage, that is to say a right of all of Her Majesty's subjects at all seasons of the year freely and at their will to pass and re-pass without let or hindrance' (ibid., citing *Ex parte Lewis* [1888] 21 QB 191, 197).[17] While the English view of the highway deems it as conditionally public property, the US view is aggressively unconditional.

Blomley cites 'a turn of the century American judge' who declared that highways 'belong from side to side and end to end by the public' (p. 78).

Not only is the sidewalk a resolutely public realm, its governing laws – administrative and judicial – act to reinforce this central tenet of pedestrianism. Hence, municipal codes, by-laws, and ordinances 'operate according to a largely spatial logic of zoning, placement, and positioning … out of concern for smooth pedestrian flow on sidewalks' (p. 33). Judges similarly see the sidewalk as 'a particular arrangement of property', where primacy is accorded to the legal requirement to pass and re-pass. The threat to this finite public resource comes from two competing sources, the neutral obstruction, and the privatizing encroachment. The former 'refers to any stationary thing (person or object) that impedes or constrains circulation.' The latter is propertied, the colonizing impulses of private owners to encroach onto the public sidewalk. As Blomley observes, while all encroachments obstruct, not all obstructions encroach:

> The encroachment seems doubly objectionable for pedestrianism. Not only does it impede and obstruct, but it also represents a departure from, or even expropriation of, the public sidewalk. They are both an avaricious enlargement of an individual's estate and an illegitimate usurpation of a public entitlement.
>
> *(ibid.)*

Facilitating flow is surely the most basic need of connection. Blomley theorizes sidewalk law and governance on this fundament. He also casts it in distinctly propertied terms, the sidewalk as defender of the public realm, resisting 'unlawful private intrusions' from adjoining 'private actors' (p. 48). Pedestrianism is also a theory that eschews abstraction. Rather, it is judged on its performative impacts or 'effects', an idiosyncratic 'particular legal knowledge, with its own networks, logic and internal truth' (p. 4). Blomley's embrace of the blue-sky in theorizing public sidewalk law presents as an imaginative, open-ended template, analogous to the pedestrian trope employed in this chapter.

Antonia Layard also writes of *effects,* the implications of interruptions and disruptions, proper and improper, in (re)creating new public spaces. Her public prescriptions are hopeful yet realistic, deeply cognizant of the English track record where publicly owned spaces have dramatically shrunk through a perfect storm of latter-day privatizations atop of centuries-old enclosures. As canvassed in Chapter 2, this crisis is existential, a looming void where, at law, the 'true public realm … does not exist':

> In England, there is no *ex ante* distinction between public and private property in land law. Both are litigated in the same courts. Other than central and local government, there is no generic group of landowners that can be easily identified as 'public'. The Crown Estate, for instance, does not describe itself as public. … The eight London Royal Parks, managed by the Royal Parks

> Agency, a central government department, on behalf of the Queen, are … perhaps public, although clearly rather distinctive. The fifteen national parks in England are made up of a patchwork of public and private landowners; designation does not make land either public or private.
>
> *(p. 27)*

With the English public estate in physical and conceptual retreat, Layard identifies only two *situs* where public real rights remain viable, sustained by 'lines' of movement that 'produce flow rather than fixity' (p. 28). The first is the lines of 'roamers', Gray's pedestrian democrats, who walk across mapped countryside and along coastal margins. However, Layard observes that roamer's rights are not rights to ownership or property, but merely rights to move. It is the absence of a 'right to stop' (p. 27), other than briefly to picnic or gather breath, which impugns their property-ness (p. 26). The other, second 'line' is that of the law on highways, 'often considered the only true public space in urban and suburban contexts' (ibid.). The public highway extends, as we have seen from Blomley, to pavements and roadside verges. But again, the emphasis is on flow, an absence of stopping that prevails. Ultimately flow is not constitutive of property rights, its very fluidity fatal to the *fixing* of the public 'stage on which the drama of communal life can unfold' (p. 29).

Flow, movement and lines find similar resonance in Olivia Barr's *A Jurisprudence of Movement: Common Law, Walking, Unsettling Place* (2016). Layard cites Barr to explain the countless 'paths and passing places' which dot the English landscape, evidence of movement's 'participating in the creation and conduct of lawful relations' (p. 25). Barr's singles out walking as one of two 'juridical practices' that unsettle the law (the other is burial). Indeed, walking is more than disruptive, since 'without movement, common law would simply not be.' Walking carries Barr's burdens of space and movement unevenly, creating diverse lawful relations in her wake as the pedestrian 'slides by'. And just as Layard uses *lines* to explain public 'rights to move', Barr also writes of their legal significance:

> We live in a world of excessive linearity, and our understanding of the dynamic place of law suffers as a result. Lines however are not so straightforward. Lines have linings; they have outlines and inlines, texture and detail, they break and cross paths, moving and wandering as they fail to meet. Set parallel and directed to the horizon, straight lines curve towards meeting, touching in a gentle kiss of blurred understanding.
>
> *(p. 13)*

Barr's connective lines and jurisprudential pedestrian assist when theorizing about public real property, in their capacity to de-construct property lines, and to imagine lawmaking anew. Public real rights in these conceptualizations are never static, constantly relational, never fixed. They stand in opposition to the private mentality, where 'legal principles predicated on boundaries and commodification …

prioritize fixity over relationality' (p. 39). Ultimately, flow is the antithesis of (private) property.

Flow, the ceaseless wake of the walker, seems thus to cut both ways for public real property. On one side, Blomley's unadorned synopsis of sidewalk governance places uninterrupted flow as the sidewalk's *raison d'etre*. This is at odds with Layard's relegation of flow to validating mere rights to move, not public rights to land. Flow is either the theoretical point, or its nemesis.

As this section outlines, the theorizing pedestrian comes in many stripes, and offers many divergent justifications. On balance, her optimal claim is that of the democrat, the walker who traverses an egalitarian public terrain (theoretically) open to all. This is starkly seen where the contrast is greatest, where public lands adjoin exclusive, expensive private property. In Sydney's affluent eastern suburbs, for example, public tracks follow the harbor foreshore from Double Bay to Watson's Bay and beyond, giving access to coves, inlets and white sand beaches.[18] These pathways cling to narrow corridors, or wind up or down awkward-to-traverse sandstone escarpments. Yet, they resolutely abut the city's most desirable real estate, the mansion homes of former prime ministers and industry CEOs. The resource that the *few* crave, harbor views or water access, is available for all, and like the doctrine of estates, it is simply the duration of the right that differs.

Likewise, at Wailea in Maui, Hawai'i, a coastal walkway carves out public rights of pedestrian access that slice (grudgingly) through the manicured lawns, horizon pools and guest-only facilities of upmarket beachside resorts. This path is a legacy of Hawai'ian customary law, an ancient highway that once circumnavigated the island, built to improve commerce and trade between its Indigenous peoples (Bederman 1996). Today, it is a narrow yet valuable link that joins the people to their idyllic beaches at Ulua or Mokapu, and frustrates the enclosing ambitions of exclusive resort-owners. Perhaps, Kevin Gray's opening epithet, 'most of us are pedestrians, some of us may even be democrats' is in truth the inverse. While some pedestrians may indeed be democrats, all democrats are pedestrians – to varying degrees of mobility. Public walking concretizes abstract calls for action, the likes of 'for the many, not the few', with an insistent constancy.

Of course, the pedestrian democrat is human; she is not perfect. In Sydney, train lines end abruptly at Bondi Junction, making it harder for western suburbanites to access the beach or harbor foreshore.[19] In Maui, the coastal path closes at night, with gates locked and bridges closed by their resort owners. In the United Kingdom, the white, middle-class nature of countryside 'roamers' is empirically proven (Monbiot 2020). The pedestrian may be a democrat by instinct, but in practice, class and race matters. As Samuel Schwarz analogously observes, public transport is not truly egalitarian until 'tuxedos feel as much at home' on the New York subway as they do on the London Tube. 'Over and over again, access to public transportation and the promotion of social equality have been joined together at the hip' (2015, p. 215). Jeff Speck describes public transport as moving capsules of public space (2012, p. 156), connective modes in which the pedestrian momentarily rests, before resuming the pace in the public outside. To the extent logistics, or class or race distinctions get in the way, the pedestrian's democratic tendencies are harder to enact.

While mostly a (flawed) democrat, the pedestrian trope also yields plausible alternative rationales for the public estate. She is a creator of lawful relations, a jurisprudent, citizen-philosopher, public health advocate, environmentalist, and beneficiary of hindrance-free flow (whatever that consequence may be). In all of these diverse roles and understandings, the pedestrian offers wide-ranging theoretical credence to the meaning, structure, and defense of public real property. In putting one foot in front of the other, and acting out her normative need to connect, the pedestrian finds much traction in the nascent theories of public real property law.

6.4 The doctrinal pedestrian

This chapter approaches its end with a sequential review of a number of enforceable public real property laws. It finds that connection and movement are surprisingly influential in the common law tradition. In both ancient doctrine and modern statute, such concepts are bedrocks upon which a smattering of real rights cling, and at times flourish. The perspective is again that of the pedestrian trope, and her footfalls across the black-letter legal landscape.

At the outset, there seem few examples of *justiciable* public real rights. Those identified in this discussion are at first glance random, haphazardly scattered across the common-law-scape (Graham 2011). The section begins with public rights of passage and roaming in Scotland and England, culturally specific contexts where the lawful pedestrian is (predominantly) legislated. Public walkways in New Zealand provide a 'newer' world example of legislated rights of way, expressed as grants 'in gross for use by members of the public'. The section next shifts to distinctly *sui generis* Australian public rights, those of the travelling stock reserve, where roaming livestock accompany the wandering pedestrian. The discussion ends on the beaches of the United States, where the pedestrian finds inconsistent, hard to find paths across dry sands to wet. In each of these public real rights, connection is of the essence, a defining feature personified by the pedestrian and her movements passing through.

As seen in Chapter 2, Scots law is a jurisdiction with a relatively sophisticated body of public real law. Its sophistication is the rationale for its inclusion in this discussion. A mixed hybrid of civilian and common law, some local jurists claim Scots property law to be 'firmly in the civilian camp' (Anderson 2016, p. 6), no doubt citing the binding influences of early institutional writers such as Craig and Stair. However, Scots law is also remarkably *common law* in its adherence to case law precedent, and indeed, how it looks to common-law outsiders from opposite ends of the Earth. For these reasons, this chapter claims Scots property jurisprudence as a cousin within the common-law fold, as much as it belongs in the civilian family.

Scots law has long recognized public real rights within its orthodox *numerus clausus* of property. This is a legal response to history and geography, the vested interests of a private few versus public conventions to access, and a largely urban population living amongst empty landscapes of hauntingly beautiful hills, mountains and coastline.[20] One of the Scots laws of property's so-called 'main real rights' is the public right of way.[21] While eclipsed by its modern statutory analogue (the right of responsible access under the *Land Reform (Scotland) Act 2003*), this real right remains an important (as well as enforceable) symbol of the resilience of public property rights in Scots jurisprudence.[22]

The right is founded on three pre-requisites. First, the public way must be a fixed route, a track from which the right cannot deviate. The way need not be the shortest route between two points, nor does it need to be visible or definite. It simply requires 'a clear indication of the direction in which the route goes', such as the contours of a hillside (Anderson 2016, p. 257). This requirement rules out common-law rights to roam, and emphasizes that the sanctioned right is one of direct passage only.[23]

Second, the public right of way must *connect* (emphasis added) two public places, *public termini*. The latter is defined as 'somewhere that members of the public are entitled to be and … somewhere of which public use is actually made' (p. 258). In clarifying the second limb, it is insufficient to simply aver a public right to be in that public place; rather it must be 'a place to which the public resort for some definite and intelligible purpose' (p. 258, citing *Duncan v Lees* (1871) 9 M 856). Case law has yielded a mixed bag of 'places to which the public resort'. In premises such as sub-post offices in private homes, geological sites of interest, or private cattle markets used four days per week; the landowner's right to exclude overrides the public entitlement. By contrast, roads, natural harbors 'used by fishermen and others', and Church of Scotland churchyards are places to which 'the public may resort'. A public place is 'invariably heritable' (Paisley 2000, p. 287).

Third, there must be a sufficient prescriptive 'public possession' of the right of way for at least twenty continuous years (Sect. 3 (3) *Prescription and Limitation (Scotland) Act* 1973). This requirement inserts a curious understanding of 'possession', one at odds with its usual private exclusivity. 'Public possession' here means regular, open and peaceable use, without lengthy interruptions. Moreover, its regular public use must be *use* as a *public* right of way,[24] which is an objective test:

> Until a right of way case arises, nobody goes from A to B to assert a right. He goes because he wants to get from A to B and he goes by the path he has been accustomed to see others take without challenge or objection. The great majority knows nothing about the legal character of the way and never address their minds to the matter. The legal character of the way … depends in the general case, not upon what was in the mind of the public or in the mind of the proprietor, but upon what the public did and what the proprietor did, considered in relation to all the surrounding circumstances. … In the general, the law presumes that the public went as of right when their user was such as presumably a proprietor would not voluntarily have permitted where there was no right.[25]

These Scots law rights, while 'encountered comparatively rarely in practice … represent touchstones of freedom' (Paisley 2000)[26] They are enforced by members of the public at large through the means of an *action popularis*. The public at large itself comprises 'natural persons, including incomers such as Ulster Scots who come to live in Scotland, and juristic bodies' (Paisley 2000, p. 69). The public right is also in theory enforceable by the Crown.[27]

In each of its three pre-requisites, this public right of way depends on the pedestrian's movement forging connection. First, the type of movement is prescribed; it must be passage only, and its trajectory must be direct. Connection is *explicit* to the second element; the way must connect two *public termini*. Third, even the limitation period inserts movement into its calculations, since its requisite public-ness of use turns *not* on how the public understands the right of way's legal character, but on what the public and landowner unconsciously *do* over time.

Public rights of way only authorize direct public passage from A to B. They do not sanction non-direct rights to roam, the generalized 'right' to wander across private Scottish countryside. Until 2003, outdoor recreational access was a long asserted, yet contested convention, at best a 'customary toleration of access' (Lovett 2011, p. 817). The passage of the Land Reform (Scotland) Act 2003 (the 'LRSA') saw a radical re-ordering of private and public real rights, where, 'the traditionally robust, modular, ex ante presumption *in favor* of the right to exclude [was replaced] with a surprisingly simple, but also robust, ex ante presumption *in favor* of responsible access' (ibid.). The LRSA overcame the doctrinal and geographical constraints of the Scots law public right of way,[28] and relegated many of the vexed legal and social narratives surrounding public recreational access to the annals of history (ibid., pp. 759–766).[29]

The LRSA adopts a 'universalist' approach to access, a right to go 'almost anywhere in Scotland' (ibid., p. 741). Section 1(1) grants a sweeping right of responsible access – a right of 'everyone' to 'land', which includes foreshores and inland waters (Sect. 32(1)). Access rights comprise *a right to be on land*, and *a right to cross land* (Sect. 1(2)). The former, a statutory right to roam, permits '(i) going into, passing over and remaining on [land] for any of those purposes and then leaving it; or (ii) any combination of those'. The latter statutory right of passage is a reference to 'passing over [land] and leaving it all for the purpose of getting from one place outside the land to another such place' (Sect. 1(4)). Exercise of these access rights is limited to purposes that are recreational or educational (Sect. 1(3)). At the heart of the statutory regime, the access right must be exercised 'responsibly' (Sect. 2).[30] Conduct excluded from responsible access includes 'hunting, shooting or fishing' or 'being on or crossing land with a motorised vehicle' (Sect. 9). The exercise of access rights does not of itself constitute trespass (Sect. 5(1)), access rights do not 'diminish or displace any other rights (whether public or private) of entry, way, passage or access' (Sect. 5(3)) and significantly for public property jurisprudence, 'a person exercising access rights is to be regarded as being in a public place' (Sect. 5(7)).

The LRSA countenances a vast spectrum of pedestrian movement and connection: from direct passage to recreational meandering, with the verbal language of the statute explicit in its *going*, *passing*, *entering*, *leaving*, or *crossing*. Impediments to free movement, such as posting no-entry signs, erecting barriers, fences or walls, or planting hedges are prohibited (Sect. 14(1)). Section 6(1) details these exceptions – places where the pedestrian's erstwhile universal access rights are not exercisable. The list includes land with buildings or other 'structures' on it, curtilages around buildings, compounds and other enclosures, and the much-litigated notion of 'sufficient adjacent land to enable persons living [in domestic contexts] to have reasonable measures of privacy in that house or place and to ensure that their enjoyment of that house or place is not unreasonably disturbed' (Sect. 6(1)(b)(iv)).

While its particularized nature imposes 'higher information and processing costs' (Lovett 2011, p. 818), the LRSA re-conceptualizes private and public real rights in ways that mirror Carol Rose's 'more fluid, less fenced-in' ideal of property. It demonstrates, as John Lovett notes, that a contextual, open-ended property regime is feasible in a 'modern, democratic nation committed to the rule of law [and] the protection of private property' (p. 816).

In England and Wales, public real rights of passage and roaming are in rough inverse correlation. The network of English and Welsh public footpaths is extensive, with almost 130,000 miles of public ways. Each square mile is said to have on average 2.2 miles of public paths (Anderson 2007. p. 381). By reason of ancient use and sheer mileage, the public right of passage therefore tends to greater certainty than its Scots counterpart (Lovett 2011, pp. 767–770). By contrast, the right to roam, given statutory force by the Countryside Rights of Way Act 2000 ('CRoW'), is far more circumscribed. Indeed, rights to roam are not the normalizing default but the bounded exception. The geographic reach of the statutory right is spatially restricted to mapped 'open countryside' and registered common lands only, contrasted to the 'universalist' guiding principle of the LRSA where 'everyone' has access to 'land'. Critics of CRoW describe it as 'timid' and 'tokenistic', one that 'serves to sustain the hegemony of the rights of private landownership in the countryside' (Mitchell 2008, p. 365).

The expansive network of public footpaths, bridleways and carriageways across England and Wales reflects an ancient usage that has existed in some cases since time immemorial.[31] Public footpaths were the highways of agrarian England, connecting village with village and the coast, their existence '[dating] back to the time when more people lived and worked in the fields, with the paths often reflecting their normal journey to work, or church or to market'.[32] The large-scale enclosure of common lands in the 18th and 19th centuries extinguished many public pathways. This was compounded by rural depopulation, paths falling into disuse, and a collective loss of corporate knowledge about their locations. However, significant numbers of public pathways survived – through enclosure orders, express dedications, or by courts applying rules of prescription or implied dedication. The National Parks and Access to the Countryside Act 1949 introduced procedures for the formal surveying and mapping of public ways. This 'produced, to a much greater extent than in Scotland, a system of "systematically confirmed public rights of way" and a procedure for resolving disputes over controversial paths' (Lovett

2011, p. 769). Importantly, 'the Act created much greater certainty regarding the existence and location of footpaths, which furthered the public's confidence in using them' (Anderson 2007, p. 403). Public footpaths are today regulated by a mix of statute and common law,[33] and constitute a cherished and jealously guarded public right in the English propertied landscape.[34]

As in Scotland, the long-standing validity of public rights of way did not enable a generalized right to roam. However, unlike Scotland, the legislative response in CRoW was not a blanket right subject to stated exceptions, but instead a limited and qualified right, one where non-access normalizes as the default position. In CRoW terms, the right to 'open-air recreation' is defined in Section 2(1) by describing what it is not.[35] 'Access lands' under the original CRoW formula were estimated to comprise 12% of the landmass of England and Wales (Anderson 2007, p. 407).[36] In 2009, this was extended to include the 'coastal margin' (Marine and Coastal Access Act 2009, Part 9), described as a 'long-distance walking route allowing two people to walk comfortably abreast along a virtually continuous four-meter-wide access corridor around the entire … English coastline' (Gray 2010, p. 47). While an impressive expansion of public acreage, the qualifications on the public right tend to be its telling feature. What is *not* accessible includes excepted lands listed in Schedule 1,[37] countryside that is neither 'wholly nor predominantly mountain, moor, heath or down', countryside below 600 meters in altitude, or countryside that is 'improved or semi-improved grassland', in sum, countryside that is not mapped by the Countryside Agency.[38] Indeed, even 'access land' can be declared off-limits for up to 28 days in a calendar year (Sect. 22). Inclusion under the CRoW regime tends to be defined by its polar opposite, the spatially demarcated parameters of exclusion.

Owner rights to (oxymoronically) close 'open countryside' permit public rights to lapse for up to nearly a month each year. Reasons include landowners harvesting or planting crops. Yet, even allowing for such periodic closures, public rights of way and rights to 'open-air recreation' enable pedestrianized movement across the rural landscapes of England and Wales, a regime where once hesitant *de facto* claims are transformed into *de jure* rights of access (Sydenham 2002), a newer narrative of passive rights to *enter* and *remain*. Connection endures, agrarian highways have been re-purposed as popular recreational routes, and ambivalent common and public rights, muddied since the enclosures, are re-validated in statutory form, connecting the mostly urban public pedestrian to remnants of her rural past.

Far from the metropole, public access rights in the New Zealand outdoors were the focus of the *Walking Access Act* 2008. New Zealand is an interesting case study for public real property, a bi-cultural society where vague public rights are wedged between uniquely powerful trespass rights and a resurgent Maori estate. From early colonial beginnings, the New Zealand state adopted an egalitarian approach to public resources, a conscious determination to avoid the exclusions and privileges of the colonial parent. For instance, Prime Minister Mackenzie's progressive government of the late 19th century was motivated by the premier's strong dislike of the concentrated private ownership in his native Scotland, an ideology legislated in the closer settlement provisions of the 1892 Land Act.

In this context, access to the outdoors is (or was) widely viewed as a birthright of New Zealanders, a convention unofficially sanctioned by the generosity of the Commissioner of Crown Lands in permitting unrestrained use of unoccupied Crown lands[39] (Hayes 2007, p. 3). This tacit national understanding was supplemented by the widely recognized Queens Chain, an historical practice of lands offices to reserve for public access a 66-foot-wide strip of land alongside bodies of water whenever land was sold to private riparian owners.[40] The Queens Chain is in practice an incomplete network, comprising a mix of formed, and unformed or 'paper' roads. Many of the latter are said to be in 'a state of nature', meaning they are infested with impassable gorse. At other locations, the paper road falls off a cliff, or cascades over waterfalls. The Queens Chain is particularly impacted by rules that fix landward boundaries for roads, but permit ambulatory boundaries on the waterside, meaning in practice that large portions of the chain have been lost to erosion.[41]

The Land Act of 1948 reinforces this curious legal rigidity, one where the law is at odds with public expectations as to access. Section 176(2)(a) states clearly that 'every person commits an offence ... who without right, title or licence, trespasses on, or uses, or occupies lands of the Crown'. The Trespass Acts of 1968 and 1980 went further, reversing the onus of proof such that pedestrians must prove they are *not* on Crown lands, and criminalizing what was otherwise the civil tort of trespass. According to former Registrar-General Brian Hayes, 'trespass under the Trespass Act 1980 is by far a more significant issue than trespass at common law' for public access. (2007, p. 45). Legislators, albeit in a minority, were likewise aware of the Trespass Act's privatization by stealth. In debates surrounding the 1980 bill, MPs offered arguments such as:

> If those station owners can prevent New Zealanders from getting access to Crown land, in effect they will be the owners of the land. ... By this legislation New Zealanders will be prevented from going on to Crown property, which in effect they own.
>
> *(Richard Prebble (Auckland Central) June 5, 1980)*

Or:

> This (farmer's selling hunting or access rights) is the true explanation for the Bill now before this House. It has been introduced so that the manner in which people have been pursuing their recreational interests will be changed, and so that people's rights to access the back country can be cut off, and those rights can be flogged off to the highest bidder.
>
> *(Geoffrey Palmer (Christchurch Central) July 1, 1980)*

After '30 years of privileging private property rights at the expense of public rights to wildlife, fisheries and water' (Philp 2008, p. 45), the national government established the Acland committee in 2005 to quell growing anxieties over the loss of 'New Zealand's culture of public access to water bodies' (p. 48). Its recommendations formed the basis of the Walking Access Act. Criticized as being captured by the farmer's lobby group, Federated Farmers, and described by trenchant critics as a 'sell-out', the legislation has two key purposes. First, to 'provide the New Zealand public with free, certain, enduring, and practical walking access to the outdoors (including around the coast and lakes, along rivers, and to public resources)', and second, to establish the Walking Access Commission (Sect. 3(a) and (b)), a Crown entity responsible for the 'negotiation, establishment, maintenance, and improvement of walking access' over public and private lands (Sects. 9, 20–32). At its heart, the statutory right of walkway access is unequivocally the pedestrian's. 'Members of the public may, at any time and without charge, (a) pass or repass over any walkway on foot; and (b) perform any activity that is reasonably incidental to that passing or repassing' (Sect. 33(1)). However, the right is no right to roam, and it only subsists over walkways established under the Act. Nor does the Act provide any clarification for the vexed paper road. It is a comparatively weak right, but a public real right nonetheless, one that reiterates the pedestrian's passing and re-passing on foot. It lacks the fertile soil of the United Kingdom, the social history and ancient usages that presaged British public real rights. However, the antipodean right does not exist in a cultural vacuum, rooted as it is in the implicit compact that is the convention of pedestrian access to inland and coastal waters.

Across the Tasman Sea, the so-called 'long paddock' or travelling stock reserve ('TSR') is another public real right, but this time an archetype with a distinctly Australian flavor. Travelling stock reserves originated in the early 19th century – as extensive networks of grassed public corridors that enabled the movement of livestock during times of drought, or the slow transport of sheep or cattle from grazing property to market or railhead.[42] These 'stock routes were heavily travelled up until the late 1940s', but declined with the advent of road transport and a 'series of wet years' in the second half of the 20th century (NPA 2011, p. 20). Today, as Crown lands, TSRs remain significant in central and western regions of New South Wales and Queensland,[43] with periodic surges in use linked to cycles of dry weather. In populous coastal zones, urban density has broken up and dispersed the TSR's interconnectivity, although pockets survive.

Many TSRs are managed in NSW by Local Land Services, a state agency once better known as Pasture Protection Boards. Under the Local Land Services Act 2013 (NSW), 'TSRs' are defined as:

> (a) any route or camping place reserved for travelling stock route or camping place under the *Crown Lands Act 1989*, or
> (b) any reserve for travelling stock, water reserve, reserve for access or crossing (where the reserve is for the purpose of providing travelling stock with access to or a crossing of water, whether expressly notified for that purpose or not), or
> (c) any stock watering place.
>
> *(Sect. 61)*

Similarly, 'travelling stock' are defined as 'stock that are being moved by being walked, and includes travelling stock that are grazing.'

These core definitions capture the traditional conceptualization of TSRs – livestock droving corridors and emergency feedlots in times of drought. In the early 21st century, evolving social, cultural and environmental values, together with multiple land use principles have led to newer roles for TSRs. These include beekeeping (Sect. 77(1)), timber management, active or passive recreation, and as cultural heritage and ecological conservation sites.[44] Environmentally, 'TSRs form a unique and continental-scale corridor of publicly-owned remnant vegetation' (NPA 2011, p. 6) possessing enormous importance for biodiversity preservation and the success of 'connective conservation' projects in otherwise heavily cleared grazing lands (pp. 8–15).

Access to TSRs for livestock droving purposes is 'lawful' under Section 72. It requires an administrative 'stock permit' to be issued, and a fee paid (Sect. 79). Ancillary uses such as 'as of right' recreational uses are permitted from 'sunrise to sunset' (Sect. 74(1)), rights of ways for adjoining owners are implied where access is otherwise unavailable (Sect. 75(1)), and 'reserve use permits' are mandatory for 'maintaining apiaries or any other (non-grazing) purpose' (Sect. 77(1)). Access to controlled TSRs thus turns on an idiosyncratic mix of statutory right, implication, or permit type. Rights to ingress and egress are further complicated by competing gatekeeping claims of other state agencies charged with the management of the TSR network.[45]

Such qualifications on access are contrasted to the clarity of connection, the historical character of TSRs as iconic 'long paddocks', public corridors that link farm to market and offer respite for travelling drought-stricken stock. Connected-ness is also reflected in the changing social, recreational and environmental rationales invoked to justify the TSR network.[46] TSRs are being reimagined as corridors for native habitat, or recreational trails for bushwalkers or horse-riders. These contemporary rationales remain true to the TSR's traditional droving origins, the *sui generis* right to:

> (a) enter a … travelling stock reserve with stock,
> (b) remain on a … travelling stock reserve with stock,
> (c) walk stock on a public road or travelling stock reserve,
> (d) graze stock on a public road or … travelling stock reserve.
>
> (Sect. 78(2))

In travelling along the New England Highway in northern New South Wales, the adjoining TSR is a constant companion, a thin, largely unbroken ribbon of native vegetation to your right or left. Its ever-presence forms a tangible, connective part of the social fabric, a place where 'travellers have long enjoyed the bush remnant … as a scenic stopover place for a quiet rest and repast' (NPA 2011, p. 23). This 'long enjoyment' is an integral part of Australian bush folklore, 'immortalised in the poetry of A.B. (Banjo) Paterson, Henry Lawson and others' (Spooner et al. 2010, p. 329). Indeed, many TSRs trace their origins (and routes) back to Indigenous traditional pathways, used for millennia for 'trade, travel, ceremonial and spiritual purposes … [routes that] formed vital links to water and food sources, and … avenues of access to various parts of the country' (ibid., p. 330). From Indigenous and colonial histories to its modern justiciable rights to *enter*, *remain*, *walk*, *travel*, *water* and *graze*, the Australian travelling stock reserve is a public real right that places movement, and the connections that movement forge, at its heart. It is also an example of English common law adapting to its colonial context, how limited rights to 'move stock' on English bridleways were given a distinctly Australian life, one where the laconic pedestrian stockman walks his cattle or sheep in the dusty 'long paddock.'

This excursus of justiciable public real rights ends with the contested notion of beach access in the United States. Public recreational easements over private property landward of the high tide line are variable and *ad hoc*, weak in so-called low water states, stronger in higher water others, and with much jurisdictional difference in between (Higgins 2005). The *situs* of this public real right is the dry sands of privately owned beaches, the littoral zone between wet sands (demarcated by the high water mark and accessible via the public trust doctrine – see Chapter 3) and private lands onshore of the vegetation line. On these privately owned dry sands, disputes over public access periodically flare, clashes over the extent of private property rights typically litigated in the context of takings jurisprudence.

On a tract-by-tract basis, individual public recreational easements may be acquired by prescription, an ancient common law doctrine based on particularized, site-specific evidence of continuous, open, non-consensual and peaceable walking. Other bases for public recreational easements include landowner grant, or implied or express dedication. As noted, prescription requires a certain *quality* of use, one that is open and peaceful. As an acquisitive doctrine, it also requires lengthy duration. At common law, legal memory of use must stretch back to *time immemorial*. In England, legal memory was fixed at the year 1189, long pedestrianized movement indeed. Under the (subsequent yet separate) doctrine of the lost modern grant, the deemed legal fiction of a 'lost' deed of grant piled one fiction atop another. Limitation statutes discarded artifice entirely, with a separate and third basis for prescription based on the expiration of a statutory limitation period, and the consequences of statute-barred counter-actions for recovery of possession.

Prescription is a rare doctrine in that it grounds both private and public real rights. Hence, its beneficiaries are not only the private owners of dominant tenements, but latterly the public pedestrian at large. In *Elmer v Rodgers*,[47] evidence that the use of a driveway on church property for beach access 'was not restricted to church members or their guests but that the public generally without permission of the owners used the premises for bathing and picnicking' (p. 514) was not fatal to the prescriptive claim. Indeed the New Hampshire Supreme Court was explicit in stating that there was 'no basis in our decisions for holding that the general public cannot acquire by prescription such rights as those claimed here' (p. 515). The argument that the general public was too indefinite a group to be the grantee of a 'lost' deed of grant was as 'disreputable' as the fictional notion of a lost grant itself.

One spatial limitation of prescription is that it is restricted to individual easement sites, and requires tract-by-tract proof. It lacks the efficacy of vesting universal *generalized* public walking rights over private dry sands. Custom, or its enabling by statute, overcomes this constraint, validating public recreational easements in 'districts' where customary usage can be demonstrated, or in a blanket fashion across entire jurisdictions. In observing the similarities between custom and prescription, David Bederman writes:

> Custom was often invoked by parties seeking some sort of right attendant with someone else's land. As a consequence, customary rights were often considered by English judges as a corollary to prescriptive rights. Both prescription and custom were created by usage and by the consent of the parties bound to them.
>
> *(1996, p. 1395)*

There is, however, a key difference, 'for while prescription always connects the right with a definite person, custom connects it with some particular locality. Prescription is personal, custom is local. … A right claimed by custom is not alleged to be vested in any definite person … but is claimed on the ground that it is vested in the shifting class of persons connected from time to time with the locality to which the right is attached' (Cheshire and Burns 1982, p. 544–545).

Bederman describes 'four ways in which customary easements of public access have come to be recognized' in the United States (1996, p. 1379).[48] First is the (mostly unsuccessful) judicial adoption of customary easements, principally in the New England states. Under this model, custom extends beach access rights to the 'public-at-large in a district' (p. 1396), a classification that sits on the uncomfortable cusp between common and public right. Bederman's second and third models broaden the public class, extending the customary right to the public at large of the state(s) in question. The second model employs statute to either enable or codify the customary easement, citing the Texas Open Beaches Act 1959 as an example of the former. In that Act, the public, individually and collectively, is given 'free and unrestricted rights of ingress and egress to and from state owned beaches'. That right is said to be 'without derogation of any right defined from time immemorial at law and custom'. The third model of 'judicial instrumentalism' is confined to the Oregon Pacific coastline, an empty, thinly populated stretch, where in the absence of formed roads, the beaches were historically used as transport corridors.[49] In the landmark case of *State ex rel. Thornton v Hay*,[50] the Oregon Supreme Court held that state's 'entire dry sand beach … was impressed with a public recreational customary easement' (Bederman 1996, p. 1419). The court invoked custom to justify a statewide public right, citing the use of the dry-sands by 'aboriginal inhabitants for clam-digging and building fires', a custom 'continued by newcomers after statehood':

> From the time of the earliest settlement to the present day, the general public has assumed that the dry-sand area was a part of the public beach, and the public has used the dry-sand area for picnics, gathering wood, building warming fires, and generally as a headquarters from which to supervise children or to range over the foreshore as the tides advance and recede.

The nature of the Oregon public right equates to a quasi-prescriptive easement, a usufruct that enables access, precludes landowner activities that impede free passage, and qualifies the right to exclude (Bender 1998). As a customary right, its application does not require forensic tract-by-tract scrutiny. Rather, the assumption is that the right applies universally, subject to spatial and socio-historic provisos being met, namely, that the disputed dry sands abut the Pacific Ocean, and that there is a requisite 'history of public use' over the 'classic' dry-sands.

This chapter's study of disparate public real rights across key common law jurisdictions is not exhaustive. For instance, the much-studied US public trust doctrine was previously traversed in Chapter 3. However, this section does provide a distinct flavor of justiciable public rights, a comparative excursus that offers common insights. First, in the absence of statute, public real rights are *circumscribed*, doctrinally constrained and given little spatial latitude. The consequences of statutory intervention however are dramatic; witness the Scottish roaming right pre and post 2003. Or, at the least they are clarifying, as in New Zealand post 2008. Second, public rights in land are *contextual*, physicalized to the contours of British pastoral hillsides, the harsh droughts of Australia, or the 'burning [of] warming fires' on wintry Oregonian beaches. Third, they are *culturally* rich; rights forged in the crucible of enclosure, iconized in bush folklore, or as accretions of enduring local practice. As culturally specific rights, perfect storms of social history and geographic exigency serendipitously merge to concertize the public right. The fourth observation, as the theories of Blomley and Barr envisage, is that these public rights are premised on flow, and the *connectivity* this enables. Couched in the language of fluid verbs, these doing words capture the movement of the pedestrian as she passes through the public outside. Public real rights variously permit one to enter, leave, pass, cross, walk, even 'range over the foreshore as the tides advance and recede'. In the two meanings of connection that this chapter explores, public real rights connect people to place, and people to places.

6.5 Conclusion: the pedestrian, connection, and public real property

This chapter argues that a defining feature of public real property is its capacity to connect. To highlight this connection, the human pedestrian is employed to locate and traverse those connections. The pedestrian, naturally, lies at the heart of walking literature, a work premised on the joys, philosophies and anthropologies of putting one foot in front of another. This literature reminds us that walking's imperative is one of enduring, of finding ways through, of connecting. This literature also gives an insight into the normative 'rules' that smooth this connective path. When it comes to public real property theory, the pedestrian is a lead actor in a small one-act play. Simultaneously, she gives form to public real rights scattered across culturally rich common law landscapes. The pedestrian is pivotal to these normative, theoretical and juristic lines of public real enquiry because she enacts connection.

Connection is not a legal doctrine. Rather, it is an example of Blomley's *own terms* thinking, a crude observation of the *effects* of public real property set amidst its scattered public real rights. As an organizing principle, connection is instrumentalist, particularly in its material version. But connection is not without rationale, as the theoretical discussion attests, and as connection's intuitive other half would inhere.

What makes connection so important, so unique to public real property? Two answers are proffered. First, it is what public property *does* – in the way performance theorists posit. We don't assume or expect that private property will connect. Private real estate gives us security; guarantees our monetized investments, safeguards our privacy, and enables personal autonomy. No doubt also, our 'castles' give us a micro-sense of belonging, as Eduardo Penalver's 'entrance to community' suggests (2005). Yet private lands do not connect, they famously exclude. Successful so-called 'private commons' like the Grove shopping precinct in Los Angeles (see Chapter 4), overcome the private estate's exclusionary tendencies by mimicking public real property. This copying is deliberate, as the Grove's developer explains, 'Its why we don't have gates. … If we're going to build a great street, it needs to do everything a street would do, which means you don't have gates. You keep it open. The more we do that, the more you become part of the fabric of the city.' (Ulin 2015, p. 78). If imitation is the sincerest form of flattery, it is the public estate's 'open-ness' that justifies the multi-million-dollar price tag paid to emulate (and flatter) the public street. Common property likewise is not connective. Members of resident's associations, strata plans, co-operatives, clubs, and the like, enjoy an inclusive sharing of common space with eligible members, yet they exclude outsiders. Only public real property defaults to connect.

Second, when connection is lost, its absence is sorely felt, and the public grievance it invokes is enduring. As noted earlier, the passing of generations did little to assuage the underlying public anger over the loss of access to the English or Scottish countryside or coast – a grievance only mollified when rights to roam were legislated in the early 2000s. Two other examples, from the United States and New Zealand, likewise highlight how *visceral* the idea of connection is to the public psyche, and how profound the implications of its loss.

In the New Zealand high country, a process of so-called tenure review beginning in the 1990s converted Crown pastoral tenure into a duality of public conservation land (usually at higher altitudes), and private freehold (usually at valuable lower altitudes and adjoining lakes). One object of tenure review is to 'make easier' public access – at the same time as facilitating the disposability of freehold private title (Sect. 24(c) *Crown Pastoral Lands Act 1998)*. This land reform policy became mired in debate, however, over loss of access to conservation lands, amongst other issues (Brower 2008).[51] Analogously to Scotland, long-held, assumed conventions about access to the 'back country' were deeply entrenched in the public mind. As in Scotland, these public expectations had contested legal bases. But unlike Scotland, much of the backcountry acreage was not tied up in private title, but a public pastoral tenure that granted run holders an exclusive right to graze, but no express right to exclude, and 'no right to the soil' (Sect. 66, Land Act 1948).[52] The conflation of an exclusive grazing right into an exclusive right to possess evolved almost imperceptibly from 1948 (Brower and Page 2012), and was unconvincingly affirmed by the New Zealand High Court in 2009.[53] To compound this connective loss, examples also came to light of newly created high country conservation lands being landlocked – often through a clumsy neglect of securing public easements (or walkways) in tenure review negotiations. The case of Hunter Valley Station, on the shores of the South Island's Lake Hawea, is a case in point. There, the sale of Crown leasehold to a former American television news journalist Mark Lauer, provided an opportunity to resolve simmering public discontent through mandating new public easements, or formalizing existing *de facto* walkways as a condition of consent under the *Overseas Investment Act* 2005. Ironically, it was argued that the best way to restore public rights of access was through the backdoor of another Act, by imposing sale pre-conditions (to a private US citizen) of 'public benefit to New Zealanders' (Sect. 16, *Overseas Investment Act* 2005). However, yet another opportunity to secure guaranteed access was inexplicably missed, the sale waved through without final agreement over access. Yet, at a broader policy level, public frustration over the ongoing, incremental loss of public connectivity proved to be not insignificant in persuading the government to end tenure review in early 2019.

Preserving public access through indirect means is likewise illustrated in the 2017 Californian Court of Appeal decision of *Surfrider Foundation v Martins Beach* 1 LLC.[54] Notwithstanding its famed beach culture, California is a jurisdiction noted for its strong protection of private property rights on dry sands.[55] Surfrider's geographic setting was judicially noted in the following terms:

> Nestled in a cove, sheltered in the north and south by cliffs, Martins Beach lacks lateral road access. The only practical route to Martins Beach is down a [private] road, Martins Beach Road, which leads from Highway 1 in San Mateo County to the beach.

In September 2009, the beach's Silicon Valley venture capital-owner, Vinod Khosla, closed the road, an action emblematic of 'wealthy landowners who have increasingly tried to buy up the internationally celebrated beaches along the California coast and turn public lands into private property' (Levin 2017). For nearly a century, Martins Beach, 30 miles south of San Francisco, had been 'a popular destination for fishing, surfing and other recreational activities'. Previous owners had opened the road over summer, erected a kiosk and public toilets, and allowed paid parking. The not-for-profit Surfrider Association challenged the 2009 closure, claiming that the owner's actions of installing a remotely controlled gate, painting over a billboard advertising access, and posting a no-entry sign constituted a 'development' under the Californian Coastal Act of 1976. This 'development' had the effect of reducing beach access, and given the statute's mandate to *inter alia* 'maximize access and public recreational purposes', a coastal development permit (CDP) was required to sanction the works. While the decision did not rule on the nature of the public 'right' (that is, whether it was simply permissive, or acquired through implied dedication),[56] the Court of Appeal nonetheless agreed that public access must remain at its pre-2009 level until San Mateo County dealt with the CDP, thereby ensuring the county's potential power to impose as a (compensable) condition of consent, the granting of a public recreational easement. The deeming of the landowner's actions as a 'development' was a blunt yet successful use of a planning instrument to preserve historic access arrangements.[57] In October 2018, the US Supreme Court refused to hear Mr. Khosla's appeal, effectively preserving public access over the private road. As *The New York Times* reported:

> Whether you have to drive an hour to the coast and picnic or whether you can spend $32 million and buy property adjacent to the coast, the beach belongs to everybody. … The Coastal Act survives the whims of a billionaire and continues to protect the people of California.
>
> *(Bowles 2018)*

Connection matters because it is a practice, an *effect* of public real property. Jane Jacobs pithily observes that 'the point of sidewalks is that they are public' (1961, p. 54). As well-worn tracts of public real estate, the sidewalk is a highly visible – and totemic – representation of a vast public realm, much of which remains hidden in plain view. The pedestrian trope walks this 'sidewalk' constantly, her steps joining the dots, making connections both material and non-material. Jacobs' unadorned one-liner reveals a deceptively simple truth, one where it could equally be said that the point of the (totemic) sidewalk is that it connects. Notions of publicness and connection are inextricably intertwined. This is what public real property does, by and through its norms, theories and laws. And when connection is lost, or threatened, this is the core truth that the yawning gap reveals.

Notes

1 *Oxford English Dictionary*.
2 Famous literary walkers include Henry David Thoreau, Ralph Waldo Emerson, Walt Whitman, William Wordsworth, Mark Twain, Robert Frost, and James Joyce (Nicholson 2009).
3 Henry David Thoreau defines 'saunter' by its French derivation, the relationship to *le terre*, the land.

4 Gros describes *private* walking in very different terms of 'hardly walking at all, but intermittent comings and goings, incessant dallying' (2015, p. 210).
5 Documented at between 12–18 inches (Schwarz 2015, p. 147).
6 For example, Tristan Gooley, *The Walker's Guide to Outdoor Clues & Signs* (Hodder & Stoughton, 2015).
7 Section 24(c) *Crown Pastoral Lands Act 1998* (NZ) requires that public access is 'made easier' when lands are converted by tenure review into either Crown conservation lands or private freehold. While access easements are measurable spatially, often the path is inaccessible, a position argued forcefully by the NZ Federated Mountain Clubs, an access advocacy group (Brower and Page 2017).
8 'When you go outside, it is always to pass from one "inside" to another' (Gros 2015, p. 31).
9 Thoreau is said to be 'the author of the first philosophic treatise on walking' (ibid., p. 88).
10 'Lowly, unpurposeful and random as they may appear, sidewalk contacts are the small change from which a city's wealth of public life may grow' (Speck 2012, p. 49).
11 Twenty years later, Olmsted used similar rationales for a Niagara Falls State Park.
12 Distractions include the intrusion of unsightly commercial developments that diminish the aesthete, 'urban, artificial element[s] plainly in conflict' with contemplative reflection. Or, they could constitute the intrusive noise and destructive churn of off-road vehicles or overhead drones.
13 For example, pioneering US conservationist, Aldo Leopold writes of the early history of hunters in lobbying for national parks in the United States, or the conservation instincts of the hunter.
14 See, for example, Sect. 23 *Wildlife Act* 1953 (NZ).
15 'Our property law system operates with a combination of formal rules and social customs to shape property rights in a manner consistent with the norms of a free and democratic society' (Singer 2009, p. 1051).
16 Fairfax writes of western public lands 'riding off into a different sunset' where once alternative ideas of adventure, relaxation, solitude or spiritual replenishment are now mainstream (Fairfax 1981).
17 See also the analogous definition in modern highway statutes, such as Section 5, *Roads Act* 2005 (NSW).
18 For example, the Hermitage foreshore track, www.nationalparks.nsw.gov.au/things-to-do/walking-tracks/hermitage-foreshore-track.
19 The new light rail network in Sydney likewise ends at Randwick, a suburb inland from the beach at Coogee. Similarly, in Los Angeles, getting to Santa Monica's beaches by public transport requires time and numerous line changes (Ulin 2015).
20 Outside the cities, a small number of estate holders owned most of the countryside. Lovett cites that in 1995, 1,411 owners held 57.8% of Scotland (2011, p. 771). There is also a 'long tradition of customary access and tolerance that took place in Scotland's hills and mountains in particular' (Combe 2012, p. 112).
21 Other justiciable common law public rights include 'certain rights in and to the foreshore, sea and territorial sea. The rights comprise the right to use the foreshore… for whitefishing (all floating fish other than salmon), recreation and navigation. The foreshore may also be used for passage along the foreshore' (Paisley 2000, p. 300). Analogous rights include 'ancient rights enjoyed by members of royal boroughs' (ibid, pp. 301–302). See also the discussion of 'community rights' in Lovett (2011, pp. 757–759).
22 The abolition of the common law public right was considered by the Law Reform Commission but not acted upon. In 2019, it was noted that the co-existence of distinct rights under the LRSA and the public common law right was confusing to some litigants (Upton 2019).

23 'This includes a right to erect directional signs and possibly some other aids to passage, as ancillary rights that tend to promote and foster the primary right. It does not include other rights such as pasturage' (p. 289).

24 Evidence of public use must also be for the right of way's *full* length, not merely part thereof.

25 *Rhins District Committee of Wigtownshire County Council v Cuninghame* 1917 2 SLT 169.

26 'The tradition of tolerated access to public places in Scotland is long established and is generally accepted as conducive to the common good' (Paisley 2000, p. 285).

27 Public rights of way differ from private servitudes in four key respects. Title to sue in a public right of way rests with every member of the public, compared to the private owner of a dominant or servient tenement; the decree granted for a public right of way is *res judicata* for or against the whole public; the public right is for the public; and in the former case, *both* termini must be public places (Cusine and Paisley (1998, p. 720).

28 In Scotland, compared to England, there were comparatively far fewer mapped footpaths and bridle paths. This has been strengthened with the concept of 'core paths'. Section 17 requires local authorities to identify a system of paths sufficient to ensure reasonable access in their area, including common law routes as well as 'other routes, waterways or other means by which persons may cross land', Sect. 17(2)(d) LRSA.

29 The historical grievances many Scots felt about loss of access to ancestral lands, the Highland Clearances, and the concentration of ownership of rural land by a small number of private landowners, all fed a widespread dissatisfaction in the years preceding the LRSA.

30 Conversely, landowners must also act responsibly in ensuring the provision of reasonable access.

31 Footpaths authorize foot traffic only and comprised 78% of the pre-2000 network. Bridleways permit pedestrians, horse-riders and cyclists and comprised 17% of the network. Bridleways also require public rights to drive animals, like the Australian TSR, House of Commons Research Paper 00/31, 'The Countryside and Rights of Way Bill, Access and Rights of Way', p. 30.

32 House of Commons Research Paper 00/31, 'The Countryside and Rights of Way Bill, Access and Rights of Way', p. 29.

33 Statutes include the CRoW Act 2000, Part II, NAPCA 1949, Part IV, the Highways Act 1980, the Wildlife and Countryside Act 1981, Part III, and the Natural Environment and Rural Communities Act 2006, Part 6.

34 For example, the walking charity, the Ramblers Association, has a Pathwatch website and mobile app where path problems or feedback may be reported. www.ramblers.org.uk/advice/pathwatch-report-path-features-and-problems.aspx.

35 It is a right to 'enter and remain on any access land … if and for so long as (a) he does so without breaking or damaging any wall, fence, hedge, stile or gate, and (b) he observes the general restrictions in Schedule 2 and any other restrictions imposed in relation to the land under Chapter II'.

36 This includes conclusively mapped 'open country' (defined as wholly or predominantly mountain, moor, heath or down) and registered common lands, Sections 1(2) and 1(3) CRoW.

37 This includes land covered by buildings and its curtilage, land within 20 meters of a dwelling, and farmland that has been ploughed or drilled within the last 12 months for the purposes of planting or sowing crops or trees, amongst others.

38 Lovett reports that mapping was concluded in 2005, with the setting of boundaries the subject of much heated litigation (2011).

39 Lands of the Crown' are defined widely in Sect. 176(1), Land Act 1948.

40 'Experts say it is a myth that among Queen Victoria's instructions to New Zealand Governor William Hobson in 1840 were orders to reserve such strips around the whole coast, lakes and rivers. … In truth it is a catch-all term for strips of publicly-owned land next to the foreshore, rivers and lakes, initially set aside for access' (Gamble 2003). The practice was formalized by Section 110 Lands Act 1892.

41 In *Attorney-General and Southland County Council v Miller,* the Supreme Court affirmed that a private owner is under no obligation to give up a corresponding part of their land where the public road is destroyed or washed away.

42 For a detailed history of TSRs from the 1830s to the 1870s, see Cameron and Spooner (2010).

43 There are 1,985,908 hectares of TSRs in NSW, www.lls.nsw.gov.au/__data/assets/pdf_file/0011/578315/factsheet-tsr-consultation.pdf.

44 As of right recreational uses include walking, running, picnicking, swimming, horse riding, fishing and pedal cycling. Recreational and sporting groups may also obtain permits for other uses.

45 In NSW, TSRs are managed by several state agencies: Local Land Services, Department of Primary Industries, and Crown Lands Western Division.

46 A 2008 review of TSRs in NSW 'raised alarm from drovers, farmers, scientists, and conservation people alike, in a concerted [campaign] to identify, protect and maintain the biophysical, cultural and social values of this important landscape feature' (Spooner et al 2010, p. 329). A further review in 2012–2013 provoked a similar coalition of affected interest-holders. The current planning document for TSRs in NSW is the State Planning Framework 2016–21, www.lls.nsw.gov.au/livestock/stock-routes/tsr-draft-state-planning-framework-faqs.

47 *Elmer v Hodges* 106 N.H. 512 (1965).

48 The fourth model is the recognition of Hawaiian indigenous customary law (Bederman 1996).

49 Bederman says that the court uncritically and without fact-finding conflated local custom in Cannon Beach as 'a surrogate for the common law of property itself,' ibid, 1421. In *McDonald v Halvorson* 780 P.2d 714 (1989), the court restricted the spatial reach of the customary doctrine to dry sands abutting the Pacific Ocean only, rejecting its application to a freshwater pool adjacent to but separated from the ocean. The court also restricted the right to beaches with 'a history of public use', so-called 'classic dry-sand beaches like Cannon Beach', *State ex rel. Thornton v Hay* 462 P.2d 671 (1969), p. 724.

50 *State ex rel. Thornton v Hay* 462 P.2d 671 (1969).

51 These include documented financial losses suffered by taxpayers in tenure review deals struck between farmers and the state agency Land Information New Zealand (LINZ), and the loss of iconic alpine landscapes and lakeside vistas, replaced by residential subdivisions, golf courses, vineyards, or dairying activities, (Brower 2008).

52 In 1909, a New Zealand court described the right as giving a 'right to vesture only'.

53 *The New Zealand Fish and Game Council v Her Majesty's Attorney-General in Respect of Comm'r of Crown Lands* (2009) CIV 2008-485-2020 (HC).

54 San Mateo County, Super Ct. No. CIV520336. It is described by the appellant's lawyers as 'one of the most important recent public access rights cases in the country'.

55 *Nollan v California Coastal Comm'n* 483 U.S. 825 (1987).

56 This question is the subject of a separate action, *Friends of Martins Beach v Martins Beach LLC 1* (Super. Ct. San Mateo County, 517634).

57 Similarly, on 6 April 2018, the Michigan Supreme Court agreed with Surfrider Foundation's submissions regarding the broad interpretation of the state's Recreational

Land Use Act – that had the effect of encouraging private landowners to grant access to their land for beach access to Lake Michigan's foreshores. A restrictive interpretation of the tort statute would have conversely discouraged beach access (www.surfrider.org/coastal-blog/entry/7908).

References

Anderson, C. 2016, *Property: A Guide to Scots Law*, Thomson Reuters, Edinburgh.

Anderson J 2007, 'Britain's Right to Roam: Redefining the Landowner's Bundle of Sticks', *Georgetown International Environmental Law Review*, vol. 19, 375–435.

Barr, O 2016, *A Jurisprudence of Movement: Common Law, Walking, Unsettling Place*, Routledge, Abingdon.

Bederman, D 1996, 'The Curious Resurrection of Custom: Beach Access and Judicial Takings', *Columbia Law Review*, vol. 96, 1375–1455.

Bender, S 1998, 'Castles in the Sand: Balancing Public Custom and Private Ownership Interests on Oregon's Beaches', *Oregon Law Review*, vol. 77, 913–947.

Berry, V 2017, *Mirror Sydney: An Atlas of Reflection*, Giramondo Books, Sydney.

Blomley, N 2011, *Rights of Passage: Sidewalks and the Regulation of Public Flow*, Routledge, Abingdon.

Bowles, N 2018, 'Billionaire's Fight to Close Path to California Beach Comes to a Dead End', *New York Times*, October 1, 2018, available at www.nytimes.com/2018/10/01/technology/california-beach-access-khosla.html?action=click&module=News&pgtype=Homepage (accessed October 5, 2018).

Brower, A 2008, *Who Owns the High Country: The Controversial Story of Tenure Review in New Zealand,* Craig Potton Publishing, Nelson.

Brower, A and Page, J 2012, 'When the Law Is Silent, Trespassers W …: Law and Power in Implied Property Rights', *Environmental Law Reporter: News & Analysis*, vol. 42, 10 242–10259.

Brower, A and Page, J 2017, 'Freeing the Land Beyond the Shadow of the Law: Twenty Years of the *Crown Pastoral Land Act*', *New Zealand Universities Law Review*, vol. 27, 975–994.

Cameron, J and Spooner, P 2010, 'Origins of Travelling Stock Routes: Early development, management, and the growing embrace of the law (1830s–70s)', *The Rangeland Journal*, vol. 32, 341–351.

Cheshire and Burn 1982, *Modern Law of Real Property* (13th ed). Oxford University Press, Oxford.

Combe, M M 2012, 'Access Rights: A Letter from America', *Edinburgh Law Review*, vol. 16, 110–113.

Cusine D J and Paisley, R R M 1998, *Servitudes and Rights of Way*, W Green, Edinburgh.

Davies, M 2016, 'Material Subjects and Vital Objects – Prefiguring Property and Rights for an Entangled World', *Australian Journal of Human Rights*, vol. 22, 37–59.

Ellickson, R 1991, *Order Without Law: How Neighbors Settle Disputes*, Harvard University Press, Cambridge, MA.

Fairfax, S 1981, 'Riding into a Different Sunset: The Sagebrush Rebellion', *Journal of Forestry*, vol. 79, 516–582.

Gamble, W 2003, 'Truth Behind the Queens Chain' NZ Herald, 12 August 2003, available at www.nzherald.co.nz/nz/news/article.cfm?c_id=1&objectid=3517579 (accessed 26 May 2017).

Gooley, T 2015, *The Walker's Guide to Outdoor Clues & Signs*, Hodder & Stoughton, London.

Gray, K, 2010, 'Pedestrian Democracy and the Geography of Hope', *Journal of Human Rights and the Environment*, vol. 1, pp. 45–65.

Graham, N 2011, *Lawscape: Property, Environment, Law*, Routledge, Abingdon.

Gros, F 2015, *A Philosophy of Walking*, Verso Books, London.

Hayes, B 2007, *Elements of the Law on Movable Water Boundaries*, MAF Policy, Wellington.

Higgins, M 2005, 'Public Access to the Shore: Public Rights and Private Property', in D M Whitelaw and G R Visgilio (eds.) *America's Changing Coasts: Private Rights and Public Trust*, Edward Elgar, Cheltenham.

Jacobs, J 1961, *The Death and Life of Great American Cities*, Random House, New York.

Layard, A 2016, 'Public Space: Property, Lines, Interruptions', *Journal of Law, Property & Society*, vol. 2, 1–47.

Levin, S. 2017 'Silicon Valley Billionaire Loses Bid to Prevent Access to Public Beach' *The Guardian*, 11 August 2017, available at amp.theguardian.com/environment/2017/aug/10/martins-beach-california-public-vinod-khosla (accessed 26 September, 2017).

Lovett J 2011, 'Progressive Property in Action: The Land Reform (Scotland) Act 2003', *Nebraska Law Review*, vol. 89, 739–820.

Lyons, S 2017, 'Psychogeography: A Way to Delve into the Soul of a City', *The Conversation*, June 19, 2017, available at https://theconversation.com/psychogeography-a-way-to-delve-into-the-soul-of-the-city-78032 (accessed 26 July 2017).

Mitchell, J 2008, 'What Public Presence? Access, Commons, and Property Rights', *Social and Legal Studies*, vol. 17, 351–367.

Monbiot, G 2020, 'Lockdown Is Nothing New: We've Been Kept Off the Land for Centuries', *The Guardian*, 22 April 2020, available at www.theguardian.com/commentisfree/2020/apr/22/lockdown-coronavirus-crisis-right-to-roam (accessed 24 April 2020).

National Parks Association of NSW, 'The NSW Travelling Stock Routes and Reserves Network: Heritage, Habitat, Livelihood', June 2011.

Nicholson, G 2009, *The Lost Art of Walking: The History, Science and Literature of Pedestrianism*, Riverhead Books, New York.

Paisley, R 2000, *Land Law*, W. Green/Sweet & Maxwell, Edinburgh.

Penalver, E 2005, 'Property as Entrance', *Virginia Law Review*, vol. 91, 1889–1972.

Philp, M 2008, 'No-Go Zones', *North & South*, August 2008.

Richardson, T 2015, *Walking Inside Out: Contemporary British Psychogeography (Place, Money, Affect)*, Rowman & Littlefield, London.

Sax, J 1980, *Mountains Without Handrails, Reflections on the National Parks*, University of Michigan Press, Ann Arbor.

Singer, J 2009, 'Democratic Estates: Property Law in a Free and Democratic Society', *Cornell Law Review*, vol. 94, 1009–1062.

Solnit, R. 2001 *Wanderlust: A History of Walking*, Penguin Books, New York.

Schwarz, S. 2015, *Street Smart: The Rise of Cities and the Fall of Cars*, Public Affairs, New York.

Shrubsole, G 2019, *Who Owns England? How We Lost Our Green & Pleasant Land & How to Take it Back*, William Collins, London.

Speck, J 2012, *Walkable City, How Downtown Can Save America One Step at a Time,* Farrar, Straus and Giroux, New York.

Spooner, P Firman, M & Yalmambirra, 2010, 'Origins of Travelling Stock Routes: Connections to Indigenous Traditional Pathways', *The Rangeland Journal*, vol. 32, 329–339.

Sprankling, J, Coletta, R & Mirrow M C (eds.) 2006, *Global Issues in Property Law,* West Academic Publishing, St. Paul, MN.

Sydenham, A 2002, 'The Countryside and Rights of Way Act 2000: Balancing Public Access and Environmental Protection?', *Environmental Law Review*, vol. 4, 87–100.

Thoreau, H D 1862, 'Walking', *The Atlantic Monthly*, June 1862, pp. 657–674.

Ulin, D 2015, *Sidewalking: Coming to Terms with Los Angeles*, University of California Press, Oakland.

Upton, A. 2019 'Access Right, Right of Access or Right of Way?' *Law Society of Scotland*, 18 March 2019, available at www.lawscot.org.uk/members/journal/issues/vol-64-issue-03/access-right-right-of-access-or-right-of-way/ (accessed 9 May 2020).

Valverde, M 2014, 'Chronotopes of Law' in I. Braverman et al. (eds.) *The Expanding Spaces of Law: A Timely Legal Geography*, Stanford University Press, Stanford.

7

OF DEMOCRACY, PROTEST, AND THE PUBLIC SQUARE

7.1 Introduction

This chapter explores the contention that public real property is 'a necessary condition of democratic life' (Honig 2017, p. xii). Beginning with US political theorist, Bonne Honig, and her thesis as to the democratic content of 'public things' (2017), this chapter's central argument is that the public estate is a touchstone for the democratic project, both symbolically and constitutively. Democracy and its robust processes play out disproportionately on public acreage, such that the former is a defining characteristic of the latter.

In making this claim, this chapter does not seek to downplay the record. Public lands are far from immune to democratic or structural inequalities. Their histories and presents conceal egregious injustices. Like citizens of color not 'properly belonging', cited in preceding chapters, or the violence inherent to settler colonial public lands, where 'one community's public thing is the product of an act of theft and dispossession to another' (Honig 2017, p. 3). Indeed, the tendency to over-romanticize public space as 'an emptiness which enables free and equal speech' comes from ignoring the 'conflicting and *unequal*' social relations that produce them (Massey 2005, p. 152, emphasis added).

Self-evidently, public spaces are not politically neutral. But neither is the story of public realty fixed, nor set on a linear trajectory. Rather, public spaces and places represent Massey's dynamic 'simultaneity of stories-so-far' (2005, p. 9) – where contests of politics and policy play out unpredictably on public ground, and the public narrative is far from settled. Such robust interactions are the gravamen of democratic discourse, the potent dialogue actualized by the greater freedoms citizens enjoy (in theory, and often in practice) on public real property. In other words, public terrain is democratic terrain. It is not always perfect, just, or predictable, but it is a space and place where free expression and political communication are most freely ventilated.

Chapter 7's structure is as follows. First, it digs into the granular of Honig's influential analysis of 'public things', an 'object'-premised exploration of the public estate that seeks to portray it as enduring and agentic. Next, it moves into doctrine, illustrating the links between public lands and constitutional laws that guarantee free speech and political communication in public forums. It also strays into the murkier domain of custom, and the enduring latency of public rights to land. Last, it reflects on democracy in performative action – the rich intersection of dissent and protest that protects and performs the public square. It closes by affirming the hopeful words of Honig, who argues that public things should 'stand out as a point worth insisting upon, something that must not be allowed to become part of the morass of despair' (p. 32). This is a reminder that notwithstanding its travails, the public estate's democratic 'thingness still enchants, even as [its] public-ness is under pressure' (ibid.).

We do live, as Honig implies, in an age of cynicism and unprecedented disruption, where public-ness is under relentless 'pressure' and for some, we stare into a 'morass of despair'. The values of neoliberalism appear normalized, the public estate has been locked into material and ideological decline for decades, democracy suffers from a disturbing loss of faith, and many democratic leaders are populist narcissists with scant regard for democratic conventions. Perhaps on two fronts, this chapter is naively backing the wrong side of history, public things and democracy? Yet, what is the alternative? This chapter makes the normative case that public realty and democracy go hand in hand. The public estate is a physicalized testament to democratic values. Its defenders are legion. Its spaces are vast. Its resilience should not be discounted. Even its national parks continue to enchant, to inspire beyond the wearying crush of cynicism, since as Honig says, 'anyone who has visited a national park can attest to this' (p. 32). Public real property and democracy share common ground, physical, legal and theoretical. This chapter traverses that commonality, to add (in its small way) to the enchantment that this intersection yields, and the noble idea that 'public things constitute [us] equally as citizens, or ought to, and can be made, sometimes, by way of actions in concert, to deliver on that promise' (p. 11).

7.2 The centrality of public things

In recent times, a handful of political theorists have contributed disproportionately to the topic of public property. Schmuel Nili's 'The Idea of Public Property' (2019; see Chapter 3) and Honig's *Public Things* (2017) are two prominent examples.[1] Yet, as Honig acknowledges, 'the importance of public things to democratic life is not currently a central concern in political theory. … [Specifically], the *res* of *res publica* is unmentioned' (p. 13). Rather, she says, civic republicans prefer to focus on the procedures or mechanics of democracy, or 'hot-ticket' issues such as the ethics of border security or immigration (ibid.).

By contrast, Honig's thesis centers on the centrality of public *things* to democratic life (emphasis added). These are the tangible things that social commentator Charles Montgomery describes as made of '[public] concrete, steel, leaf and lawn'

(2013, p. 233). Her argument is 'that democracy is rooted in common love for, antipathy to, and contestation of public things' (p. 4). In provoking this diversity of political opinion, public things thereby 'constitute us, complement us, limit us, thwart us, and interpellate us into democratic citizenship' (p. 5). In sum, public things provide the physical framing of civil society, the anchor-points around which an untidy, disruptive, yet ultimately resilient body politic coalesces and takes democratic form. Jane Jacobs said something similar in *The Death and Life of Great American Cities* (1961) (at least in terms of city planning), describing how beneficial city diversity is fostered by a public estate that 'stands staunch while [private] money rolls around … and begs them to roll over' (pp. 254–255). In Jacobs' formulation, the public estate is depicted as an analogous anchor-point amidst the frenetic creativity of private property:

> In our American cities, we need all kinds of diversity, intricately mingled in mutual support …. Public and quasi-public bodies are responsible for some of the enterprises that help make up city diversity – parks, museums, schools, auditoriums, hospitals, some offices, some dwellings. However most city diversity is the creation of incredible numbers of different people and different private organizations, … planning and contriving outside the formal framework of public action. The main function of city planning and design should be to develop … cities that are congenial places for this great range of unofficial plans, ideas, and opportunities to flourish, along with the flourishing of the public enterprises.
>
> *(p. 241)*

The value of public things therefore rests not only in themselves, but also in their robust and proportionate presence amidst civil society. Yet, the irony, as this book's Introduction argues, is that public things (and public property) have become lost to plain sight. This is the paradox of the simultaneous ubiquity and invisibility of public things. In the New York of post-Hurricane Sandy, it is the functional presence of public payphones that Honig uses to highlight this paradox. The hitherto invisible (and unloved) payphone and its public network of copper-wire proved crucial in keeping the city's residents connected throughout the crisis. As one resident told Honig, 'it's funny what's hiding in plain sight … it's invisible, but when you need it, it's there' (p. 30). This epitomizes the democratic value of public things, overlooked and integral, yet in danger of being taken for granted, and thus, at risk of loss. 'What is funny, invisible, but hiding in plain sight is the very idea of public things, things that conjoin people. Shared amongst users from all kinds of backgrounds, classes and social locations, the public thing calls out to us, interpellating us as a public' (ibid.).

Interestingly, Honig feels no compulsion to define public things. Like Jacobs' quote, Honig simply engages in list making, ticking off on a range of prosaic, quite mundane *res*: public telephones, sewage treatment plants, railroads, public schools, public cemeteries, records offices, and so on. Rather than seeking definitional clarity, Honig's analysis turns on establishing a number of key elements. First, that public things are in substance, and of themselves, 'objects'. Second, that their permanence endures beyond the brevity of human life, a deeply powerful and symbolic reassurance. And, third, that as an enduring institution, public things possess their own innate agency.

Honig calls the first and second qualities 'object permanence'. Translated to the public estate, this emplaces public realty as an enduring thing of the external world, 'objects' outside of, and beyond our finitudes. The advantages of objective-ization are several. Politically, a focus on 'the objects rather than the subjects of democracy' (p. 25) mitigates the ennui that comes from what passes as modern political apathy, of the citizen's failure to engage with democratic processes. The focus shifts from the *subject*, by-passing narratives of low voter turnout, hollowed-out political parties, or generational disillusionment, to the higher architecture of democracy; the physical *objects* that constitute its framework, buttress its continuity, and sit above the ephemeral swings and roundabouts of public mood. In a broader sense, to (re) think public things as objects also shifts the discursive paradigm. '[W]e are switched to questions of orientation and receptivity, from subjectivity to object-ivity, from identity to infrastructure, from membership to worldliness' (p. 28). This emphasis on public *infrastructure* likewise creates a 'holding environment of democratic citizenship' (p. 5), a tangible world that supports, subverts and challenges us, 'providing *fixed* points around which collectivities may constellate, generating unexpected and self-surprising actions in concert' (p. 6, emphasis added).

This centrality to democratic life is vindicated when public things go missing, or fail. 'Without public things, action in concert is undone and the signs and symbols of democratic life are devitalized' (p. 4). Honig cites examples of bridges that collapse without warning to highlight the shock caused when '[public things] let us down' (p. 6). Or, as we have seen in 2020, when underfunded or ill-equipped public health systems fold under the exponential arithmetic of pandemics. In their failures, and the tragedies that their failures are powerless to prevent, public things reveal the vast gap that they otherwise quietly and un-assumedly fill.

Their *permanence* is also central to their democratic mission. These are things beyond our short life span, given significance by a solidity and physicality that endures. We count on public things to outlast our relative transience. Hence, national parks are rarely, if ever, de-gazetted.[2] The shrinking in size of national monuments in the United States was thought to be beyond political convention, let alone executive or legal power.[3] Such public things are akin to what Massey calls (in the English context) 'venerable' institutions (1980), public things beyond commoditization and disposal. Like the 'unthinkable' of ever selling off New York's Central Park, London's Victoria Embankment Gardens, or Sydney's Domain.

In the neoliberal mindset however, venerable institutions aside – perhaps – most public things are/were fair game. This transactional disposability derives from another time, the early 1980s, when certain values, particularly *efficiency,* were emboldened to step outside their 'spheres of relevance' to become, analogous to exclusion, the top stick in the values woodpile:

> Efficiency is no longer one value among others. It has become rationality itself, and it is the standard by which everything else is assessed. It has infiltrated everything, it has no rivals. All spheres submit to its homogenizing powers.
>
> *(p. 14)*

Efficiency's risk lies in its agnosticism for democracy. Indeed, its antagonism for its time-consuming, (allegedly) inefficient processes. And yet, even by the standards (and statistics) of English neoliberalism (see Chapter 3 and Christophers 2018), certain public things remain outside efficiency's logic, that small percentage of public acreage that stubbornly stays public. Honig might describe these things as the 'translational objects of democratic life', whose endurance comes from the 'sense of futility they sometimes visit upon us when they remind us that they are more permanent than we, … and that in any case, we are not always in charge' (p. 11).

Last, the idea that something external 'takes charge' resonates with the public estate's own independent *agency*, the third plank in Honig's analysis of the democratic public thing:

> It seems to me deeply politicizing … to grant to [public] things some agency in the civic contests that surround them and us. At the very least, public things press us into relations with others. They are sites of attachment and meaning that occasion the inaugurations, conflicts and contestations that underwrite everyday citizenships and democratic sovereignties.
>
> *(p. 6)*

In 'calling' on us to act, we engage with public lands in escalating ways, from passive use, to principled debate, to passionate protest. But more importantly, public lands themselves are implicated as participants. For instance, the US Interior Department's decision of February 2020 to reopen to cattle grazing 'the spectacular country neighboring the Escalante River' in Utah's (now diminished) Grand Staircase-Escalante National Monument, not only implicates the usual protagonists, but the monument itself. For 20 years, a deal between ranchers and conservationists saw grazing permits relinquished in return for financial compensation, and 'allowed the flora and fauna in the remote red rock canyons of the monument to flourish once again' (Leshy 2020). 'Wildflowers, willows, fish and wildlife, including beavers and otters, now flourish where there was once only fouled water and clouds of biting cow flies tormenting hikers' (ibid.). Here, not only are private interests and federal agencies given voice, but the national monument (and its resurgent environment) also has agency, 'calling' out the risks that these new grazing arrangements pose.[4]

Honig's 'public things' lays important theoretical groundwork for the democratic significance of public real property. In its object-ivity, permanence, and agency, the public estate provides a fixed 'holding environment' around which a self-regulating civil society coalesces and takes democratic shape. For analogies, think of Carol Rose's 'inherently public property', and the unorganized public's self-policing, democratic governance of these liminal yet physical spaces (Chapter 3, 1985). Or from Chapter 4, where the democratically elected Mayor of Bogota, Enrique Penalosa, momentarily transformed his city's 'unhappiness' through the medium of enhanced public things, 'using concrete, steel, leaf, and lawn' to share public wealth 'in service of a philosophy of radical fairness' (Montgomery 2013, pp. 233–235). Of course, authoritarian states also possess public things, or at least state-owned corporate equivalents, like sewage treatment works and subways and sidewalks. Why don't these assets equally 'interpellate' their citizens into the ranks of 'democratic citizenship'? Or, in a similar vein, instill the 'democrat' into Kevin Gray's 'pedestrian democrat' of Chapter 6? Maybe, these are not truly 'public' things, but rather the diminished basics of the autocratic state?

Public thing-ness lays down a critical formwork, but clearly, there are other factors at play, further overlays that transform the skeleton of civic infrastructure into an enlivened public thing. This chapter next builds on Honig's foundational analysis to suggest two additional factors that enliven public things, the jurisprudence of the democratic public square, and the clarifying flashpoint of civil protest.

7.3 Free speech, political communication, and the public square

The Greek Agora and the Roman Forum illustrate how public squares have served as centers for urban public life for millennia, as 'a meeting place for citizens in which they handled their common affairs, traded goods, enjoyed dances and games, and *exchanged news and opinions*' (Lehavi 2013, p. 123, emphasis added). As a core feature of urban design, the public square has been replicated across time and place, endowing many cities, old and new, with a public heart of city halls, courthouses, public libraries, post offices and parks. Away from the 'concrete, steel, leaf and lawn' however, the public square also exists in our democratic imagination, a conceptual dimension where political communication is robust and open. Rich in symbolism and meaning, the public square is both a forum of democratic discourse, and hallowed public acreage. Or, as Antonia Layard observes of the ancient world, 'the agora was both a place *and* an idea' (2016, p. 43, emphasis added).

Rebecca Solnit likewise draws the link between the abstraction of the 'democratic citizen' and the thing-ness of public space, and the rich overlap of idea and place. And again, like Honig, Solnit claims its significance is laid bare when public things disappear:

> [W]hen public spaces are eliminated, so ultimately is the public, the individual has ceased to be a citizen capable of experiencing and acting in common with fellow citizens. Citizenship is predicated on the sense of having something

> in common with strangers, just as democracy is built upon trust in strangers. And public space is the space we share with strangers, the unsegregated zone.
>
> *(2001, p. 218)*

This 'unsegregated zone' – where the democratic citizen congregates and mixes on public ground – takes a multiplicity of *legal* forms, from the bright-letter of constitutional law to the murkiness of custom. In the United States, one perspective is provided by the public forum doctrine, based on the Free Speech Clause of the First Amendment. In another democracy, Australia, it manifests less explicitly. There, the High Court reads between the lines of a late-19th-century colonial compact to construe political communication as an implied freedom of a constitutionally prescribed system of government. The public square also exists beyond the rarefied atmosphere of constitutional law. Ancient public rights can be likewise reduced to the physicality of public acreage, famously in Speakers' Corner in London, or indeed, to an everyday myriad of localized places far less known. This section explores these various *legal* convergences of public property, and free speech and assembly, to exemplify this chapter's core claim – that public terrain is democratic terrain.

At the heart of express constitutional doctrines like the American public forum is the principle of free speech. As Carol Rose observed in the 1980s, 'speech helps us rule ourselves; the more ideas we have through free speech the more refined will be our understanding and the better our self- governance' (1986, p. 778). Rose's (then) characterization of free speech as an integral social glue has become somewhat unstuck by the explosion of hate-speech on social media, and the partisan politicization and cultural war-gaming of free speech by Right and Left. Free speech has become a right to make (often noxious) noise. Yet what has not come unstuck is the jurisprudential connection with public real property.[5]

Thus, the application of First Amendment public forum rules in the United States turns on the requisite character, and category, of the public real property in question.[6] Some jurists criticize such a narrow propertied focus, and the 'misleading' analysis it engenders,[7] yet the doctrine remains fundamentally framed by superior courts' interrogating what they understand to be the external parameters – and internal gradations – of the public estate:

> In general outline, these rules focus tightly 'on the character of the property at issue' in order to determine whether it is a 'public or non-public' forum. If the property is a public forum, the government's ability to regulate the public's expressive use of the property is subject to strict constitutional limitations; if it is a nonpublic forum, the government is given great latitude in the property's regulation'.
>
> *(Post 1987, p. 1715)*

Thus, in determining what is a public forum, a (contested) spectrum of publicness ranges from 'traditional' or 'quintessential' public forums, to 'designated' public forums, and ending with 'nonpublic' forums, where free speech activities can be widely curtailed. Of course, private property is outside this continuum, and beyond constitutional reach.

Traditional public forums are famously the 'streets, parks, and other public spaces' that have been used since time immemorial 'for purposes of assembly, communicating thoughts between citizens, and discussing public questions'.[8] This comprises what Layard may call the 'true public realm' (2016), core public property that also includes the grounds of state capitols or city halls, but not military bases and the public highways that bisect them.[9] At the other spectral end, nonpublic forums are spaces where the public owner acts 'as if it was a private owner of property' (Post 1987, p. 1726), with 'the power to preserve the property under its control for the use to which it is lawfully dedicated.'[10] Here, American courts confront an entrenched dilemma as old as public real property, distinguishing between openly accessible public spaces, like streets and parks, and C.B. Macpherson's corporate public property, where the public owner enjoys the same trespass powers of the private. In the middle ground, 'designated' public forums are described as public spaces 'opened up' to public assembly and debate. They occupy a 'chimerical' zone rendered by later judicial decisions as 'an empty category' (Post, pp. 1754, 1757).

While public forum jurisprudence has all the hallmarks and inexactitudes of arbitrary taxonomy (as explored in Chapter 2), it nonetheless is premised on drawing lines in (and within) the public property sand. In so drawing, it sequesters 'traditional' public forums as places where democratic freedoms are freely exercised. In such streets and parks, and analogous 'open spaces, meeting halls, street corners, or other public thoroughfares' (Post 1987, p. 1734), democracy and the public estate find common expression and common ground. While '[t]here is no magic talisman to distinguish public from nonpublic forums' (p. 1834), such taxonomic imprecision does not derogate from the underlying tenet that '[i]n a democracy like our own [the United States], the public realm coincides with the arena in which common values are forged through public discussion and exchange' (p. 1788).

Of course, as observed in this chapter's opening, public lands are imperfect, and 'common' democratic values are unevenly shared. Understandings of democracy are inexorably the subject of contest. Don Mitchell notes that the *rationality* of the public forum doctrine has been 'closely defined in terms of gender, class and race', and originally resided only 'in the bodies of certain men' (2003, p. 51). For much of the history of the 'American common', it excluded 'women and the majority of men' (ibid.). 'Public space', he argues, (and in this context he means public property) 'occupies an important – but contested ideological position in democratic societies' (p. 130).

By contrast to the black letter of US constitutional law, the sparser Australian Constitution 'contains very few rights and a paucity of related case law' (Clark and Page 2019, p. 26). There is certainly no express right to free speech. In this near-empty context, the Australian High Court, starting with a series of cases in the 1990s, moved to imply a freedom of political communication as a necessary corollary to '[the maintenance of] the system of representative and responsible government that the Constitution prescribes' (Stone 1998, p. 128). Most cases under this implied freedom have turned on questions of press freedom and laws of defamation.[11] Few cases have concerned forum, and where so, only in passing, until the landmark decision of *Brown v State of Tasmania*[12] in late 2017.

Early cases, however, show how the public forum was being incrementally weaved into the implied constitutional fabric. In 1997 in *Levy v Victoria*,[13] state regulations that restricted access to seasonal 'duck hunting areas' were challenged for their inconsistency with the freedom to enter and protest 'from an informed and persuasive basis'.[14] The plaintiff was charged with unauthorized entry into a prescribed 'duck hunting area', where he variously filmed the shoot, confronted hunters, and collected dead and injured birds. While the regulations were ultimately held not to be oppressive of the implied freedom of political communication, Justice Kirby, influenced by US public forum jurisprudence, observed the significance of context, stating that these 'duck hunting areas', mostly public wildlife reserves, were 'no Hyde Park'.[15] In other words, these public lands were not traditional public forums as understood in the American parlance, 'United States authority … especially hostile to regulation that occurs in traditionally public fora and, to some extent, other public property' (Stone 1998, p. 133).

Later cases hinted of the public estate, particularly *O'Flaherty v City of Sydney Council*,[16] where an Occupy protestor (unsuccessfully) argued that Council bans on overnight sleeping in one of Sydney's main public thoroughfares, the pedestrianized Martin Place, was 'incompatible with the implied freedom, because it unreasonably restricted his capacity to communicate his political opinions and support for the worldwide Occupy movement' (Clark and Page 2019, p. 31).

In was not until *Brown*, however, that the loop between public real property and the expression of democratic rights was closed. In *Brown*, protestors fighting the logging of old-growth eucalypt forests in Tasmania sought to invalidate that state's *Workplaces (Protection from Protestors) Act 2014* ('the Protestors Act'). Their argument was that the Act, and its banning of protestors within defined 'business premises' and/or 'business access areas' (logging operational areas and surrounding curtilage) was an impermissible burden on the implied freedom. A majority of the High Court agreed, striking down the Protestors Act as invalid, and noting in various judgments the backdrop of public context. In *Brown*, the 'public forum' was the Tasmanian public forest estate, ancient forests that were the setting of decades-long protests against logging and hydropower construction, protests defined by their locus of dissent on Crown land:

> More significant to an assessment of the relevant burden imposed by the impugned provisions is the long history of political protest on Crown land in Australia. Most significant is the history of on-site political protests on Crown land in Tasmania, directed to bringing about legislative or regulatory change on environmental issues, beginning with the protest activity between 1981 and 1983.[17]

In this spatio-temporal context, there was 'an expectation on the part of the public in Tasmania, residents and visitors alike'[18] that access to public forests was lawful, an 'expectation' that the High Court 'recognised' as an underlying (and amorphous) body of law.[19] Interestingly, this latency is revealed by the state's need to enact its power to exclude, exposing to sunlight what had lain deeply subliminal. Clark and Page argue that this public 'expectation' 'did not arise in a vacuum' (2019, p. 35), harking back to the influences of the reformist *Forest Charter of 1217*, which 'disafforested' vast tracts of England and restored the customary rights and 'liberties of the forest' to 'all good and lawful men'.[20]

The Forest Charter is an unlikely diversion from 21st-century Tasmania. But nonetheless it is an insightful (forested) segue, since its narratives tells similar tales, and remind us of the enduring latency of ancient laws. Moreover, the Forest Charter suffers from a similar fate of being lost to plain sight. According to Lucy Finchett-Maddock, its invisibility arises from the higher profile of its 'better-known twin', the Magna Carta of 1215, which 'eclipsed' its companion charter, and affirmed a systemic bias which privileges individual rights and 'archives' any 'memory of the commons' (2016, p. 130). Its endurance is seen in the Forest Charter remaining good law for over 750 years. Arguably, it persists via the saving provisions of the *Wild Creatures and Forest Laws Act* of 1971 (UK), that in section 1(5) retains 'rights originating in the forest law'. The Forest Charter, and its invocation of 'liberties of the forest' remind us, like the forest rights in *Brown*, of the underlying force (and persistence) of ancient customary rights as a provenance of public claims to land.

Chapters 3 and 6 have already observed custom's under-regarded role in the jurisprudence of the public estate, citing instances where it forms a surprising basis of lawmaking, like beach access in Oregon. Disaggregated, socially constituted, and pluralist in character (Thorpe 2018), customary rights and practices represent an *other* understanding of the democratic governance of public space. As already observed, Rose's 'Comedy of the Commons' is an analogous thesis, wherein custom forms an unlikely juridical basis of the 'unorganized public's' self-policing of its 'inherently public property' (1986). Politically, custom 'formed both the property and the political practice of poor and laboring classes in England and America … one of the normative weapons of the weak against the strong, [and] one of the ways in which power was disciplined and concessions enjoyed' (Hartog 1985, p. 912). And of course, in modern law, custom is often reduced to, or modified by statute; public rights to fish, public highway rights, or latent entitlements to the public forest estate – where 'residents and visitors alike' may enter, protest, forage, gather firewood, and so on[21]– being examples in point. Custom's fingerprints are all over public real property. One just has to look carefully for its signposts, a governance of public space that serves an egalitarian, at times, radical idea of democracy.

Such qualities are openly on show at London's famous Speakers' Corner. Situated on the northeast edge of Hyde Park, Speakers' Corner is an unremarkable, 'relatively small scrap of land, one that is easy to miss' (Cooper 2013, p. 189). Widely cited as a 'trope for open public debate and a marketplace of ideas' (p. 186),[22] its reputation as a forum for political and intellectual debate has been in purported decline for years. No longer a 'university for the working classes' as it was in the 1940s, Speakers' Corner is often dismissed as sliding into a degraded 'freak show', dominated by 'nutters, religious fundamentalists or lunatics' (2006 p. 759). Yet as Davina Cooper observes, it is 'a complex, contradictory place. In some ways it appears to be a typical site of male camaraderie and casual misogyny, yet it is also a place where those lacking social capital or other forms of recognition have gathered … the Corner is rooted in a long history of dissent' (2013, p. 191).

This dissent has egalitarian and radical elements. Egalitarianism is measured by the Corner's preference for speakers 'lacking social capital' over those with middle class credentials, education or expertise. Its 'antithetical relationship to social privilege' (2006, p. 763) levels inequalities, undermines hierarchy and, enacts one of Cooper's 'everyday utopias' that imagines society otherwise (2013, p. 190). This egalitarian spirit builds on history. In the 19th century, Hyde Park was widely seen as a 'park for the working class' and a 'genuine expression' of a 'unique plebian concern for public space in London' (2006, p. 763). Its *radicalness* is likewise a legacy of history, although perhaps, no longer a descriptor of its more sanitized present. As a site of public executions until the end of the 18th century, Marble Arch saw many impassioned calls to arms from the gallows, such that it came to embody a 'long-standing, independent, metropolitan radical tradition' (Cooper 2013, p. 192 citing Antony Taylor 1995). These histories marked out Speakers' Corner as a particular public place of dissent,[23] a particular territoriality codified by the Royal Parks Regulation Act of 1872 'which created an officially demarcated [space] for public address' (2006, p. 754 citing Roberts 2000).

Unlike the 'no Hyde Park' duck-hunting reserves in *Levy v Victoria*, Speakers' Corner is literally part of Hyde Park, a customary (now legislated) public square where free speech and public acreage meet in the abstract and the physical. However, as hinted, Speakers' Corner's rich history of protest is also highly cogent. This further overlay – that of protest and dissent – comprises the concluding section of this chapter.

7.4 Democracy in public action – of protest and dissent

In democracies, protest occurs on public real property. Protestors rarely take to the shopping mall; they take to the streets. Or parks, or city squares. This section depicts protest's close links to the public estate. Conversely, it shows how effortlessly privately owned public spaces (POPs) drop any pretense of 'public-ness' at the first sign of dissent. The public estate's wide-open 'boundlessness' reveals it as a bellwether of democratic protest – and a flashpoint in the struggle for spatial justice.

There is a rich history to what Finchett-Maddock calls the '*proprietorial* right of resistance' (2016, pp. 121, 221, emphasis added). This resistance is a centuries-old struggle for space, an ongoing contest between the enclosing, dispossessing DNA of private property, and the oppositional claims of customary public rights to land. This resistance is described in diverse ways, and is the subject of a vast literature. Karl

Polanyi (1944) detects it in the 'counter-movement', periodic moments in history when 'human societies tend to react forcefully to the privatization of land, to its treatment as a commodity to be bought and sold in the market, and to the negative outcomes … that often flow from such treatment' (Christophers, 2018, p. 324). In the rural histories of England, it is epitomized as the struggle against enclosure, the epochal privatization of common lands that peaked in the 18th and 19th centuries and unleashed a social, political, demographic and legal upheaval that reverberates today (McDonagh and Griffin 2016, Clark and Page 2019). In the literature of the urban commons, it takes shape in 'the right to the city', the ground-up alternative to capitalist conceptions of bounded and exclusionary space, and an *oeuvre* in which citizens participate (Mitchell 2003, p. 17). As a verb, it is expressed as 'commoning'. Whatever its nomenclature, at its heart lies the struggle for spatial justice. And as Finchett-Maddock discerns, it is a struggle which implicates *property*, since it is land 'where the practices and performances, the processes and products of state laws, and a law of resistance … converge' (2016, p. 44). It is also a struggle about how we conceive property; a theoretical counter-narrative to what Nicholas Blomley terms the 'universalizing and totalizing' logic of private property (2004, p. 102).

This struggle for spatial justice has been, and remains, lopsided. Turbocharged by Garrett Hardin's tragedy of the commons thesis (1968), the dominance of private property has proved (almost) unidirectional. Yet, resistance is not futile. Claims to public property are exercised on a daily basis. Such performances, peaceful and quotidian, are taken for granted. Yet, as Honig observes, the loss of public things is telling. Often this loss goes unchallenged. Or it may be lamented in private, unactioned. But sometimes it may precipitate a tipping point to be crossed. This is the flashpoint when 'proprietorial resistance' conflagrates into active protest, a political 'taking back' that evokes and ignites a 'memory of the commons':

> [This taking back] harks back to an era when there were no fences, no borders, nothing enclosed. Autonomy is a reaction to this dispossession, and the memory that it ignites is that of the commons. … This is the era prior to enclosure, or the resistances to such an early form of privatization through the likes of the 'Diggers' of the 17th century, led by preacher Gerard Winstanley who believed that the earth was a common treasury for all. … It is the continuation and memory work of the commons.
>
> *(Finchett-Maddock 2010, p. 38)*

Finchett-Maddock likens the memory work of the commons to a 'haunting', a collective mourning that runs from the 'common fields of the fifteenth century, through to the abandoned spaces of the twenty-first' (p. 145). By drawing on this 'archived' memory of the commons, we are remembering 'not to forget' a different way of relating to land. A remembering that is, of itself, an act of resistance:

> Resistance and laws of resistance are like ghosts, they rely upon memory, resentment, forgiveness and history. There is similarly a role of memory

> within the history of the commons; the commons are reawakened through the memory of the past, and the commons stand for the past itself.
>
> *(p. 149)*

Ghosts and their hauntings are also employed by Sarah Keenan to symbolize an awareness of spatial loss, the memory of 'a seething presence of something that is absent' (p. 168), yet a haunting that still connects the 'then to now, [and the] there to here' (p. 167). Cristy Clark and John Page analogously write of protestors re-conceiving relationships of people, property and place via a 'glimpsed "thought of utopia"' (2019, p. 29). Such 'hauntings' or 'glimpsings' speak to an unconscious, yet deeply relational yearning for an *other* way of relating to land.[24]

This re-kindling of long-buried landed memories is a public activity that materializes on public acreage, a gravitation to its physical and metaphysical sense of wide-open-ness. Like forest rights in *Brown*, the public right to protest is vindicated by the state's need to modify or proscribe it. Hence, authorities respond to escalating protests by spatial means, through restricting access to public real property. A common tactic is to clamp down on the rights of free passage on public highways.[25]

This section cites two well-documented 'counter-movements' to exemplify the close links between protest and the public estate. The first is recent, the Occupy social movement that began in 2011. The second is historical, the short-lived Diggers' camps of 1649–1650. While centuries apart, both protest movements sought to 'unsettle hegemonic space and force it to adapt' (Keenan 2015, p. 96). Both are interesting because of their *public* spatial aspect, the struggle against dispossession that manifested in a public 'taking back'.

As a global protest movement, Occupy has provoked widespread academic scrutiny. This section's intent is not to repeat the breadth or detail of this particular literature, but rather, to highlight, through example, the inextricable links that Occupy shared with the public estate.

The Occupy movement was seeded in a post-GFC 'loss of faith in the political and economic system', but as activists told Jeremy Gantz, it also came to be increasingly defined by 'the struggle for public space' (2017, pp. 217–218). Its camps were 'not just "places"; these are our communities that we've built. … It's a model of the new society that we're all struggling to develop in these encampments … [places where] incredible transformation happens' (p. 218). Utopian experiments, or at least efforts to build community, needed public real property to take root and (briefly) flourish. In London, it was the grounds of St. Paul's Cathedral, in New York it was Manhattan's Zuccotti Park, in Sydney, it was the pedestrianized Martin Place, and in Istanbul, it was one of the city's few remaining green spaces, Gezi Park near Taksim Square.[26] Public things soon materialized on these occupied public lands. Honig says that the first facility built at Occupy Wall Street was a public library (p. 20). In Occupy Sydney, 'musical performances, film nights, and free yoga and meditation classes' were opened to protestors and public alike (Clark and Page, 2019, p. 32). In Gezi Park, occupiers established 'a clinic, communal kitchen, nursery, library, communications office and a market garden' (Erensu and Karaman 2016, p. 12).

Despite the proliferation of public things, public real property did not provide a lasting tenure for Occupy. Occupy St. Paul's was dismantled and removed 'at the will of the landown[ing]' highway authority – after the protest site was determined by a court to be on a mapped public highway. Layard calls *City of London Corporation v Samede*[27] a victory for Blomley's logic of pedestrianism (see Chapter 6), a judgment where the imperatives of highway flow overrode any counter-right of Occupy protestors to stop (2016). Yet, the public estate (in all its inexactitudes and ambiguities)[28] allowed Occupy a critical breathing space, and in so doing, to 'unsettle hegemonic space and force it to adapt, however slightly.' As an idea, Occupy St. Paul's endures because of the temporal and spatial liberties public real property afforded it.[29] Compare these four and a half months of occupation to initial experiences at nearby Paternoster Square, a 'public' quadrangle sold in 1986 to a consortium of property developers under a 250-year lease. There, protestors confronted private security guards who directed them off the Square (Layard 2016, p. 9; Shrubsole 2019, p. 70). In the end, Layard concludes that 'public ownership did make a difference. It meant that once away from Paternoster Square … the protestors were able to engage their ECHR rights to free assembly, assembly and association on the (publicly-owned) land next to the Cathedral' (2016, p. 19).

In Sydney, the site of Occupy Martin Place played to local politics, pitting a sympathetic Sydney City Council against a less than sympathetic state government. It took extraordinary state legislation to move protestors on, again illustrating that public rights to land are seen most clearly in their abrogation. In Istanbul, what started as a 'modest sit-in' (some 18 months after the first Occupy protests), rapidly transformed from a protest about the loss of a small city park into a 'fully-fledged anti-government revolt in which myriad grievances against authoritarianism, discrimination, and the increasing commodification of common spaces … were voiced' (Erensu & Karaman, 2016, p. 1). It is this (in part) revolt against the central government's 'neoliberal interventions in public spaces' that piques interest. The privatization and commercial re-development of 'the most centrally located public park in Turkey' reduced to a 'highly condensed form' the spontaneous, grassroots nature of this struggle for spatial (as well as social and political) justice (p. 3).[30] The Gezi protest lasted only two weeks. Once dispersed by police, protestors re-assembled at a nearby public park, and from there, so-called 'park forums' rapidly spread throughout Istanbul and other cities.[31]

Again, public real property provided the physical platform that for a while sustained a post-Gezi ethos. Above all, Erensu and Karaman underscore that the 'unprecedented energy and form of the revolt are undoubtedly linked to the centrality of the park … in Istanbul's most central open public space' (p. 16). This is a centrality that is both geographic and conceptual, a notion of the public square that yields 'concrete' as well as abstract utopias (Butler 2012, pp. 133–137).

Occupy's radicalism matches a recent re-kindling of academic interest in the Diggers (McDonagh and Griffin, 2016), a short-lived social movement whose brief moment in 17th-century history may have passed into obscurity but for the prolific writings of its intellectual leader, the preacher Gerrard Winstanley (Willard 2012).

The Diggers haunt modern-day Occupy because each movement enacted a relational vision of property in land that challenged the established social and politically landed order. As Briony McDonagh and Carl Griffin argue, the Diggers' 'very *public* and dangerously radical politics … meant the Diggers colony [and the precedent it set] was never going to be tolerated' (p. 6, emphasis added). The Diggers' settlement on the wastelands of St. George's Hill at Walton-on-Thames, Surrey is perhaps the most famous of their utopian encampments,[32] yet its tenure (like Occupy's) was also short-lived, and opposition to it was equally complex, and at times, violent.

What sets the Diggers apart from much of English rural history is that their actions were not protests against the enclosure of customary common rights *per se.* Rather, their spatial claims were something far more radical; one that treated land as a common-wealth, 'the common Treasury of all', or a 'stolen birthright of the people'.[33] Theirs was a different 'taking back'. Thus, the Diggers burnt the heath, planted crops, built makeshift houses, and practiced a way of communal living that not only challenged the private interests of the landed gentry, but also threatened the long-established common rights of local villagers. This threat to the propertied *status quo* produced an unholy alliance of private and common, which acted in concert to erase the Diggers' camps (and their propertied alt-potential) through legal and illegal means[34] (Clark and Page, pp. 42–44, McDonagh and Griffin, pp. 5–7).

The Diggers' camp at St. George's Hill occupied a 'particularly barren stretch of land' of 'scrubby heath and woodland', variously described as a patchwork of manorial wastes, unstinted commons, and Crown land (McDonagh and Griffin, p. 5; Shrubsole 2019, p. 211).[35] It was almost the lands 'no-one wanted', a phrase used in another time and place to describe the public rangelands of the American west (see Chapter 2). The 1649 execution of Charles I in particular opened up the Diggers' claim to what they saw as vacated Crown land, which lay ready to be 'returned to the common people in equal benefit' (Willard 2012, p. 877). Contemporaries described the Diggers as 'crack brained people' who 'thought because the[se lands] were called commons, they belonged to any body, not considering that they are commons only for the inhabitants' (McDonagh and Griffin 2016, citing Gurney 2007, p. 123). Their concept of land as a 'common treasury of all' or 'belonging to anybody' enacted an almost public claim to land, although politically, it was 'proto-communist.' As Chapter 2 notes, public real property was a 19th-century English creation, such that the Diggers' *public* relationships with land must have appeared as 'crack brained' and dangerous as their fundamental misunderstanding of 1649 property orthodoxy.

Today, paradoxically, St. George's Hill is a gated enclave of London's rich and famous, a place of exclusivity, of private golf courses, tennis courts and mansions on multi-acre lots (Willard, p. 888). Activist/blogger Guy Shrubsole chronicles his attempts to breach the perimeter fences of St. George's Hill, eventually spotting a break in the chain-link to enter and make his own small gesture of protest, 'treading in the footsteps of Winstanley, trespassing upon land once held in common but now held offshore' (p. 213). Shrubsole notes the 'cruel joke' that is St. George's Hill, the 'supreme irony of history' how a once 'radical communal experiment came to be completely enclosed and privatized' (p. 212). That Shrubsole is forced to make his (illegal) gesture of protest surreptitiously and alone; 'digging up the earth, sinking my fingers in the leaf mould and the thick black loam, smelling its rich peaty scent' (p, 213), exemplifies the fiercely anti-protest nature of private property.

Twenty-first-century St. George's Hill, or the 250-year lease of Paternoster Square, exemplify what happens when the public estate retreats from the propertied landscape, or as Honig puts it, the rhetorical 'bridge' collapses. In these so-called POPs, the agenda-setting power of the private owner is paramount. 'Public-ness' is seen for its thin varnish, condoned only to the extent that it suits the private owner's overriding commercial needs. As Lessard writes of this psychology, 'there must be nothing disturbing to the consumer in a mall, nothing to interfere with the impulse to buy. Unrelenting vigilance and diligence [i]s required. If a soda [i]s spilled, the cleanup crew must be there in minutes. Political activity [i]s … out of the question' (2019, p. 210). In these privatized public spaces, public conduct is privately surveilled, rights of assembly are strictly qualified, and the arbitrary power to exclude is omnipresent. Protest is indeed out of the question. In the 'Public Plaza' of 1330 Avenue of the Americas, New York City, rules that ostensibly '*increase* public enjoyment and safety' include prohibitions on skateboarding, roller blading, roller skating, loitering, littering and vandalism. There is (quaintly) no radio playing, no food or beverages to be consumed, all chairs and benches are to be left cleared of personal items, and Shopping Carts and Obstructive Packages are prohibited. Disregard of these rules will subject you to removal.[36] Of course, there is nothing extraordinary in singling out this particular 'Public Plaza', other than to observe the ubiquity of its rules writ large. And of course, to record that such sites are not even on the US public forum doctrinal radar.

Property jurists such as Layard, and Kevin and Susan Gray (1999), likewise observe the loss of freedoms synonymous with the rise of 'quasi-public spaces.' In Bristol's Cabot Circus, typical of the privatized, 'retail-led' re-development of city centers in England, re-purposed '"*visitors*" are unable to walk a dog, play a guitar, take a photograph or smoke a cigarette in places previously understood as being in the public realm' (Layard 2010, pp. 415–416).[37] Gray and Gray write of a group of young, unemployed, mostly Black youth in Wellingborough exiled for life from the (privately enclosed) civic center of their hometown for 'trifling defaults' such as 'whistling in public' (1999, p. 47).[38] Privatized public spaces consummate an enclosure that is 'spatially, legally and temporally complete' (Layard 2010, p. 416). Their chilling effect is to displace sites of protest and democratic dissent to a shrinking public acreage.[39]

7.5 Conclusion

In 1986, Carol Rose writes of the essential 'democratic give-and-take' that comes from public recreation on public lands. Her support for the democratizing effects of public property is qualified by the plain truth that 'these are not always easy arguments to support, and are extraordinarily difficult to prove' (pp. 780 and 781).

Regrettably, in the decades since, prosecuting this argument has only become harder. There is a dispiriting litany of recent public and democratic failings: the statistical loss of faith in democratic governance, the seeming 'success' of authoritarian states, the rise of populist leaders, the corrosive influence of big money, and in landed terms, the ongoing privatization of public spaces, and its flipside, the proliferation of privately owned public spaces. In both its idea and its grounded practice, the democratic public square is in retreat, in deficit, and the subject of existentialist scrutiny.

Yet, there persists an optimistic counter-narrative, given voice by Honig's hopeful reminder that 'public thingness still enchants, even as [its] public-ness is under pressure' (p. 32). Public things still enchant because as Honig opines, they 'furnish a world in which we encounter others, share the experience of being part of something that is larger than ourselves, and work with others, acting in concert to democratize access to it, to better it, to desegregate it, to maintain it' (p. 36). Massey's hopefulness likewise stems from the constitutive qualities of physical public space as sites of democratic expression. Especially, the 'elements of chaos, openness and uncertainty' that play out on public ground, and act as 'potential creative crucibles for the democratic sphere' (2005, p. 153). Disruption is the key, 'democratic politics' requiring that social inequalities are 'brought to the fore, making them visible so that they can enter the terrain of contestation' (ibid., citing Mouffe 1993, p. 149).

In the context of public rights to land, a number of property jurists express similarly hopeful sentiments. Like Kevin Gray's 'geography of hope' with its phalanx of pedestrian democrats (2010, see Chapter 6), or Antonia Layard's 'unashamed optimism amidst genuine and very real concerns about social, cultural and physical privatization' (2016, p. 5). There is a residual endurance in the 'object permanence' of public things, the civic infrastructure of 'concrete, steel, leaf and lawn' around which an untidy, sometimes unruly society coalesces and individually feels part of a greater democratic whole.[40]

Pragmatically, as observed, public things are neither 'innocent [n]or pure' (Honig 2017, p. 36). Indeed, as Massey argues, that is the point, The 'very fact that [public places] are sometimes riven by antagonism, always contoured through the playing out of unequal social relations, is what renders them *genuinely* public' (2005, p. 153). Howsoever flawed, their true net worth is realized when they are gone, leaving in their stead an ascendant, universalizing private estate with its 'insidious culture of exclusion' (Gray and Gray 1999, p. 47) and anti-democratic tendencies.

This chapter argues that public terrain is democratic terrain. It does so acknowledging the institutional decline in both, and how the weakness of each frays the collective sum. But there is a core from which a rebuilding may come. We see it in remnant constitutional doctrines dependent on public real property. And through the lens of protest, we see how public lands are inherently sites of subversion, their shared spaces 'shaped differently from networks of hegemonic power relations' (Keenan 2015, p. 92). If there is one compelling counter-argument to the inexorability of Honig's 'morass of despair', it is the alternative, a propertied landscape without public real property. We glimpse it in the privatized town centers, the shopping malls, and corporate public plazas, the dangerous (and anti-democratic) illusion of private property masquerading as public.

Notes

1 An earlier seminal work in political science that touched on public (or 'common') property was that of Canadian political theorist, C.B. Macpherson (1978).
2 One counter-example is the former Urewera National Park on the North Island of New Zealand, de-gazetted by the *Te Urewera Act 2014* (NZ) to create its own unique, self-owning entity (see Chapter 3).
3 The fierce debate surrounding the de-classification of millions of acres of public lands in Utah in the Bears Ears and Grande Escalante-Staircase National Monuments is discussed in Chapter 3.
4 That public lands have an independent agency is a concept consistent with Christopher Stone's prescient argument that 'trees have legal standing' (1972). Stone writes of a parched lawn 'speaking' of its need for water, its agency told though its yellowing, dying grass. Since Stone's groundbreaking article, a 'rights of nature' or ecological jurisprudential worldview has emerged, with legal personhood conferred on certain natural objects. For example, in New Zealand, the Whanganui River (once a public thing) became its own legal person, 'Te Awa Tupua', legislated in 2017 (Clark et al., 2019).
5 Rose says as much.

> Thus it is not surprising to find that in recent years, there are hints that property used for political speech has come to be viewed as inherently public. In *Members of City Council v. Taxpayers for Vincent,* for example, Justice Brennan suggested in dissent that certain publicly owned properties – here, utility poles – are uniquely suitable for the dissemination of political speech, and should be held open to the 'time-honored' practice of posting signs. This could be stated as a public trust concept: this property is needed for the public's political communication, thus governments hold the property in 'trust' for this communication, and have only limited abilities to divest the public of its trust rights.
>
> *(1986, p. 778)*

6 There have also been cases where public ownership is less clear, such as airport terminals owned by port authorities, or commercialized public spaces like Chicago's Navy Pier, *Board of Airport Commissioners for City of Los Angeles v Jews for Jesus, Inc.* 482 ULS 569 (1987); *ISKON v Lee* 505 U.S. 672 (1992); and *Chicago Acorn v Metropolitan Pier and Exposition Authority*, 150 F. 3d 695 (1998), all discussed in Coggin (2019, pp. 76–79).
7 For example, Post (1987), and Coggin (2019).
8 *Hague v CIO* 307 U.S. 496 (1939) at pp. 515–6. Robert Post dates the rise of the 'public forum' as a 'technical term of art' to the Supreme Court decision of *Police Department of Chicago v Moseley* 408 U.S. 92 (1972), which was, in turn, heavily influenced by a law review article written by Henry Kalven in 1965 that engaged in a post-hoc analysis of Supreme Court decisions from the 1930s and 1940s. Kalven wrote '[i]n an open democratic society, the streets, the parks and other public places are an important facility for public discussion and political process. They are in brief a public forum that the citizen can commandeer; the generosity and empathy with which such facilities are made available is an index of freedom' (1987, p. 1718, quoting Kalven).

9 *Greer v Spock* 424 U.S. 828 (1976).

10 *Adderley v Florida* 385 U.S. 39 (1966) at 47–48,

11 The Australian implied freedom of political communication is not restricted to the act of speech *per se*, but catches within its wider ambit, acts of 'expressive conduct' or 'appeals to emotion' (Stone 1998).

12 (2017) 261 CLR 328.

13 (1997) 146 ALR 248.

14 Ibid, p. 250.

15 Ibid, p. 289.

16 (2013) 210 FCR 484.

17 (2017) 261 CLR, 328, 387 (Gageler J.) The period 1981–1983 represents the epochal protests over the damming of the Franklin River in Tasmania, protests that assumed a national prominence, and proved instrumental to the election of the Hawke Labor Government in 1983.

18 (2017) 261 CLR, 328, 345 (Kiefel CJ, Bell and Keane JJ).

19 The High Court majority did not rule on the *nature* of the public right of access to the public forest estate. Only one justice (Edelman J) ventured an opinion, suggesting it was a 'statutory license' under the relevant forest legislation. The majority approach was one of 'acknowledgment' and 'recognition' of an existing general law right (Clark and Page 2019).

20 'Disafforested' is a technical term that refers to the removal of parcels of land from the jurisdiction of forest law. Forest laws imposed by the Norman conquerors in the 11th, 12th and 13th centuries covered at their height nearly one-third of the English landmass, and were deeply unpopular. In effect they transformed open spaces (including but not limited to treed forests) into private game reserves, and imposed fines and cruel punishments on residents who interfered with the Crown's game, some of whom were simply adhering to their customary rights. The *Forest Charter of 1217* is analyzed in Clark and Page (2019, pp. 35–38). For further detail on forest law, see Green (2013) or Langton (2015).

21 In *Brown*, the High Court listed a series of non-exclusive incidents of the public right, including 'recreation, organized events, recreational vehicle use, hunting and firearm use, fossicking and prospecting, firewood collection, [and] indigenous rights use' p. 345 (Kiefel CJ, Bell and Keane JJ). Edelman J added the right to 'peaceful protest activities such as … filming and investigation', p. 490. In Tasmania, these rights are modified by, and subsidiary to the safety and reasonable operational needs of forestry practice, as stipulated in forest management statutes.

22 Davina Cooper adds that Speakers' Corner has 'generated surprisingly little scholarship' (2013, p. 186).

23 "During the 17th and 18th century, last dying speeches at Hyde Park became a place for public dialogue about diminishing customary rights against the growing imposition of capitalist social relations and the rule of private property' (Cooper 2013, pp. 191–192, citing Roberts 2008).

24 Why the memory of the commons is archived is moot. Hannah Critchlow argues that memory persists in DNA for up to seven generations, stored in brains hard-wired to 'process inputs via circuits that have been laid down by our genetic inheritance, … complex processes [that] give rise to outcomes in the form of thoughts, decisions and choices' (2019, 2020). It may also recur as a stirring of folk-memory. Guy Shrubsole says, 'the dispossession of England's peasantry is mostly forgotten' and untaught in schools, but 'a powerful folk-memory of the Scottish Highland Clearances rightly persists' (2019, p. 78).

25 See for example, Layard (2012, pp. 263–271); Montgomery (2013, pp. 173–175); and Mitchell (2003, pp. 56–57).
26 Of course, this is not the end of the list. To give other examples, in Toronto, Canada, Occupy protestors occupied St. James Park, and in Minneapolis, Minnesota, the relevant *situs* was the Hennepin County Central Government Plaza. In *Batty v Toronto* (2011) 108 OR (3d) 571 a trespass notice issued by the City of Toronto was held to not infringe the protestors' Charter rights. Conversely in Minneapolis, *Occupy Minneapolis v Hennepin County* 866 F Supp 2d 1062 held that sleeping in a public park was protected free speech (Hamill 2012, pp. 380–388; Clark and Page 2019, p. 32).
27 [2012] 2 All ER 1039.
28 Layard says that the ownership of most of the King's/Queen's highways in England is 'lost in the mists of history' and 'has long been resolved by convention' (2012, pp. 268–269).
29 'It bought for protestors that key ingredient: time' (Layard 2016, p. 20).
30 Erensu and Karaman describe Gezi Park as a 'public refuge in a highly congested and commercialized area and a meeting ground for LGBTQ individuals at night' (2016, p. 9).
31 Within a week, some 65 forums were being held daily on different squares and in public parks in Istanbul, and in more than 50 locations across the country' (Erensu and Karaman 2016, p. 14).
32 There were other Digger's colonies at Iver, Buckinghamshire, Wellingborough, Northamptonshire, and elsewhere in Kent, Nottinghamshire and Gloustershire (McDonagh and Griffin 2016, p. 6).
33 These claims were in part motivated by Protestant radicalism, and in part, a particular interpretation of history that saw the 'Norman yoke' as the cause of the common people's 'miserable poverty' (McDonagh and Griffin 2016).
34 In one especially surreal incident, 'two local freeholders led a procession of men dressed in women's clothing to the hill where they attacked the Diggers with staves and clubs' (McDonagh and Griffin 2016 p. 6).
35 There is an argument that the land at St George's Hill was almost all Crown land, citing surveyors at the site in 1649–1650 (Gurney 2007, pp. 82–83).
36 From a photograph of the 'Welcome to 1330 Avenue of the America's Public Plaza' sign, taken 30 May 2019.
37 In privatized city centers, public highways are often the subject of 'stopping-up' orders that close public roads and facilitate their private re-use (Layard 2010).
38 CIN *Properties Ltd v Rawlins* [1995] 2 EGL 48 (Court of Appeal).
39 Private lands are not subject to the *Human Rights Act 1998* (UK), which governs property owned by public bodies. As such on private lands, the right of trespass trumps any 'right' to protest (Layard 2016, p. 6). On public lands, English courts have ruled that protest must be 'proportionate' and 'non-obstructive' in the absence of the public landowner's consent, *Appleby v UK* (2003) 37 EHRR (Layard 2012, p. 261).
40 'These are the hallmarks of a horizontal, open society, one that is often inefficient but ultimately more innovative and resilient than closed, top-down systems' (Slaughter 2020).

References

Blomley, N 2004, *Unsettling the City: Urban Land and the Politics of Property*, Routledge, New York.
Butler, C 2012, *Henri Lefebvre: Spatial Politics, Everyday Life and the Right to the City*, Routledge, Abingdon.

Christophers, B 2018, *The New Enclosure: The Appropriation of Public lands in Neoliberal Britain*, Verso Books, London.

Clark, C et al., 2019, 'Can You Hear the Rivers Sing? Legal Personhood, Ontology, and the Nitty-Gritty of Governance', *Ecology Law Quarterly*, vol. 45, 787–844.

Clark, C and Page, J 2019, 'Of Protest, the Commons and Customary Public Rights: An Ancient Tale of the Lawful Forest', *UNSW Law Journal*, vol. 42, 26–59.

Coggin, T 2019, 'Judicial Imaginations of Everyday Space: A Hohfiedlian Critique of Spatial Relationships in US Jurisprudence', SJD Thesis, Fordham University, New York.

Cooper, D. 2006, '"Sometimes a Community and Sometimes a Battlefield": From the Comedic Public Sphere to the Commons of Speakers' Corner', *Environment and Planning D: Society and Space*, vol. 24, 753–775.

Cooper, D 2013, *Everyday Utopias: The Conceptual Life of Promising Spaces*, Duke University Press, Durham, NC.

Critchlow, H 2019, *The Science of Fate: The New Science of Who We Are – And How to Shape Our Best Future*, Hodder & Stoughton, London.

Critchlow, H 2020, *The Science of Fate*, presentation in conjunction with the Byron Writers Festival, 30 January 2020.

Erensu, S and Karaman, O 2016, 'The Work of a Few Trees: Gezi, Politics and Space', *International Journal of Urban and Regional Research*, 1–18.

Finchett-Maddock, L 2010, 'Finding Space for Resistance through Legal Pluralism: The Hidden Legality of the UK Social Centre Movement', *The Journal of Legal Pluralism and Unofficial Law*, vol. 42, 31–52.

Finchett-Maddock, L 2016, *Protest, Property and the Commons: Performances of Law and Resistance*, Routledge, Abingdon.

Gantz, J 2017, *The Age of Inequality: Corporate America's War on Working People*, Verso Books, New York.

Gray, K & Gray, S 1999, 'Civil Rights, Civil Wrongs and Quasi-Public Space', *European Human Rights Law Review*, vol. 4, 46–102.

Gray, K. 2010, 'Pedestrian Democracy and the Geography of Hope', *Journal of Human Rights and the Environment*, vol. 1, 45–65.

Greene, J 2013, 'Forest Laws in England and Normandy in the Twelfth Century', *Historical Research*, vol. 86, 416–431.

Gurney, J 2007, *Brave Community: The Digger Movement in the English Revolution*, Manchester University Press, Manchester.

Hamill, S 2012, 'Private Rights to Public Property: The Evolution of Common Property in Canada', *McGill Law Journal*, vol. 58, 365–403.

Hardin, G 1968, 'The Tragedy of the Commons', *Science*, vol. 162, no. 3859, 1243–1248.

Hartog, H. 1985, 'Pigs and Positivism', *Wisconsin Law Review*, 899–935.

Honig, B 2017, *Public Things: Democracy in Disrepair*, Fordham University Press, New York.

Jacobs, J 1961, *The Death and Life of Great American Cities*, Random House, New York.

Keenan, S. 2015, *Subversive Property: Law and the Production of Spaces of Belonging*, Routledge, Abingdon.

Langton, J 2015, 'Royal and Non-Royal Forests and Chases in England and Wales', *Historical Research*, vol. 88, 381–401.

Layard, A 2010, 'Shopping in the Public Realm: A Law of Place', *Journal of Law & Society*, vol. 37, 412–441.

Layard, A 2012, 'Property Paradigms and Place-Making: A Right to the City; a Right to the Street', *Journal of Human Rights and the Environment*, vol. 3, 254–272.

Layard, A 2016, 'Public Space: Property, Lines, Interruptions', *Journal of Law, Property & Society*, vol. 2, 1–47.

Lehavi, A 2013, *The Construction of Property Norms, Institutions, Challenges*, Cambridge University Press, Cambridge.
Leshy, J 2020. 'A Trump Plan Breaks a Great Deal for Ranchers and Park Lovers', *The New York Times*, March 3, 2020, at www.nytimes.com/2020/03/03/opinion/environment-ranchers-trump.html?searchResultPosition=1 (accessed 22 March 2020).
Lessard, S. 2019, *The Absent Hand: Reimagining Our American Landscape*, Counterpoint, Berkeley, CA.
Macpherson, C B 1978, 'The Meaning of Property' in C B Macpherson (ed.) *Property: Mainstream and Critical Positions*, University of Toronto Press, Toronto.
McDonagh B & Griffin C 2016, 'Occupy! Historical Geographies of Property, Protest and the Commons 1500–1850', *Journal of Historical Geography*, vol. 53, 1–10.
Massey, D 1980, 'The Patterns of Landownership and its Implications for Policy', *Built Environment*, vol. 6, 263–271.
Massey, D 2005, *For Place*, SAGE Publications, London.
Mitchell, D 2003, *The Right to the City: Social Justice and the Fight for Public Space*, Guildford Press, New York.
Montgomery, C 2013, *Happy City: Transforming Our Lives Through Urban Design*, Farrar, Straus and Giroux, New York.
Post, R C 1987, 'Between Governance and Management: The History and Theory of the Public Forum', *UCLA Law Review*, vol. 34, 1713–1835.
Rose, C M 1986, 'The Comedy of the Commons: Custom, Commerce, and Inherently Public Property', *University of Chicago Law Review*, vol. 53, no. 3, 711–781.
Solnit, R 2001, *Wanderlust: A History of Walking*, Penguin Books, New York.
Shrubsole, G. 2019, *Who Owns England? How We Lost Our Green & Pleasant Land & How to Take It Back*, William Collins, London.
Slaughter, A 2020, 'Forget the Trump Administration: America Will Save America', *The New York Times*, March 21, 2020, at www.nytimes.com/2020/03/21/opinion/sunday/coronavirus-governors-cities.html?action=click&module=Opinion&pgtype=Homepage (accessed 22 March 2020).
Stone, A 1998, 'Case Note: *Lange, Levy*, and the Direction of the Freedom of Political Communication under the Australian Constitution', *UNSW Law Journal*, vol. 21, 117–134.
Stone, C 1972, 'Should Trees Have Standing? Toward Legal Rights for Natural Objects', *Southern California Law Review*, vol. 45, 450–501.
Thorpe, A 2018, 'Pop-Up Property: Enacting Ownership from San Francisco to Sydney', *Law & Society Review* vol. 52, no. 3, 740–772.
Willard, T. 2012, '"The Free Enjoyment of the Earth": Gerrard Winstanley on Land Reform' in A. Classen (ed), *Rural Space in the Middle Ages and Early Modern Age: The Spatial Turn in Premodern Studies*, De Gruyter, Berlin.

8

CONCLUSION

8.1 The lie of the (public) land

This book set out with a number of objectives. The first was to engage with a little-traversed subject, a study of the public realm through the lens of property. As observed in the Introduction, the cognate topic of public space attracts much scholarly attention – in disciplines from geography to urban design and beyond. But the *legal* study of public real property is sparse. Such scholarly unevenness deserves redress. Moreover, this book's terms of reference were narrow; a survey of the *common law* public estate that yielded in its wake an inevitably Anglo-centric and unrepresentative worldview. A wider public project is needed, perhaps, for another time. To partly offset this attenuated focus, *Public Property, Law and Society* occasionally casts a wider net, drawing on the insights of political science, social commentary and journalism to fill the legal lacuna. But ultimately, its intent was, and remains *proprietorial*.

The second was a corollary of the first: to compile a literature review of this scattered public jurisprudence, its practices, customs, laws and theories; and its scholars and their writings. In so doing, this book has ranged across the vast common law public plains to gather a disparate, mostly disconnected jurisprudence; from the Division of Public Things, to the public trust doctrine, the laws of roaming, the conventions of sidewalk flow, the nuances of the public forest estate, and so on. This review reinforces that while the public property estate may be little visited; a number of esteemed property scholars have laid down important signposts. Carol Rose's foundational contributions to public theory are one standout. The insights of Antonia Layard, Sarah Hamill and Kevin Gray are likewise extremely valuable. And the groundbreaking legal geographer Nicholas Blomley has long written of property outside the private modality.

The third was to suggest a series of innovative organizing principles around which these laws, practices and theories could coherently coalesce. Five organizing principles were identified – and interrogated – *ownership*, *sociability*, *belonging*, *connection* and *democracy*. Some frameworks have proved more compelling or extensive than others, yet, as the chapters have progressed, each has contributed in valuable and innovative ways to the public property discourse.

The fourth fed off the third, to develop a nascent theorization of the public estate, and to amplify the book's sub-title, such that concepts of 'public ownership', 'public belonging' and 'public connecting' are better equipped to explain our relationships with the public domain. While much groundwork has been laid so far, the final push remains the task of this concluding chapter.

Given that these objectives have been (to greater or lesser extents) documented, the telling question remains; what lessons does this book reveal for the public estate? What are the individual and collective learning's of taxonomy, ownership, sociability, belonging, connection, and protest? Answering these questions necessitates an initial distilling of each chapter's essence, a drawing together to frame the book's wider project.

Chapter 2 puts forward not so much an organizing principle as a selective lesson in history and geography. It argues that the public taxonomic project has been underwhelming; a halting, inconsistent exercise that has generated a plenitude of loose, untidy ends. Yet, notwithstanding the record, the task of *finding public order* is not universally futile. As observed, taxonomy instils a certain rigor in legal thinking, as helpful to the jurisprudence of the public estate as it is to any other areas of public or private law. The process also demonstrates the rich diversity of the public estate, and the concomitant need to accommodate this vast public storehouse – with all its untidiness – under the one overarching banner. Last, it highlights that when it comes to one particularly (recurring) organizing filter, that of public purpose, that *public* rationales are both desirable and necessary. Public real property best serves public purposes, not maladapted private ones.

Chapter 3 is an important chapter. It asks the ownership questions, who is the public owner, and why do we publicly own? It exposes the weaknesses of cutting and pasting private answers into the public context. With its unhelpful bundle metaphor and premise of individual ownerships, the private estate offers few lessons to resolving the public conundrum of ownership. Nor are public 'rights' the automatic inverse of the private, the superficially plausible case of *inclusion* highlighting the flaws in this binary logic. Generally, public owning aligns, and is consistent with a beneficial understanding of ownership, where entitlements to share, use or enjoy the public resource is limited only by the things we cannot do. Public owning can also disrupt, challenging assumptions about the identity of the 'public' in the public ownership equation. Like Chapter 2, this chapter also observes the significance of purpose, positing that the better ownership question may be one of public-owner purpose, not public-owner identity. This shift in emphasis may render the latter enquiry subsidiary to the overriding consideration of *why* we own, an altogether more plausible and persuasive interrogation of public ownership.

Chapter 4 builds on Carol Rose's genius of the sociable comedy of the commons (1986). Turning Hardin's polemic tragedy on its head, the sociable thesis argues that public real property serves the social goods of human flourishing, the well-lived life, (even) happiness. This is an attractively sunny view of the public estate, one that is undoubtedly true, but also one that is far from ubiquitous. Think of the sociability of public beaches, or imagine city parks packed with Sunday crowds. Yet equally consider the plight of the lonely commuter, shuffling from far-off home to work and return on the public concrete of the public interstate. Nor does public sociability uniformly take place on public acreage. The popular rise of privately owned public spaces, and their attendant rules and omnipresent threat of exclusion, diminishes sociability as a *public* lodestar. Yet, as the chapter concludes, when it comes to public sociability, the public realm may be the best, or the least-worst, property show in town.

Belonging in Chapter 5 shifts the property focus to the spatial and the contextual. Along with ideas of place making and community, belonging clears a discrete theoretical space for public real property. It does so through its rejection of (private) property's exclusionary or subject-focused theories, myopic perspectives that 'miss or mis-recognize' what happens on the ground. Radical and utopian, belonging nonetheless speaks a plain truth or authenticity to the connections that public realty forges, the ties of affinity that link individual parts to collective wholes, connections that resonate in both theory and relationally. As the chapter concludes, belonging's narratives have an empathy for things public, and a capaciousness for place, community life, and (be)ing.

Chapter 6 segues from the intuition of belonging, to a more instrumentalist version of connection. In so orienting, this chapter concentrates on the physical and material ways in which public conduits (sidewalks, highways, public easements, countryside rights of way) connect A to B. Utilizing the trope of the human pedestrian, and her movements through the public outdoors, this chapter shows how the idea of connection informs an understanding of public real property, its norms, theories, and black-letter laws. Connection is not a property law doctrine. Nor is it an elegant theoretical construct. Rather, it is an example of Blomley's *own terms* thinking, a crude observation of the *effects* of public real property. Yet it is a critical feature of the public estate for two compelling reasons: put simply, it describes what public realty does, and likewise, what it doesn't do when public connection falls away.

Chapter 7 completes the excursus by examining how democracy and dissent inform and explain public real property. This is a simultaneously dispiriting, yet stubbornly hopeful organizing point. To the extent that democracy and public property are degraded, declining institutions, the blame lies at the feet of those who have through policy or action impugned either or both. The wholesale disposal of public acreage, the ideological assault on public ownership, the privatization by stealth, the hollowing-out of democratic conventions, all have corrosive, cynical effects. Yet, in a perverse way, this (im)perfect storm proves the point. Public terrain is democratic terrain, such that when one fails, so does the other, in a correlative, lock step stumble. Even the structural flaws of one taint the other, the incidence of proportionately greater public acreage in affluent neighborhoods an affront to the democratic fabric. The interest of political theorists in public things, expressed by thinkers such as C.B. Macpherson and Bonnie Honig, is yet another hint of this public/democratic conjunction.

These chapters speak to a number of common themes: the need to let go of inapt private paradigms, embracing blue-sky ways of thinking anew and afresh, the *public-ness* of public purpose, an egalitarianism that underpins public thinking, and more. Importantly, they also provoke a series of dualities, which this chapter next explores.

8.2 Public property vs. public space

From time to time, this book falls unwittingly into the trap of conflating public space with public property. This is a well-laid trap, one that goes beyond mere semantics. In sum, not all public space is public property. Equally, not all public property is public space. As Antonia Layard remarks, '[p]ublic space is not property. Or better put, public space is not *just* property' (2016, p. 43; see also 2010, pp. 437–438).

The first logic (not all public space is public property) can be seen through the lens of POPs. The popular embrace of private property as a site for public gathering and recreation has been observed in several chapters. Of course, privately owned public space may be better than literally nothing. Yet, this trend is a pernicious phenomenon. POPs inculcate an 'insidious culture of exclusion' (Gray and Gray, 1999, p. 47), an objection of *effect*: of the primacy of private rules, the conformity and homogeneity this generates, the counter-expression it stifles, and the exclusionary power it executes. POPs also enliven inapt *values*. As canvassed, private property's strength lies in alienation. When translated to a public setting, this value casts a shadow on the lasting tenure of (disposable) privately owned public spaces, but more significantly, it privileges and normalizes the commodification of land. Simultaneously, it marginalizes its non-commodity values. Despite superficial 'public' appearances, Chapter 7 shows how privatized town centers or shopping malls do likewise, alienating (and estranging) from civic space certain members of the community whose spatial needs extend beyond the marketplace. Last, POPs muddy the institutional waters, obfuscating an already blurred distinction between public and private property. This feeds an entrenched, pre-existing discourse wherein 'property' and 'private property' are interchangeable and equivalent, a corrosive relativism that fails to call out the ubiquity of everyday encroachment and enclosure – since it fails to see it.

The second logic (not all public property is public space) is altogether different. Examples abound of public real property that is not public space. This is a latent, yet deeply significant issue, flagged in Chapter 2 where early taxonomic endeavors struggled to account for a public real estate that is 'private' in its owner's agenda-setting powers. Roman lawyers invented *res universitas* to capture this type of public realty, public places that stood outside the 'wide-open synergies' of *res publicae*. *Res universitas* were the 'bounded' corporate property of 'municipal theaters, racecourses and other income-producing public property' (Rose, 2003, pp. 106 and 108). Scots Institutional Writers toyed with different categories of *regalia* to account for the distinction – at least with the sovereign's property. C.B. Macpherson's seminal hierarchy of property as either 'private', 'common' or 'state' (1978) produced the misnomer of 'common property', which arose in part from problematizing 'state property' as a form of corporate (and therefore private) property. With state property, the public owner is said to be 'apt to be as jealous of its property as a privately owned one' (p. 5). The logic in setting aside 'state property' (along with its owner's corporate right to exclude) may be sound, but the resultant nomenclature of 'common property' it produced – as a catch-all descriptor for non-private property – is unfortunate. As seen in Chapter 3, Macpherson's typology – and terminology – has proved enduring and distorting, witness Mariana Valverde and her depiction of sidewalks in Toronto as the 'private' property of the City (2013).

Not only has (publicly inaccessible) public property sown the seeds of taxonomic and terminological confusion, it fosters a problematic mentality around public property – best summed up by Sarah Hamill as 'a clear attempt to force all property into a private property model', one that 'emphasizes the government's use of the land rather than the public's benefit in it' (2012, p. 365). This 'government as owner' paradigm is no less harmful to the public realm's integrity than unchecked privatization. Indeed, it's possibly worse, since it degrades and de-legitimizes what's left of the public realm. Where governments arbitrarily close or restrict access to publicly owned lands without regard to the public's benefit in them, a corrosive loss of shared ownership follows. 'This is ours' begins to ring hollow. In the end, public lands are reduced to a quasi-private status 'owned' by cities or state agencies. This is unsurprising, given the enclosing logic of private property, and the orthodoxy that impugns public property. Such concerns go not only to institutional integrity and public entitlement, but especially to spatial justice, a critical subject that this chapter will return to in closing.

So, what should be done with Macpherson's 'state property'? Despite the risks and inexactitudes, the lessons of taxonomy suggest the desirability of its discrete recognition as a particular species within the public genus. The converse of doing nothing, of a sweeping under the public carpet is counter-productive, reinforcing the 'government as owner' mentality, and encouraging the indirect privatization of public resources. If there is any justification, any intellectual rigor in resorting to a rudimentary bifurcated classification, it is the benefit that flows from separating out this public variant from the public rest. In so compartmentalizing, its public corporate attributes can be seen for their own particularity, without unduly tainting the estate as a whole. Yet, retaining these lands within the public ledger is equally defensible. They are government-owned, even where the state owner is compelled to ape private-sector attributes or behaviors. And their holding serves a clearly defined public purpose, whether it's the education, health, national defense, taxation, or general administration of its state's citizens. Questions of accessibility are rendered moot, or better put, relegated to the mechanical or logistical. Overall, in so doing, we are exceptionalizing the exception, not normalizing it.

The boundaries of public space and public property demand constant vigilance – and education. It is surprising how this distinction is misunderstood, or simply unknown. Yet it is not misunderstood, nor unknown, by those at its coalface. In 2011, Occupy protestors were peremptorily ejected from London's Paternoster Square, yet they lingered for months in the grounds of St. Paul's Cathedral. In 1649, the ambiguity of vacated Crown lands bought the Diggers time and some official sympathy at St. George's Hill (Willard 2012). And across time and place, the homeless are routinely moved on from privately owned 'public' plazas, yet they may linger on less trafficked public sidewalks, in public parklands, in public tunnels, or under public bridges. This is the consequence of Jeremy Waldron's plain truth that 'everything that is done has to be done somewhere' (1992, p. 296). Private property rules carve out where we may be(long), and where we may not. For those lucky enough to own private property, we can confidently *be* within its secure confines. For those who are societally disenfranchised, or for whom their only propertied claim is a public one, the public realm's significance to public be(ing) and belonging is critical. This is a guarantee that only the public realm, not generic public space, can promise.

8.3 The commons vs. the public

This dichotomy has already crept into this concluding chapter through a critique of Macpherson's 'common property'. As Chapter 2 argues, the intellectual mixing of the 'commons' with the 'public' has led to an unfortunate imprecision in property discourse. The commons are traditionally understood – in the English customary context – as common use rights shared amongst the inhabitants of discrete villages or parishes, rights governed by localized, idiosyncratic rules. Such use rights over common lands, while inclusive within, are off-limits to outsiders. In its *external* effect, the common fence is no less exclusionary than the private one.

Also, common property rights have largely failed to migrate to the settler colonial state (Page, 2017, pp. 73–74). Instead in these colonial geographies, public lands are vast storehouses of acreage. Where common rights exist in the 'modern' sense, it is the 'limited common property' model observed by Carol Rose (1998, p. 132; see also Page 2017, pp. 74–76). These are the rights of eligible members of clubs, co-operatives or condominiums to use and share common swimming pools, lifts, foyers, gardens, and the like. Common rights can also be seen in rural land-sharing communes that for example, date from the flower-power days of the Age of Aquarius (Page 2010). Generally speaking, however, the forces and logic of enclosure have dispossessed common property to the physical and conceptual periphery.

Conversely, public rights to land are unfenced entitlements open to all. Or, in the *res publicae* tradition, entitlements open to the citizens of the nation-state. This was the doctrinal misunderstanding that Gerrard Winstanley's Diggers prematurely visited upon the commoners of 17th-century Surrey, a mistake with fatal consequences for their fledgling settlement (see Chapter 7). It is the same misunderstanding that follows the near-uniform non-migration of the 'commons' to the settler colonial state, yet persists in obfuscating the latter's vast public-ness. Commons and commoning are likewise terms that have proliferated in recent scholarship, such as the 'urban commons' liberally cited in rights to the city discourse, or the utopian sentiment of the 'commons' in protest literature. While this book is highly sympathetic to communitarian thinking, it baulks at this admixture. In a pedantic sense, it symbolizes Hohfield's cautionary advices of adopting terminology of a 'blended sense' that 'convey[s] no definite meaning whatever' (1913, p. 18). More substantively, this ambiguity plays to private property's playbook. If there is private property and non-private property – or indeed private property and nothing else – then it helps the private cause to keep the other on its existential toes, to maintain an ambiguity that de-legitimizes the integrity (and intrinsic distinction) that exists in and between the common and public estates.

Such an insistence on the commons/public distinction may seem trivial, or arcane. Yet, it is a distinction fundamental to this book's core mission – as it traverses the wilds of property in the *public* realm. As noted elsewhere (Page 2017), the literature of the commons is rich and extensive. Yet, there is a corresponding dearth of public real *property* scholarship, a paradox remarkable given the vast acreage of public lands, or the extensive tracts of private lands over which public real rights subsist. This paradox is only entrenched by ignoring, or at the very least, smoothing over the substantive doctrinal and conceptual differences that define and delineate the public and common estates. Keeping the terminology consistent maintains the structural integrity of both.

8.4 Flow vs. fixity

This duality is one that is clearly identified and argued in the scholarship of Antonia Layard (see Chapters 6 and 7). Public rights to land may guarantee a right to flow, but they fail in substantiating any rights of fixity, a right to stop on (public or private) land in the exercise of the public entitlement. Public highway rights of passage, ramblings across countryside rights of ways, the meanderings of roaming, or the connections that public easements avail to landlocked beaches, each highlight how public real rights are rights of flow. On the ubiquitous public sidewalk, Blomley's logic of pedestrianism (2011) concludes similarly. In Chapter 3, the seemingly infinite array of public uses (from ranging over the foreshores of Oregon beaches to children building sandcastles) is transient and mobile. In chapter 4, public sociability is premised on cheery comings and goings. Flow is the *raison d'etre* of the pedestrian trope so integral to Chapter 6. In Chapter 7, protestors cannot stop indefinitely in their politically symbolic occupation of public real property. As each chapter exemplifies, flow not fixity lies at the heart of public real property.

Layard argues that the absence of any right to stop denies public rights an essential propertiness (2016, pp. 21–29). Public entitlements are more in the nature of usufructs, not estates or interests in land. Stopping implicates a right to possess, and where that possession is exclusive, a right to exclude others from stopping at the same time and same place, the classic indicia of (private) property. From this angle, this duality is problematic, undermining this book's core claim that public entitlements are things of property. Yet, this duality also reveals – in a different light and with an alternate slant – a fundamental point of difference between the private and public estates. While public rights, claims and uses may be premised on movement, as Chapter 6 contends, private rights are not. Mostly, they are rights to stop, to take possession, to stake a Blackstonian claim to absolute dominion, to construct fences, to exclude all others, to exploit, and so on. Exceptionally, they may envisage movement, as in the case of the private easement, or the profit a prendre/rendre. But these are circumscribed and technical exceptions to the norm. Easements have a history as grudging property concessions to the rights of others, whether a consequence of 18th-century enclosure orders, or the trade-off for a favorable tenure review determination in the 21st-century New Zealand high country (see Chapter 6).

Flow is the gravamen of the public realm. It is the one property type that does not rely on the fence (or hedge, or CCTV, or threat of private security) as a weapon of exclusion, as a means of impeding flow. As noted earlier, there is little *external* difference between the private and common fence. But as Chapter 3 ponders, public fences are at most *defensive* in nature, pushing back against private encroachment (Solnit, 2001). The public side of the public fence is like the public estate itself analogously under-studied, a construct that is curiously atypical, porous and non-binary (Blomley, 2005, 2016). Such characteristics and qualities give a glimpse into the estate that lies within.

8.5 Public purpose vs. public use

The insights of critical geographers such as Doreen Massey and Brett Christophers cast light on this important dichotomy, a 'public use' versus 'public purpose' binary that reveals two potentially very different threshold rationales for the public realm. Does public real property serve the needs of public use or public purpose? Of course, this does not have to be a purely either/or proposition. Often the answer is both; especially where public use *is* the public purpose.

Yet there are many instances where public real property cannot be *used* by the public-at-large, or its use is subject to qualifications. These range from Macpherson's inaccessible 'state property' (government offices, defense bases, and so on) to the pre-conditions imposed on access to public institutions, such as paying entrance fees into national parks or public museums. Other examples include the eligibility criteria that filter access to public schools (limited to students, parents or authorized visitors), public housing (income or employment criteria), or classified public lands (restrictions based on say forestry operations, or fauna/flora preservation). Moreover, public use may be curtailed or suspended for overriding public health or safety reasons (evidenced by the closing of beaches and parks during the COVID-19 pandemic). All these examples, and more, illustrate that public use is a variable, porous and qualified concept. In a related sense, Chapter 3's analysis of *inclusion* as a prospective gatekeeper 'right' for public property, not only invokes the unhelpful baggage of private property, but is similarly problematic through its patchy, variable application. Likewise, that chapter's observation of the theoretical under-development of any public right to use and enjoy portends the current limits of 'public use'.

Public purpose, conversely, is highlighted in Chapters 2 and 3. It follows the arguments of Massey and Christophers (amongst others) that public owning requires a specifically public purpose or public justification, not some maladapted private analogue. Otherwise, as Christophers surmises, what is the point in public ownership if we simply ascribe to it private justifications (2018, p. 141). 'At least let the state function as a public owner … rather than requiring it to ape private-sector approaches and values. … Public ownership must be allowed to mean something *truly different* from private ownership for it to have any real worth or significance' (ibid, emphasis added).

As Chapter 7 canvasses, the reification of (private) efficiency as an all-encompassing, universalizing standard was not always thus. Bonnie Honig lays the blame on neoliberalism, that has 'undone' public values through its 'unremitting calculations of instrumental worth and its incapacity to imagine a world-building project that is not entrepreneurial by nature (2017, p. 14). Neoliberalism's preferred 'benchmarks' or 'best practices' are not 'mere verbiage but in fact promote an epistemic sea change that… leaves the fundaments of democratic life behind' (ibid.). The corrupting effects of efficiency can be seen in the bleeding of private property's values, especially its land as commodity mentality, into the public realm, and with it, the deemed superiority of the 'efficient' private ownership model. As Christophers and Shrubsole (2019) observe (in the context of the politics of land in England), the outcomes of this corruption are all too plain to see, with the large-scale disposal of public lands and/or the corporatization of public land-owning entities.

What came before, when efficiency stayed within its 'own sphere of influence' and was neither 'a vice [n]or a threat' (Honig 2017, p. 14) can be glimpsed from relatively recent public estate history. The rapid growth of public housing in post–World War II England enlivened the 'simple decency' of a public ownership that served distinctly public ends (Boughton 2018, and chapter 2 generally). Similar altruistic, egalitarian rationales underpin the founding of national parks in the United States in the later 19th century (see Chapter 6). Or the design principles of Frederick Law Olmsted, who saw New York's Central Park as the physical embodiment of democratic values, and a rejection of the elitist premise that 'when you try to do things for everyone you end up with the low[est] common denominator' (Honig 2017, p. 16). What are these uniquely public purposes? Or to put the question another way, what are the hallmarks of a *purposive* understanding of public real property?

Again, this requires a selective rejection of inapt private values, a modicum of blue-sky imagination, and as noted above, due deference to historical precedent. Much can be gleaned from the understated notion of *public-wealth*.[1] Private wealth is well understood as the accumulation of private capital, but public-wealth suffers from the all-too-familiar curse of under-thought. Public-wealth may well be framed by the thematic organizing principles charted in this book, the overlap that is the beneficial sum of public sociability, public belonging, the terrains of connection, and an egalitarianism that is for all, not some. 'Public purpose' is a statutory benchmark of public realty in Aotearoa/New Zealand (see Chapter 2), variously defined as 'the use, benefit, enjoyment, safety, or defense of the people of New Zealand, or the inhabitants of any district or locality therein' (Sect. 2(2) Reserves Act 1980). Elsewhere, public purpose is also referenced by values of 'recreation, environment, landscape, ecology, community, and access' amongst others (Sect. 3(1)). As seen, this New Zealand understanding of public purpose is also malleable to context, evolving alongside social and cultural change.

In the United Kingdom, postwar public housing policy was described as motivated by 'a spirit of companionship' and 'wartime sentiments of *social solidarity and shared purpose*' (Boughton 2018, p. 67, emphases added). Such ideals continue to imbue left politics. In 2019, the opposition Labour Party went to the national election with a land policy titled 'Land for the Many'. Its manifesto made explicit reference to *public-wealth*, stating that '[t]he expansion of public wealth in land creates more space for everyone, while the expansion of private wealth in land reduces the space available for others.' Its guiding principle was 'private sufficiency and public luxury' (Monbiot et al 2019, p. 12). In the pursuit of 'public luxury', an ambitious expansion of public wealth was advocated; from the codification of an urban right to roam to the creation of new parks and green spaces, protections for the County Farming Estate, and enhancements to the Allotments Act 1908 (pp. 60–70).

And finally, from the United States, and its rich public trust jurisprudence, the *Mono Lake* judgment of the Californian Supreme Court (see Chapter 3) declared that the interests of state-wide public trust holders were akin to a 'process of public expression' not a mere 'aggregation of private interests' (Ryan 2015, p. 632–633). In walking back from a private-centric view of ownership, the court gave voice to the sum of 'public expression' over the sum (or aggregation) of individual rights. Not only was this *obiter* a refutation of past thinking (like Macpherson's), but it also left the public purposive door ajar, inviting future enquiry as to what a 'process of public expression' may look like.

Such examples give illustrative content to the vast diversity of 'public purpose'. Rather than seeking a perfect (and arguably unattainable) definition, it is perhaps safer to err on the side of explanation through example, citing Honig that 'a definition is not needed to initiate the sort of rumination called for here' (2017, p. 4). The 'sort of rumination called for here' is an appreciation that the public purpose of public real property is one that serves truly different and public ends.

8.6 Spatial justice vs. private privilege

The final duality explored in this chapter is that of spatial justice, and its counter of private privilege. While the inclination of private property is to sequester, public property possesses what Rose calls 'wide-open synergies' (2003, p. 108).

These are, of course, sweeping generalizations as to the nature of private and public property. Nor is there any bright line that quarantines the public estate as spatially just and pure. Far from it, as seen in previous chapters, the Indigenous dispossession intrinsic to the colonial project, or the insider/outsider dynamics of public non-belonging, represent two egregious examples of spatial injustices on public lands. Sarah Keenan similarly describes contexts where injustices pervade public space as much as private (see Chapter 5). Nonetheless, the public/private divide throws out two very different institutional (and instinctual) perspectives about space, and entitlements to it.

The tensions at the heart of this duality manifest in several ways. One is the spatial injustice that flows from the physical loss of public real property, the *dimensional* accumulation of centuries of encroachments, enclosures and privatizations that have collectively reduced public acreage. The scope of this physical loss periodically motivates protestors to resist, and engage in counter-acts of 'taking back' (see Chapter 7). Another is *conceptual*, the marginalization of the idea of public property that impugns its validity, and fosters a false sense of equivalence, such that 'private public space' suffices for the real thing. Yet another is a matter of fate or good fortune, whereby one's class, race, wealth or other socio-economic or demographic differentiator determines one's proximity to public real property, and the spatial injustice such unevenness of access distributes and entrenches.

The COVID-19 stay-at-home orders have brought into sharp focus the latter tension. In many jurisdictions, emergency laws require citizens to shelter in place to minimize the risk of infection and the spread of the virus. Leaving home demands a 'reasonable' or 'lawful' excuse. In New South Wales, Australia, from where this final chapter is written, four lawful excuses permit outside activity; to obtain food or other goods or services, to travel for the purposes of work or education, for medical or caring reasons, or to exercise.[2] In such extraordinary and supervening times, the right to exercise finds itself as one of the few residual public property rights condoned by authorities.

The Order contains no definition of 'exercise'. Nor is there any reference to the distance citizens may travel to engage in essential exercise. Section 5(4) states that travel from the city (presumably Sydney) into regional areas is not a 'reasonable excuse', but otherwise the geographic ambit of the public right of exercise is vague, and open to arbitrary interpretation. In this lacuna, police instruct citizens to exercise locally or within their postcode, such that residents who live in neighborhoods blessed with a proliferation of public real property enjoy a rich bounty of exercise choices. They also enjoy a freedom from being in breach of the Public Health Order. Conversely, those who live in communities with far fewer parks or open spaces, or no access to beaches, have far fewer choices, and greater exposure to punitive fines when they 'stray' outside their own communities. The unintended consequence of (otherwise) sound public health policy throws into stark relief the spatial justice implications of ready access to public real property.

The pandemic also reveals the ugly face of localism, whereby (typically wealthier) coastal residents use the cover of the public health emergency to close 'their' local public beaches to outsiders. In a curious propertied twist, locals exhort the transformation of public property into common property, open to those within the local commons, but excluding those without. Such sentiments have provenance, for instance witness the public trust judgments from the United States where competing public ownerships pitted locals against the wider public for the trust resource (see Chapter 3).[3]

In England, George Monbiot writes that the experience of COVID-19 lockdowns is 'nothing new'. Rather, where 92% of land remains off-limits, lockdowns simply affirm the old normal – that 'we've been kept off the lands for centuries' (2020). Monbiot calls for an expanded public real property right; a post-pandemic right to roam that embraces both *the city* and the countryside (emphasis added). Monbiot points to the 131 golf courses that comprise over 11,000 acres in Greater London,[4] closed school grounds, or locked private green squares, as private lands over which public rights of access could feasibly subsist. In the meantime, 'millions of people swelter in tiny flats or edge round each other in miniscule parks, desperate for a sense of space and freedom' (ibid.). Monbiot's imagery of 'miniscule parks' around which urbanites anxiously 'edge' as they socially distance, paints with ever-greater starkness the spatial inequalities that a desperate lack of public real property delivers. In densely crowded cities, the scarcity of public open spaces plays out in nightmare scenarios where (healthy) space[5] is a private privilege, not a public right.

The inequalities of space implicate public real property, or specifically, correlate to its absence. In England, the private dominance of space means that any expanded public estate must take a predominantly incorporeal form to achieve a modicum of spatial justice. In dispersed geographies, the expansion of corporeal public acreage is an arguably more feasible route to #EquityOutdoors (Reis 2019). Likewise, abandoned or under-utilized spaces may be re-purposed to create new public acreage, seen in the post-industrial transformation of former rail lines into parks, best practice examples including Chicago's 606 (see Chapter 4). Finally, in neighborhoods with entrenched structural disadvantage, spatial injustice is particularly acute, matched (and correspondingly reinforced) by their paucity of public open spaces (see Chapter 3). Charles Montgomery says this unfairness is 'compounded by the way cities are organized. … We have known for decades that poor people and minorities in the United States have less access to parks, green spaces and recreation centers, and they have even fewer trees on the streets where they live' (2013, p. 241). Montgomery writes of a deficit of public wealth, or more accurately, its disproportionate distribution. Yet, as Rose confidently predicts, creating more is the merrier since '[t]he expansion of public wealth in land creates more space for everyone' (Monbiot et al. 2019, p. 12).

We all own property. Some just own more property than others. Property's diversity means that our ownerships extend across a rich spectrum: from fee simple title to the finite term of leasehold, and from sharing the benefit of an easement to buying into a co-operative with its structured private and common entitlements to space. But that's only a slice of the property pie. What we regularly fail to see is our public owning; our vast repository of *public-wealth*. Or, if we do intuit a sense of propriety in public things, it is vague, ill defined, and contested. As such, its marginality and ambiguity render it something less than proprietorial. In property law terms, the public realm becomes lost to plain view.

As discovered, there are many reasons for this obscurity, and the existential myopia it generates. If we are to begin peeling back the universalizing and totalizing logic of private property (Blomley 1994) to make room for the public estate, perhaps one place to start may be Hamill's 'government as owner' modality. The corrosive view that 'emphasizes the government's use [and *control*] of the land, rather than the public's benefit in it' (2012, p. 365). If we can shift the rhetoric from 'this is the government's' to 'this is ours', then we have accomplished a critical first step along the journey. Restoring the simple decency of public wealth, re-building the democratic fabric, and re-balancing *public purpose* are important others.

In the end, there is no single silver bullet that best sums up public real property, much like there is 'no magic talisman to distinguish public from nonpublic forums' (Post 1987, p. 1834). Yet, in writing of the public estate, this book engages a lot with *doing*, observing the power of *verbs* to describe the plenitude of ways in which public owning, public belonging, public connecting, and more, are actualized. To publicly own is to enact a diffuse beneficial ownership, one that escapes the straitjacket of private rights and individual entitlements. To publicly belong is to garner a sense of the public whole through affinity to part. To publicly connect is to materially link place and context, to traverse the everyday journeys from A to B. Of course, these are not the only verbs open to public proprietorial imagination. Building sandcastles, hiking, sitting on the park bench in the springtime sun, these are all pleasant doing words. The grind of daily commuting along public highways, or driving through anonymous 'atopias' (Lessard 2019) is less so. And thieving is a brutal verb that tells the uncomfortable truth of public lands in the colonial settler state. As April Anson surmises (2019, p. 59; Chapter 3) perhaps public lands, and by extension all public real property, are verbs, publicly owned spaces and places characterized by their wide-open synergies, and their near-limitless potential of public *doing*.

Notes

1 Sometimes also referred to as 'commonwealth', as in the Commonwealths of Australia or Virginia. Again, the interchangeability or synonymy of these underutilized terms reflects the systemic blurring of 'common' and 'public' observed elsewhere.

2 *Public Health (COVID-19 Restrictions on Gathering and Movement) Order* 2020 under the *Public Health Act 2010* (NSW), dated 30 March 2020.

3 American public trust law is clear that public trust resources belong to the citizens of the state, not those in the immediate neighborhood and its environs (see Chapter 3). In Sydney, the re-opening of beaches following a relaxation of lockdown orders triggered a war of words after the Waverley mayor (in the city's beachside eastern suburbs) indicated that beaches were open for locals only (Fitzsimmons 2020).

4 Monbiot's example of golf courses, and their thousands of acres of inaccessible land, is attributed to the exclusionary excesses of private property. However, such places could equally fit the definition of Rose's 'modern limited common property', where access is limited to 'only to those who pay fees or are members' (Monbiot 2020).

5 Said to be four square meters per person.

References

Anson, A 2019, 'The President Stole Your Lands: Public Lands and the Settler Commons', *Western American Literature*, vol. 54, 49–62.

Blomley, N 1994, *Law, Space, and the Geographies of Power*, Guildford Press, New York.

Blomley, N 2005, 'Flowers in the Bathtub: Boundary Crossings at the Public–Private Divide', *Geoforum*, vol. 36, 281–296.

Blomley, N 2011, *Rights of Passage: Sidewalks and the Regulation of Public Flow*, Routledge, Abingdon.

Blomley, N 2016, 'The Boundaries of Property: Complexity, Relationality, and Spatiality' *Law & Society Review*, vol. 50, 224–255.

Boughton, J 2018, *Municipal Dreams: The Rise and Fall of Council Housing*, Verso Books, London.

Christophers, B 2018, *The New Enclosure: The Appropriation of Public Lands in Neoliberal Britain*, Verso Books, London.

Gray, K and Gray, S 1999, 'Civil Rights, Civil Wrongs and Quasi-Public Space', *European Human Rights Law Review*, vol. 4, pp. 46–102.

Hamill, S 2012, 'Private Rights to Public Property: The Evolution of Common Property in Canada' *McGill Law Journal*, vol. 58, 365–403.

Hohfield, W 1913, 'Some Fundamental Legal Conceptions as Applied in Legal Reasoning', *Yale Law Journal*, vol. 23, 16–59.

Honig, B 2017, *Public Things: Democracy in Disrepair*, Fordham University Press, New York.

Fitzsimmons, C 2020, '"Locals Only": How a Mayor's Rogue Sentence Re-Ignited Old Tensions on the Beaches' *Sydney Morning Herald*, 3 May 2020, available at www.smh.com.au/national/nsw/locals-only-how-a-mayor-s-rogue-sentence-reignited-old-tensions-on-the-beaches-20200430-p54otj.html (accessed 4 May 2020).

Layard, A 2010, 'Shopping in the Public Realm: A Law of Place', *Journal of Law & Society*, vol. 37, 412–441.

Layard, A 2016, 'Public Space: Property, Lines, Interruptions', *Journal of Law, Property & Society* vol. 2, 1–47.

Lessard, S. 2019, *The Absent Hand: Reimagining Our American Landscape*, Counterpoint, Berkeley, CA.

Macpherson, C B 1978, 'The Meaning of Property' in C B Macpherson (ed.) *Property: Mainstream and Critical Positions*, University of Toronto Press, Toronto.

Monbiot, G et al., (2019), *Land for the Many: Changing the Way Our Fundamental Asset Is Used, Owned and Governed*, Labour Party, London.

Monbiot, G 2020, 'Lockdown Is Nothing New: We've Been Kept Off the Land for Centuries', *The Guardian*, 22 April 2020, available at www.theguardian.com/commentisfree/2020/apr/22/lockdown-coronavirus-crisis-right-to-roam (accessed 24 April 2020).

Montgomery, C 2013, *Happy City: Transforming Our Lives Through Urban Design*, Farrar, Straus and Giroux, New York.

Page, J 2010, 'Common Property and the Age of Aquarius', *Griffith Law Review*, vol. 19, no. 2, pp. 172–96.

Page, J 2017, *Property Diversity and Its Implications*, Routledge, Abingdon.
Post, R C 1987, 'Between Governance and Management: The History and Theory of the Public Forum', *UCLA Law Review*, vol. 34, 1713–1835.
Reis, A 2019, 'Equity Outdoors: Public Land and the Decolonial Mediascape', *Western American Literature*, vol. 54, 63–78.
Rose, C M 1986, 'The Comedy of the Commons: Custom, Commerce, and Inherently Public Property', *University of Chicago Law Review*, vol. 53, no. 3, 711–781.
Rose, C M 1998, 'The Several Futures of Property: Of Cyberspace and Folk Tales, Emission Trades and Ecosystems', *Minnesota Law Review*, vol. 83, 129–182.
Rose, C M 2003, 'Romans, Roads and Romantic Creators: Traditions of Public Property in the Information Age', *Law & Contemporary Problems*, vol. 66, 89 110.
Ryan, E 2015, 'The Public Trust Doctrine, Private Water Allocation, and Mono Lake: The Historic Saga of National Audubon Society v Superior Court', vol. 45 *Environmental Law*, vol. 45, 561–640.
Solnit, R 2001, *Wanderlust: A History of Walking*, Penguin Books, New York.
Shrubsole, G 2019, *Who Owns England? How We Lost Our Green & Pleasant Land & How to Take it Back*, William Collins, London.
Valverde, M 2013, *Everyday Law on the Street: City Governance in an Age of Diversity*, University of Chicago Press, Chicago.
Waldron, J 1992, 'Homeless and the Issue of Freedom', *UCLA Law Review*, vol. 39, 295–324.
Willard, T 2012, '"The Free Enjoyment of the Earth": Gerrard Winstanley on Land Reform' in A. Classen (ed), *Rural Space in the Middle Ages and Early Modern Age: The Spatial Turn in Premodern Studies*, De Gruyter, Berlin.

INDEX

Note: Page numbers in *italics* indicate figures and in **bold** indicate tables on the corresponding pages.

For Product Safety Concerns and Information please contact our EU
representative GPSR@taylorandfrancis.com
Taylor & Francis Verlag GmbH, Kaufingerstraße 24, 80331 München, Germany

www.ingramcontent.com/pod-product-compliance
Ingram Content Group UK Ltd.
Pitfield, Milton Keynes, MK11 3LW, UK
UKHW022125190926
475702UK00013B/1645
9780367375980